CLIMATIC CHANGE

CLIMATIC CHANGE

Evidence, Causes, and Effects

edited by HARLOW SHAPLEY

contributors:
Harlow Shapley, Carleton S. Coon, Paul B. Sears,
Hurd C. Willett, H. Wexler, John Wolbach,
Donald H. Menzel, Barbara Bell, P. L. Bhatnagar,
Max Krook, A. J. J. van Woerkom, Dirk Brouwer,
Richard Foster Flint, John T. Hack, C. C. Nikiforoff,
J. Laurence Kulp, Edmund Schulman, John H. Conover,
Victor Conrad, Elso S. Barghoorn, Edwin H. Colbert,
Edward S. Deevey, Jr.

HARVARD UNIVERSITY PRESS · CAMBRIDGE

Library of Congress Catalog Card Number 53–9041

SBN 674–13550–4

PRINTED IN THE UNITED STATES OF AMERICA

PREFACE

As is well known, those who complain about the weather rarely do anything about it; and still less is done about the climate, except occasionally to exaggerate in the interests of tourism. Sensitive to this situation, the American Academy of Arts and Sciences and its Rumford Committee assembled from many sciences and institutions the climatic experts, with their knowledge, theories, and plans. A two-day conference was held in May 1952 at the Academy's House, where a score of students of the wide science of climatology and three score of the specially curious analyzed and debated the evidences of climatic change and the possible sources of such variations. The success of the five sessions encourages the belief that valuable advances in knowledge can arise from planned conferences of specialists from neighboring disciplines.

The twenty-two papers that are brought together in this volume are solid, sometimes fairly solemn, and at all times authoritative. The meetings were in similar vein, but the solemnity was alleviated by the informalities of the gatherings, and by the quizzing and private arguments.

In the beginning the speakers were reminded that the conference owed its existence not only to the Rumford Committee but also to the climate-indicating fossils of the paleozoic and subsequent eras. The protozoa and protophyta of the Pre-Cambrian ages were in their time confronted with climate and its changes, as are we. All the intermediates between those simple organisms and the complicated speakers at the conference — all the conodonts, trilobites, cycads, tyrannosaurs — faced the terrestrial climate and frequently survived its changes. Biological evolution proceeded through the millennia. We grew up. Hence our present obligation to the biota of the past. Hence our dedication of this effort to our necessary protozoic ancestors as well as to our less necessary contemporaries.

The climatology of the past and present is one of the most penetrating and wide-spreading of the disciplines that bring scientific friends and strangers together. Biology and physics in their many phases converge on the climate problem, for climate is much more than persistent weather. Its study requires a fusion of the inanimate and the living. Next to the genes and chromosomes, and the mysterious and perhaps nonexistent "life essence," climate is the major factor in organic evolution. It is the prime factor also in demography, for the spread and tribulations of the races and nations of men are directly dependent on the climatic environments. Our cultures and civilizations are tied closely to climate and its vagaries. Even modern folkways, as Paul Sears points out, come into the picture, as in the devotion of the human stomach to maize and rice, which are dependent on climate and affected by its changing.

The central sciences in the study of climatic change are of course meteorology, oceanography, paleontology, and those parts of geology that deal with the rise and subsidence of mountains, continents, and seas. More basic than these is the radiation of the sun — that genial nearby star to which we owe our existence, our food, our warmth, and our April showers. Especially, as animals and plants, we owe a deep debt to the essential constancy of sunlight throughout the past two billion years. But here we encounter a paradox. As the theme is developed in this multiscience volume, it turns out that we are most indebted not to the constancy but to the deviations from constancy of sunlight for those climatic changes that have contributed to organic development from lowest protozoa to highest primate. An absolutely steady sun and earth-crust for the past 400,000,000 years might have left us living as Silurian ooze-browsers, unambitious, deprived of climatic stimulation.

The Pleistocene Ice Ages yield the most conspicuous evidences of hard weather in ancient times. Actually we are in current contest with the ice sheets — current, that is, on the cosmic time scale. The last major Ice Age of the Pleistocene really ended, as Willett, Flint, and others remark on later pages, only four thousand years ago in North America, somewhat earlier in Europe; and since then there has been a Little Ice Age from which we just now appear to be emerging.

Our climate is now reasonably comfortable over a wide latitude — neither too muggy nor too frigid. If solar radiation is the dominant influence in climatic behavior, one might (futilely) urge the sun: Steady now, hold it! But do we really want an equable epoch? Climatic and continental changes usefully force us inhabitants of this sun-controlled planet to evolve in adaptability. If the warm spell and vegetable lushness of the mid-Mesozoic era, which prevailed for a hundred million years, had persisted to the present, we almost certainly would not be here to write essays on climate. The flowers and the bees and the other facets of life derived much inspiration and experience from the rising mountains and the climatic changes that together led terrestrial biology into the highly adaptable forms that successfully faced the oncoming Ice Ages and survived them.

Returning to the breadth of climatology, let us see how our twenty-two contributions can be classified. Here is a listing, made with the realization that some of the authors are writing in two or three fields at once:

Astronomy, six items, some with a considerable touch of astrophysics and geophysics;

Geology and geography, three items;

Meteorology, four items;

Paleontology, four items, of which three deal with botanical records;

Paleoanthropology, two items that help to put man in his place among the storms and calms of the past million years;

Geophysics and geochemistry, each one item.

One contribution, my own, is decidedly miscellaneous; it touches on probabilities of "other worlds," treats of the earthly conditions that are necessary for the occurrence of organisms, and lightly previews much of the subsequent argument.

Some of the contributions provide good over-all summaries for particular fields: for example, Willett on atmospheric circulation, Coon on the races of men in contact and contest with the climate, Wolbach on the geographical evidences and their limitations in providing satisfactory clues to the origin of climatic change, and Deevey's exhaustive survey and bibliography of lake beds — a treatment of fossil pollen and animal forms that is little less than a handbook on limnology.

The reader will discover that the experts from the various fields that contribute to climatology do not agree in all details; they do not even wholly agree when in the same field handling the same material. This is fortunate for the science. It suggests that we shall not all be simultaneously wrong. It means that searching and critical analyzing must go on.

An occasional unevenness appears in the texture and intensity of the contributions in this volume. Two or three of the contributions might have been more suitably published where the specialist alone would look for them. But a true picture of climatology cannot be attained until we recognize the width and depth of its contributing technologies. The celestial mechanician needs his heavy equations before he pronounces on the possibility of long-range climatic changes, engineered from the heavens; the moon and neighboring planets get into the analysis, and even the little planet Pluto on the fringe of the solar system cannot be wholly ignored as a factor in paleoclimatology until we examine its tiny perturbing effects. We cannot properly ignore bog deposits, soil environments, or the solar corona. We have therefore included all the papers of the Conference, long and short, simple and technical. This volume will indeed be something like the weather — soft and easy-going at times, occasionally cold, rugged, and enigmatic, and at other times, whether tough or tender, possibly a bit monotonous.

They tell of an ancient schoolboy who not only did not know where the Dead Sea is, but said he did not even know it was sick; and we read, in our paleolimnological contribution, that "a certain dystrophic lake's metabolism is overbalanced and it cannot work the dy into a less humic gyttja." This is too bad — not the resulting congestion in the lake, but the fact that sometimes we must use such technical terms for clarity and space economy.*

Some readers will never before have met a few of the other technical terms that are prominent in this volume, such as *paleoecology*, the science that deals with the totality of the evironmental relationships of the geological past; *pedogenesis*, the science and classification of the soils; *radioisotopic*, pertaining to that form or isotope of a chemical element that is naturally radioactive; *Pleistocene*, the latest of the main geological periods, sometimes called Quaternary, and famous for its series of Ice Ages; *interstadial*, between stations in space or time; *xerophyte*, a plant that is found in the desert heat and drought, and can take it; *meromixis*, permanent stagnation; *megascopic*, nonmicroscopic; *ectothermic*, cold-blooded, in contrast to *endothermic*, warm-blooded; and *edaphic*, influenced by soil rather than climate; but now the readers have met these words and know their approximate meanings. There are a few others of this sort, but the authors have kindly refrained from exhibiting too much of their stock of technicalities.

In this preliminary orientation in the subject matter I cite as examples five peripheral studies that are surprising and unexpected phases of the investigation of climate — unexpected at least to much of the public, and perhaps to the weatherman. They bring in silviculture, astrophysics, physical chemistry, celestial mechanics, and physiology.

(1) The skillful analyses of tree-ring measures by paleodendrologist Schulman, carrying forward the pioneer work of Douglass, not only reports the successes and dangers of the association of tree growth with climate, but also shows the necessity of examining both the habits of forests and the many factors other than rain that regulate ring width.

(2) The application of Menzel's new theories of solar and planetary magnetism brings his analyses into the climate argument; and Miss Bell has used his work to suggest that climate-affecting warm spots may be found at the magnetic poles — warmth produced by corpuscular radiation from the sun.

(3) The magic of the radioactive carbon 14 isotope, produced by

* Both of these words refer to the muck that forms in lake bottoms; dy is mainly organic, while gyttja contains mineral material in varying proportions.

cosmic radiation at the top of the earth's atmosphere, is presented as a climate-exploring tool by Kulp, who, along with Libby and others, dates accurately the glacial products of the late Pleistocene and finds the ages of water samples deep in the slowly circulating oceans.

(4) Prolonged computations on the orbital characteristics of Pluto are a part of the future budget of climatic research, and Brouwer writes that he is fairly confident that further study of the problem "will yield a pleasing and perhaps elegant solution of the difficulty."

(5) The melting point of the marrow fat in the leg bones of Alaskan caribou is used by Coon in his exploration of the effects of recent climatic changes on the lives and ranges of man and animals. The red-corpuscle counts for Andean Indians are also indicators.

Other peripheral studies are mentioned in the first communication of this volume, where I illustrate further the breadth and fascination of the multiscience attack on the ancient, present, and future climates of the earth.

HARLOW SHAPLEY

CONTENTS

CLIMATIC CHANGE

1

ON CLIMATE AND LIFE

Harlow Shapley

Although climate is chiefly a
matter of winds, ocean currents, sunshine, rains, and snow, it
involves also the responses of plants and animals to these physical factors.
What plants grow on the mountain sides and control the evaporation?
What animal affects the weather by meddling with the water courses,
thereby producing lush vegetation in arid regions? Clearly life and climate
interact on each other. If life had never appeared on the earth's surface,
the local climates would have been different from those which have
prevailed. And if the climate had everywhere been unchanging throughout geologic time, the varied life we know — the millions of species —
might not have come about; possibly the organisms would never have got
their start in the dim Pre-Cambrian ooze.

One of the sessions at our American Academy Conference [1] was an
extemporaneous discussion without preparation of any kind except a
preliminary list of questions that I had assembled for participants in an
Open Circle inquiry into climate and life. The subject of the discussion
was spelled out in the ample title: Climatic Conditions Required for the
Origin and Continuance of Life on This and Other Planets. The session
was serious, deep, cheerful, and inciting, for on the inner circle of chairs
we had representatives of biochemistry, paleontology, astrophysics,
meteorology, geophysics, physical chemistry, geology, and astronomy,
and they were not amateurs. The discussion ranged from the Moon and
Mars to the presumed giant planet of the star 61 Cygni; from the atomic
structure of carbon to the chemistry of algae; from the Oparin soup at the
bottom of the primitive oceans to the salts of the Dead Sea and the hot
liquids of Old Faithful.

In this introductory chapter I shall refer to some of the most fertile
arguments, reflect on the multiple factors in climatic change, and also
consider the probable distribution of life throughout the sidereal universe.
If we find domiciles for life out among the stars, we must grant, of course,
that those distant climates are for the play of the imagination only.

We asked many questions at the Open Circle session — hard questions that elicited soft replies, and only tentative answers, for however out-standing the work and wisdom of the participants, the unsolved problems were the more impressive. Did life start once or many times? Did spores or other pansperms get across space from somewhere to impregnate our otherwise infertile planet? What climatic violence can man and other biota withstand as the sun dies down or flares up? Did a wretched climate do in the doughty dinosaur, or had his Class run its full cosmic race when it settled down from the living into the fossiliferous rocks? Those were questions that stimulated the conferees and brought life to climate and climate to life.

To begin with, let us evade a close definition of life. The reader probably knows what we mean by life, even if we cannot clearly define it. We start astronomically, and ask about this organic livingness elsewhere in the universe. What chance is there for life like ours in other planetary systems, in this or any other galaxy? And if there are other life-infested planetary surfaces, is that life "high" or "low?" Are we alone?

THE ABUNDANCE OF LIFE-BEARING PLANETS

Before we go, with provincial vanity, into the possibilities of organisms existing on the other planets in our own solar system, we may find it interesting to speculate about life near other stars. We speculate rather than pronounce because of our ignorance of one basic factor important to this inquiry. We ask: how does a system of planets originate? And we get no fully satisfying answer. There are half a dozen competing hypotheses, such as the one involving the contraction of a vast dust cloud, another that appeals to the tidal disruption of stars. Also we have the double-star collision theory, the planetesimal hypothesis, and my own "aboriginal chaos" theory. All of these hypotheses are defective as first stated and are now worn thin; but some of them are subject to fairly successful patching.

We do not need to know in detail, however, the method of the origination of planets before we proceed to speculate on the sidereal distribution of life. From a rough evaluation of circumstances and opera-tions throughout the stellar universe, we can arrive at a lower limit of the probability. There may be many more life domiciles than we estimate, but likely not less.

Some theories suggest that nearly every star has its system of planets, that they are a natural by-product in the origin of stars. But probably more than half of all stars are double, and the gravitational perturbations in most double systems would eject planets or absorb them, or permit to exist only those that are far out in a dim and death-dealing cold, too remote from the stellar heat sources to permit biological experimentation.

Theories of planetary origin that depend on the collision or near collision of two stars would make planetary systems exceedingly scarce because of the extreme isolation of stars, one from the other. Collisions among stars of our Milky Way system are well-nigh impossible in these days; but in the crowded days of the birth of our Galaxy, when the now expanding Metagalaxy was young and violent, the planet-making collisions could be and probably were numerous.

Let us be skeptical and suppose that, in whatever way they come, only one star out of a million is blessed with a family of planets. This number is chosen on the basis of knowledge of the separations and motions of stars. We can see only a few thousand stars with the naked eye, and on the ungenerous hypothesis of only one in a million, probably not one of our visible neighbors has a planetary family. But there are a hundred billion telescopic stars in our Galaxy, and therefore one hundred thousand of our galactic stars would qualify for planets and even for planetary life. But such a high probability of life in our galaxy would hold only if planets and life always go together, and certainly they do not. Of the nine planets in our system, only one is definitely suited to the sort of life we practice. Mercury and Pluto are unquestionably barren. If the earth's orbit had been eccentric like that of a comet, or if its mass had been as small as that of the moon, or as big as that of Jupiter, the living spark might never have survived, or never have flashed up in the first place. The atmosphere, temperatures, and other properties must be proper.

Suppose we skeptically guess that only one star family out of a thousand has a planet with the happy requirements of suitable distance from the star, near-circular orbit, proper mass, salubrious atmosphere, and reasonable rotation period — all of which are necessary for life as we know it on the earth. That is, we assume that, of the hypothetical one star in a million that has planets, only one family in a thousand has a planet suitable for the life experiment. It will require, therefore, a billion stars, on the average, to provide one life-bearing planet.

Maintaining our stubborn skepticism, we may argue that even in this one-to-a-billion chance, the first step (Creation?) may not have been taken — the step that starts organisms off in the persisting way; and we may further argue that even if life did start it may not have persisted long enough for the complicated biochemistry that leads to high mammalian life; or there may have been some intervening volcanic activity or sidereal collision that would totally erase the embryonic biology. Very well; let us then grant that among the suitable planets a single one out of a thousand goes all the way to the higher life.

Does this final one-out-of-a-thousand chance rule out life everywhere in the universe except on this one planet, which is located near one of the hundred billion stars at the edge of this one galaxy among the billions of galaxies? No, life is not ruled out even by these stringent demands. The odds against life are found to be $10^6 \times 10^3 \times 10^3 = 10^{12}$ — that is, the odds are one to a trillion that any given star supports life of the "high" sort. But the total number of stars in the sidereal universe is in excess of 10^{20} and therefore we compute (by subtracting the exponents) that there must be at least 10^8 other planets with a long history of high-life forms. These one hundred million life theaters, scattered throughout the Metagalaxy, indicate that the life phenomenon is widespread and of cosmic significance. We are not alone. And we should admit, of course, that the animal, vegetable, or other organisms on other happier planets may have far "surpassed" the terrestrial forms. There is no reason whatever to presume that *Homo sapiens, Apis mellifera,* and *Corvus americanus* are the best that biochemistry and star shine can do.

We have, by this ungenerous argument and computation, ruthlessly cut down the frequency of life-touched planets and allocated to ourselves a bit of uniqueness in our own galactic system. But, considering the total of galaxies and stars, the stellar universe that the astronomers probe must contain abundant life as well as novel climates.

HOW MUCH LIFE ON MARS?

But let us return to the solar system and its climatic problems. The existence of life on Mars is still an open question, although astronomers have for years rather uncritically assumed that the seasonal color changes on the surface must mean that life is present. An observer looking at the planet Earth from a moderate distance, say a scientist on the moon, would also see our winters come and go. He should be able to locate the positions of the poles of the earth by watching the alternating color changes due to winter snowfall and summer melting in our northern and southern hemispheres. He would note that we have much water on the surface, in strong contrast to the small amount on Mars, where it is weakly recorded by the skin of hoarfrost at the polar caps. The color changes on the surface of the earth, visible to the observer on the moon, could be quite independent of vegetable or other life. Even in the absence of snow, the moisture on desert lowlands should produce colors that would fade out with the drying up in the annual rainless season. Fog on a lifeless desert could produce a widespread color change. In other words, variations in the color of Mars do not necessarily mean that vegetation is present. The Martian problem is still open.

Some of the climatic changes on Mars can be readily deduced. The surface is relatively free of high elevations and certainly free of large bodies of water. Air and water currents must be relatively uncomplicated. The mass is low, and the air is rarefied even at the Martian surface. The inclination of the equator to the plane of the orbit is like that of the earth and consequently the seasonal phenomena are similar. The rotation of the planet is a little more than 24 terrestrial hours; the year is 1.9 terrestrial years, and the months may be ignored because the two little moons are ineffective, both tidally and photometrically. We can predict the daily and annual meteorological changes from our own experience, after making allowance for the low temperatures and the weak effects of air currents on the lowland elevations. The orbit of Mars has an eccentricity of 0.093, compared with 0.017 for the earth; and therefore the Martian temperature (and climate) will be somewhat affected by the fact that Mars is 26 million miles nearer the sun at perihelion than at aphelion — a change of 18 percent in the distance. The perihelion effect on the earth's temperature and climate is relatively small, in comparison with the many other factors that contribute to terrestrial climatic change, for the difference in distance, perihelion to aphelion, is only 3.4 percent.

If we knew how life got started on our own planet, we could better guess whether the Martian conditions have been hostile or friendly to the origin of organisms. Certainly the mean temperature is painfully low, the atmosphere at the surface is rarer than on our highest mountain tops, and both oxygen and water vapor are scarce. Carbon dioxide has been detected and we all agree that argon, produced by the radioactivity of one of the isotopes of potassium, is almost certainly a constituent of the thin Martian atmosphere. The dominant gas presumably is nitrogen, which has not yet been recorded. Could it be detected without going to the planet? Dr. Rupert Wildt suggests the possibility that Martian aurorae may sometime be observed, and, if so, they would probably indicate the presence of a deep but low-density atmosphere composed mostly of nitrogen surrounding the dry cool planet.

In the course of our Open Circle discussion of other-planet life, I put the pointed question directly to Professor Henry Norris Russell, who has long pondered and written on the subject of planetary atmospheres: "Is there life on Mars?" We received the following full summary, which was generally accepted: "We don't know!"

The moon, of course, is lifeless, waterless, and essentially airless. Hydrogen, helium, nitrogen, and oxygen gases would all leak away from the surface of this small-mass satellite. The moon might not even permanently retain by gravitation the inert argon, produced radioactively from potassium 40. Very little of it could get to the surface in the absence of water erosion and volcanic action. The writer interpolates the suggestion, however, that the ever-impinging meteors, with their consequent explosions, would produce, throughout the three or more thousand million years that the moon has been under meteoric bombardment, various gases, including some that are relatively so heavy that they would not easily escape from the surface. The meteoric impacts would also release from the surface some of the entrapped argon. The moon must therefore have an atmosphere, but in quantity perhaps not many lungfuls and in character not very salubrious.

The cloud-shrouded surface of the planet Venus remains as yet something of a mystery. In general, the students of planetary atmospheres find little likelihood of life of the terrestrial sort on that planet, notwithstanding its earth-like mass and its fairly suitable location with respect to the sun. Is it covered with oceans of water? Does the rotation period permit an equable alternation of night and day? Is the oxygen situation suitable for air breathers? Some of the astrochemists have positive answers to some of the questions of this sort; but doubts still prevail and we must await improved technologies before we penetrate the shroud and agree on the living conditions.

The other planets of the solar system are too hot or too cold for life, and they have other limitations. For example, Mercury is too hot on the sun side, too cold in the endless night of the hemisphere that is never exposed to the sun; and life of our sort would be impossible in Mercury's twilight zones because of the lack of atmosphere and water. Jupiter, Saturn, and the other distant planets, out in the icy cold that is inevitable so far from the sun, have poisonous atmospheres, heavy with methane and ammonia; and they have other hostile characteristics.

Earth-sized planets have never been detected around other stars. Even though the probability of their existence is high, their discovery is with present techniques impossible for at least two good reasons: first, the dominating glare of a star overwhelms the feeble reflection from a nearby planetary surface; and second, a small planet cannot gravitationally disturb the motion of a star to the point where the deviation from rectilinear motion could be detected by a terrestrial observer. A very large planet, larger than our greatest, can of course produce a measurable effect on the motion of a star. That is the situation with respect to the nearby star 61 Cygni, and perhaps one or two others; but such disturbances in the motion cannot be found, and used to predict the existence of an unseen giant planet, if the star is more than 30 light years distant. Frequent and accurate measuring of the motions of nearby stars for the next century or two should uncover half a dozen systems like 61 Cygni, perhaps many more if large planets are common; but it would take much longer to demonstrate earth-size planets among the neighboring stars. These times could be shortened, of course, if new highly accurate techniques of position measurement were developed.

SIX CONDITIONS FOR PLANETARY LIFE

Climate is not the only important factor that determines the possibility of life on a planetary surface. Expanding somewhat the list of conditions mentioned above, we propose the following as necessary for the origin and continuance of life:

1. Water, the practical solvent for living processes, must be available in liquid form. The kind of life we are talking about and thinking of does not live in uncondensing steam or unmelting ice. The basic requirement, therefore, is that the living planet must be at a proper distance from its star — in the liquid-water belt — not as close as Mercury is to the sun nor as remote as Jupiter.*

2. The planet must have suitable rotation period so that nights do not overcool nor days overheat.

3. The orbital eccentricity must be low to avoid excessive differences in the insolation as the planet moves from perihelion to aphelion and back (most cometary orbits would be lethal for organisms).

4. The chemical content of air, ocean, and land surface must be propitious, and not perilously polluted with substances inimical to biological operations.

5. The controlling star must not be variable by more than 4 or 5 percent; it must not be a double star, and of course not subject to catastrophic explosions like those of the novae.

6. Finally, life must get started and establish a tenacious hold on the seas, shores, or inland. Once firmly established it apparently can diversify and spread; much of it can meet and survive the changing climatic and physiographic situations. The records show, however, that thousands of highly developed organic forms fade into oblivion as the eras unfold.

There are a number of other conditions that life like ours requires, such as a planetary mass sufficient to hold a good oxygen-rich atmosphere,

* There is the fanciful possibility that a planet with life could be independent of the gravitation and radiation of a star, and be loose, alone, and wandering in interstellar space, with its necessary heat generated by its own radioactive mineral constituents. Such a planet would have no proper day and night; it would probably be entirely dark except for weak starlight and luminescence incited by radioactivity; it would have a strange atmosphere, be devoid of tides, and have a most unusual climate and certainly an exotic biology.

a high inclination of the planet's axis of rotation to the plane of its orbit, and freedom from excessive bombardment by short-wavelength radiation and meteors; but a good deal of variation from present terrestrial conditions can be allowed if enough time is given for the gradual adaptation of the animals and plants to changing conditions. If the sun were as bright as Rigel, any life-bearing planet would have to be more than ten times as far away as we are. If the life-energizing star has a low surface temperature, the life-bearing planet must be closer to its star. If the planet's mass is much greater than ours, with the size the same, the life must adapt itself to enhanced gravity, stronger winds, more violent storms, and a somewhat different atmospheric chemistry. If oxygen is scarce, a modified breathing apparatus would be required; and other adjustments would be needed by plants if carbon dioxide had a greatly different availability.

Certainly many adjustments could be made by organisms on a planetary surface to physical conditions unlike those we experience, but the major requirements still stand. The most important requirement is of course that life must in some way get started.

SPECULATIONS ON THE PRIMITIVES

The specialists at the Conference on Climatic Changes discussed extensively the primitive biochemistries that must operate in that narrow zone between the inanimate and the living. The classic treatment by Oparin of the conditions for the origin of life [2] is a good starting point. Contributions to various phases of the life problem by Schroedinger,[3] Bernal,[4] Urey,[5] and C. G. Darwin [6] have their greatest significance, perhaps, in showing that some of the leading physical scientists are currently concerned with speculations on the most primitive organic operations. Unquestionably, basic contributions and fertile suggestions can be expected from the fields of physics and chemistry.

Neither biologists nor astronomers have much interest in the pansperm hypothesis, which visualizes life sprouting on the earth's surface from seeds (spores) that have floated in from other planets. Even if such a seeding were possible, it merely transfers the basic question — "Life, what is it and how did it start?" — to some still less accessible place than our Pre-Cambrian sediments. Experiments have shown that some spores can long survive at interstellar temperatures and can resist a reasonable amount of ultraviolet radiation. It takes an ingenious imagination, however, to get the spores away from their distant hypothetical homes and across the light years to a planet such as this. They are speculators, not scientists, who surmise that interstellar space may be full of life spores, which are continually caught up by planetary atmospheres and slowly settle down into fertile soil. It is better to consider our life an endemic phenomenon, originated on the earth and up to now bound to it.

The protozoölogists and biochemists appear to agree on one important and to me rather incredible point, namely, that if micro-life were once started and established it would prevent later origins. This fact (or dogma?) would indicate that all the myriads of forms now existing came from Pre-Cambrian ancestors. But it would not follow literally — even if we accept the conclusion that probably there was organic "success" only in those Archeozoic times some two or three thousand million years ago — that we of the mammal stock must be lineal descendants of Pre-Cambrian sponges. Temperature and chemical conditions in Archeozoic times could have been propitious for life's origin simultaneously in several well-separated places on the planet. Several starts, spreads, and upward developments could have been made in ancient days before the total planetary surface was overrun and new originations of life out of the inanimate were blocked. Incidentally, it is easy to believe that we ourselves may some day accomplish the creation of life by a magic synthesis in the biochemical laboratory.

One of the most interesting recent contributions in the field of the origin of terrestrial life has come through studies by Urey and others of the evolution of a planetary atmosphere. Undoubtedly there were gradual changes in the ancient atmospheres. The methane and ammonia that are now dominant in the gaseous envelopes of Jupiter and Saturn were not strangers to the early atmosphere of this planet. In Pre-Cambrian times, Urey argues, conditions would have been much more favorable than they are now for the origin of life. The primitive oceans, much less extensive than now, might have been a 10-percent solution of organic compounds, which would provide a very favorable situation for the origin of life. "Many researches directed toward the origin of life have assumed highly oxidizing conditions and hence start with the very difficult problem of producing compounds of reduced carbon from carbon dioxide without the aid of chlorophyll. It seems to me that these researches have missed the main point, namely, that life originated under reducing conditions or as reducing conditions changed to oxidizing conditions, and it was only necessary for photosynthetic pigments to become available as free oxygen appeared." [5]

The arguments for the origin of life under reducing conditions, before oxygen became too dominant in air and soil, have been outlined by Oparin, who visualizes the steps from organic compounds to colloidal compounds, and on to the most primitive of living organisms. Somewhere and somewhen the trick of using sunlight effectively by way of photosynthesis entered the biological enterprise that has now populated the earth. Early in the Paleozoic Era living forms came ashore and learned to take their oxygen raw, and to run, crawl, and fly over the earth's surface. At that moment they became immediately and directly dependent on the climate. In an empirical way the plants and animals have ever since studied the climate and climatic changes, and made adaptations that range from the desiccation of simple plants in the desert dry season to the extraordinary adjustments of migratory birds, fish, and other animals.

NOTES ON THE PLEISTOCENE

Several of the contributors to this volume have discussed special problems that relate climate to life. Comment on some of the facts and arguments presented by them will further illustrate the complicated nature of climatology. The weather of the Pleistocene has naturally received much attention. In that most recent and clearly defined geological epoch, which lasted for a million years or so, the great ice sheets advanced and receded several times. Also in that time, buffeting the changing and vigorous weather, the primate *Homo* emerged and began to take over terrestrial biology.

Slight irregularities in the radiation of the sun are held chiefly responsible by many investigators for climatic changes; and when the irregularities are coupled with suitable continental elevations, glaciers creep further from the poles. No other astronomical contribution to the climatic variations, such as the effects of cosmic dust clouds or orbital changes, approach in significance the solar variability.

Because the data on sunspots are readily available, they are frequently introduced into correlation studies of terrestrial meteorology. The spottiness of the sun, rather than measures of solar radiation, or of solar flares, faculae, corona, and prominences, is correlated with weather conditions. But the spots themselves are doing little to us or to the weather directly. Specialists agree on this point. The abundance or scarcity of sunspots is simply an indicator that the sun's radiation, in waves and corpuscles, whether it comes from the total surface of the sun or from its flares or corona, is more or less than average. The spots are indexes of solar unrest, not of weather change. We need not carry umbrellas when a spot is seen.

How to construct an ice age is a technical problem the solution of which is beginning to be understood by glaciologist and meteorologist. Let us start with the present interglacial climate, with few glaciers outside of arctic zones. First, the sun must get hotter and radiate more energy than at present into the earth's atmosphere, and especially into the water bodies on its surface. A few degrees rise in temperature will suffice. The increased evaporation and atmospheric circulation leads to increased precipitation, and snow accumulates in the higher latitudes, increasing the temperature contrasts of the earth's surface. Concurrently with the heavier snows of winter, there must be heavier cloudiness and cooler temperatures in the summers so that the snow will not melt away. We keep this machinery going for a century or two. Glaciers will begin to appear at favored locations in higher middle latitudes and, at least in temperate and arctic zones, the earth's surface will cool. But there must also be high land if glaciers are to prosper and leave records for deciphering by future glaciologists; from the Silurian, Mississippian, and Jurassic periods, when the land was low, we have no glacial records.

The association of high continents and mountains with increased evaporation and precipitation, and perhaps with more than a little volcanism, apparently prevailed at the time of the Pre-Cambrian glaciers, and most clearly for the Permian and Pleistocene ice sheets. One actor in this icy drama, however, must be carefully watched: the sun must not radiate too much more than average while the Ice Age is under construction or the summers cannot be cool enough to maintain the winter's contribution of snow. With too much solar radiation the increased precipitation that follows increased evaporation will not in the high latitudes be of that solid variety out of which glaciers and ice sheets are made.

The recorded warming-up of the earth during much of the first half of the twentieth century may represent merely the gradual clearing of the upper atmosphere of the fine volcanic dust that Krakatoa, Katmai, and other volcanoes have contributed to the climate problem; or that warming-up may be a continuation of our retreat from the Ice Age (Cochrane Readvance) that appeared in North America as late as the pyramid-building operations along the Nile; or it may be an early stage in that increased solar radiation that presages enhanced evaporation and precipitation, which in turn go along with the beginning of a new ice age. The meaning of the current temperature trends is not clear. Time, it is trite and true to remark, will tell. Actually the warming of the Arctic has been going on, the glacial and biological records indicate, for about forty years. Arctic meteorology deserves and is now receiving much attention in the interests of today's weather and yesterday's climate.

Notwithstanding the local success of the professional rainmakers, man has as yet little prospect of controlling world-wide weather or climate patterns. The growth of industry, and the increasing population of fuel-burning inhabitants of the earth, have in the past seventy years put enough additional carbon dioxide into the atmosphere to affect (perhaps quite slightly) the atmospheric control of climate. The accompanying smog, of course, has in the last half century affected more perceptibly than has carbon dioxide the natural weather patterns. But even smog is probably negligible in the totality of multiple factors that produce changes in weather and climate and in the human lives that exist amidst the mixed gases of the planet's atmosphere.

REFERENCES

1. See the preface to this volume.
2. A. I. Oparin, *The origin of life* (Macmillan, New York, 1938).
3. Erwin Schroedinger, *What is life?* (Macmillan, New York, 1945).
4. J. D. Bernal, *The physical basis of life* (Routledge and Kegan Paul, London, 1951).
5. H. C. Urey, *The planets — their origin and development* (Yale University Press, New Haven, 1952).
6. C. G. Darwin, *The next million years* (Rupert Hart-Davis, London, 1952).

2

CLIMATE AND RACE

Carleton S. Coon

T HE TENOR OF THE COMMUNICATIONS
that follow seems to be that throughout geological time
terrestrial climate has grown increasingly variable and that the speed of
the changes has also increased. In response to these changes in environment both vegetable and animal forms of life have grown increasingly
capable of adaptation, permitting them to cope with variations of climate
in time and space. At the same time the kinds of ecological adaptation
have become more numerous, and the end product of environmental and
ecological adaptability seems to be an increase in intelligence. The most
adaptable animal of all, and we presume the most intelligent so far
evolved, is man. His adaptation has taken two interrelated forms, physiological and cultural. The first is my subject; the second is Dr. Sears's.

Despite our alleged intelligence as a species, and despite the efforts
of several little-heeded men, it has taken a long time for scientists to
learn the facts of life as they pertain to the chain reaction of climate,
physiological function, organic adaptation, and certain aspects of race,
in animals in general, man included. In 1877, exactly three-quarters of a
century ago, J. A. Allen,[1] a zoölogist at the American Museum of Natural
History, wrote: "The study of man from a geographical standpoint, or with
special reference to conditions of environment, offers a most important
and fruitful field of research, which, it is to be hoped, will soon receive
a more careful attention than has as yet been given it." Allen's paper
dealt with geographically correlated variations in North American animals
and birds, on three axes: color, general size, and the relative size of the
peripheral parts; or, more simply, color, size, and form. The first of these
had already been studied in 1833 by Gloger; the second by Bergmann
in 1847.[2] Only the third was new with Allen. In the zoölogical field few
scientists have concerned themselves with the subject of geographical
variations within species. Outstanding in this respect is Rensch,[3] who,
during the late 20's or 30's, tested these three correlations and added
several observations of his own; but even with this work available, Ernst
Mayr [4] was moved to write in 1941: "The study of these ecological correla-

tions and the establishment of definite rules is such a new field that we may consider ourselves at the beginning of the work."

If, 64 years after Allen's statement, an authority of Mayr's stature could say that we were at the beginning of the work, it is clear that this aspect of biology had been grossly neglected, and eleven years later such is still the case. During those 64 years the study of biology passed through several phases of emphasis. The first phase was in the Darwinian epoch, in which Allen's work could clearly be rejected as Lamarckism; and then came the era of genetic orthodoxy, during which it could be tossed into the bin of discredited interests, for it was then fashionable to call people interested in taxonomy naturalists. Mayr himself, probably more than any other man, has brought taxonomy back into the biological social register. He has shown how essential is the study of systematics to a comprehension of the total life process. Although his interest in ecological rules does not represent a complete rediscovery, yet his emphasis on this aspect of biology may turn out to be an equally important landmark in biological history.

If the study of ecological rules has been neglected by biologists, physical anthropologists have slighted it even more. The study of race in man has been influenced not only by biological fashion but also by current political ideologies. In each country of Europe, as in America and in some African and Asiatic nations, a small but persistent group of men has continued to pile up objective data on the metrical and morphological characters of human beings. But in some European and Asiatic countries, before World War II, politicians and propagandists concocted theories of racial superiority and inferiority with which to bolster their political schemes. In other European countries, corresponding politicians and propagandists interested in internationalism concocted opposite theories, first, to claim that all races are equal in every respect, and second, to deny completely the existence of races. In America we have followed both these fashions in turn. Each has served the political motives of its period. The second movement, unfortunately for the progress of science, is still with us. So strong is the feeling against thinking or talking about race that, as far as I can find out, only one college course specifically devoted to the subject of race, and so labeled, has been given in America during the current academic year. For these various reasons the study of ecological variations in man has been neglected, and the study of race itself is nearly at a standstill. But fashions come and go. What is laughed at in one decade becomes the rage in another. Perhaps our turn will come.

Just as Rensch was the only voice crying in the zoölogical wilderness, the combined plea of three men, Garn, Birdsell and myself, has raised a feeble noise in the desert of physical anthropology. In our small and conceptually indiscreet book, *Races*,[5] we suggested that some of the racial variations in man may be due to adaptations, by a mechanism or mechanisms unknown, to extremes of environment. At the time we wrote it, I, at least, had never heard of Allen, Gloger, Bergmann, or Rensch. It was only in a review of our book by Dr. M. T. Newman [6] that I learned of their work. Since then I have found a little time to read what these zoölogists have written, and to think about how their findings may possibly apply to man. Just this small amount of contemplation has made it abundantly clear to me that if a person is to study the racial variations in man in terms of ecology, he must be a superscientist, thoroughly conversant with not only his own subject, including anatomy, but also physiology (particularly heat-and-sweat physiology), nutrition and growth, radiation physics, optics, body mechanics, genetics, and cultural anthropology in time and space. With all due respect to my colleagues, I know of no one individual who can meet these qualifications. Hence it looks as if the fulfillment of Allen's hope would have to be still further delayed.

Nevertheless, the problem can be stated. According to the modern concept of species formation, expounded by Mayr and others, the majority of animal species are polytypic; that is, they extend over a varied geographical range, and in a number of observable characteristics the local populations vary gradually from one end of the spatial range to another. A minority of species is monotypic, that is, lacking in geographical variation in any known character. Monotypic species are usually confined to small and isolated areas. Man is a polytypic species. Instances of genuine isolation, like that of the Polar Eskimo, are rare, and the isolation is probably of short duration. Like other polytypic species, man varies from place to place, and the different forms which his variations take appear to follow, in some but not all cases, the same ecological rules as other warm-blooded animals. Three of these rules, the oldest, concern us here.

(1) *Gloger's Rule*: "In mammals and birds, races which inhabit warm and humid regions have more melanin pigmentation than races of the same species in cooler and drier regions; arid regions are characterized by accumulation of yellow and reddish-brown phaeomelanin pigmentation." [7] "The phaeomelanins are subject to reduction in cold climate, and in extreme cases also the eumelanin (polar white)." [8]

(2) *Bergmann's Rule*: "The smaller-sized geographic races of a species are found in the warmer parts of the range, the larger-sized races in the cooler districts." [9]

(3) *Allen's Rule*: "Protruding body parts, such as tails, ears, bills, extremities, and so forth, are relatively shorter in the cooler parts of the range of the species than in the warmer parts." [9]

The rest of this paper will be devoted to an inquiry into the possible application of these three rules to man. They cannot be called laws in the sense of Newton's laws or the second law of thermodynamics, although these laws, and other well-established physical principles, no doubt contribute to whatever validity the three rules may be shown to possess. That no one simple law is involved in any case is shown by Rensch's discovery[3, 10] that these three rules, along with several others of his own formulation (Rensch's clutch rule and hair rule, for example), are subject to exceptions of 10 to 30 percent. The rules cannot be called laws, because controls have not been sufficiently established to eliminate outside functions, and because not enough experiments have been made. However, a hibernating animal that defies Bergmann's rule is no more a valid exception than a helicopter is to the law of gravity. If all exceptions were run to the ground and all leads followed, the physical basis for these observations could in each case be established, or the rule refuted.

In the case of man we have several advantages, and one disadvantage. We are dealing with a single species, or *rassenkreis*, to use Rensch's term,[3, 10] which for a mammal is extremely rich in individuals, and which covers a larger geographical area than that of almost any other mammal. More human beings have been "collected" than any other kind of fauna. Our measurements, while far from adequate, are relatively numerous. Another advantage is that we know quite a lot about the history of man. One principal disadvantage is that man possesses culture. In addition to his enormous capacity for physical adjustment to many climates, he has developed artificial adaptive aids, such as the use of fire, shelter, clothing, food preservation, and transportation. These aids have permitted him to occupy every single part of the land surface of the world, except the Greenland and Antarctic icecaps, and by means of them he is already looking for further conquests on other planets and in outer space. There neither Gloger, nor Bergmann, nor Allen can help him. In studying the putative applicability of these rules to man, our eyes are shifted not to the future but to the past, when man was a rare animal among millions of others, a relatively defenseless creature lacking defensive teeth, horns, or claws, but an animal who by his cunning brain and skillful hands conquered the forces of nature, making the beasts his servants, changing the face of the earth, growing in numbers, and learning to control everything except himself.

For the best part of a million years, some kind of man has existed, probably occupying not one but several environments, and during his evolutionary life span the climates of most if not all of the regions in which he has lived have changed, generally more than once. As part of the cultural growth of man, two principal evolutionary changes have been achieved.[11] The brain has gone through two major increases in size, quite independently of body size, which for primates seems to be standard procedure. The earliest hominids of which we know, the South African Plesianthropi, had a cranial capacity of about 660 cubic centimeters; Sinanthropus and Pithecanthropus hovered about the 900- to 1,000-cubic-centimeter locus; and the rest of fossil and all living varieties of men have a capacity in the neighborhood of 1350 cubic centimeters.[12] If we treat the brain as a square rather than as a cube, and measure the flattened-out area of the cerebral cortex, we arrive at tentative figures of 600 square centimeters for Plesianthropus, 1200 for Sinanthropus, and 2400 for modern man.[12, 13] In other words, man's brain may have evolved by two consecutive doublings of the cortical area. This concept, while controversial, at least has the advantage over others that it can be explained by currently popular genetic theory. Its acceptance (if it is to be accepted) will mean that two major steps in human evolution may have taken place since the ancestors of man became erect bipedal primates feeding themselves with their hands. This further means that some if not all of the climatically adaptive changes which distinguish modern races from one another may have been acquired in stage one or stage two of this process, rather than in stage three, the modern level of potential cerebration. The late Franz Weidenreich postulated that the Mongoloid face began with Sinanthropus in stage two.[14] Whether or not he was correct, that anatomist was prepared to accept the thesis of presapiens raciation, and the concomitant thesis of multiple evolution from an earlier evolutionary level. Whether or not one or several human stocks made this jump, we do not know, but for present purposes both possibilities must be taken into consideration.

We must not, however, assume that any or all stocks which passed through the first two cerebral size stages to the third were any more ape-like in many respects than the readers of this volume. Schultz [15] has shown that some of the features that distinguish man from his fellow occupants of the great primate house are more conservative and ancient in man than in the apes. For example, the heavy hair on the human scalp is also present in the newborn chimpanzee, which has hair elsewhere only on its eyelids, eyebrows, and arms. The erect position of the head on the top of the spine, with the position of the face and orbits below the braincase, is another example of what Schultz calls ontogenic retardation, or conservatism, using this term rather than the less palatable and perhaps less truthful, if commoner, word, foetalization. The human position of the great toe falls also in this class of conservative phenomena, while the smaller size of the other toes is due to shortening, rather than to an increase of the length of the big toe itself. Furthermore, we cannot assume that all earlier human types had big teeth and prognathus jaws. The gibbon's face is no larger in proportion to its brain and body than that of man. The siamang, in a few cases, has a chin.

In the basic evolutionary characters, all men are equally human as far as we can tell; if some races resemble one or another of the anthropoids in some particular feature, that may mean only that that particular race is more specialized, more differentiated from the common stock, than the others. No earlier evolutionary status is necessarily implied, at least until we know all the pertinent facts.

Schultz has shown that just as much variation is seen among the apes as among men, if not more. He says that the "skin color of the chimpanzee varies from black to white . . . the writer [Schultz] has the body of a young chimpanzee, born of black-haired parents, which had straw-colored hair at birth, and later this color changed to a reddish tint . . . Giants and pygmies have developed among chimpanzees and orangutans, and long-armed and short-armed varieties among gorillas . . . Of the great apes . . . each has a very limited distribution, in contrast to man, yet each has produced several species or subspecies which are morphologically but not geographically as different from each other as the main races of man." [16]

Schultz's statement shows that many of the differences between men which we consider racial also occur individually and racially among the apes. This means that the early human forms must have possessed the capacities for these same variations, some of which can therefore be very ancient, and can go back to the earlier evolutionary stages. In other words, a Negro may have become black before he became a man, a Nordic's ancestor blond and blue-eyed while his brain was still half its present cortical size. The evidence used in this paper does not favor any such interpretation, but neither does it render it impossible.

Taking up Gloger's rule first, we find that it was originally formulated to account for the color of feathers and fur, rather than of skin. Birds and beasts of humid forested regions, both in the cooler latitudes and in the tropics, tend to adopt somber colors; the association is with humidity and shade, rather than with temperature. Since individual birds and animals have been seen to grow darker or lighter when carried from one environment to another, it is clear that whatever influence produces this effect reflects a genetic capacity of considerable latitude. At any rate, it does not apply to man. His color variation is primarily concerned with the skin, which in a precultural state must have been wholly, except for the scalp, exposed to the elements, and in some racial and cultural situations still is.

Speaking very broadly, human beings have three kinds of skin. One is the pinkish white variety which burns badly on exposure to the sun, and fails to tan. Such skin is found in a minority of individuals in the cloudy region of northwest Europe, also among descendants of the inhabitants of this area who have migrated elsewhere, and among albinos anywhere. It is quite clearly defective skin, and causes its owners trouble anywhere anytime they step out of the shade. Clothing, lotions, wide-brimmed hats and sun-glasses help to mitigate its deficiency. Luckily for the rest, relatively few of mankind possess it.

At the opposite extreme is black or chocolate-brown skin, familiar as the integumental garb of the full-blooded Negro. Persons who wear skin of this type are the same color all over, except for their palms and soles. As I discovered in Ethiopia, the unexposed skin is sometimes even darker than the portions exposed to the sun, such as the hands and face, perhaps owing to an increased thickening of the horny layer in contact with solar radiation. Once this layer has thickened, a man with such a skin can travel anywhere without fear of the sun; he can roll up his sleeves, take off his shirt, or run naked in any climate where he or any other human would not be hindered by the cold. Negroes have gone to Alaska, and to the North Pole.

In between is the range of integumental color possessed by the majority of mankind, belonging to skins which although appearing as white, olive, yellowish, reddish, or brown, have one feature in common. The skin that is covered by clothing, if any, is relatively light. Exposed areas, if the light is strong enough, tan. In some populations this tanning can approach the darkness of the black-skinned peoples. However, skin that can tan can also bleach. Peoples who live in mid-latitude regions where the air is dry and the sky cloudless in summer, while in winter dampness and clouds are the rule, can shift their skin color with the seasons. This capacity for developing pigment in response to light and losing it when the light is gone, is probably the original genetic situation with man.

The physiological advantages for the second and third types of pigment are simple enough. They concern entirely, as far as we know, ultraviolet radiation. As Luckeish and others have shown,[17] the lower limit of solar energy that reaches the earth's surface is located at about 2900 to 2950 angstrom units. Any ultraviolet waves shorter than this are absorbed by the atmosphere, particularly by ozone. Radiation between 2950 and 3200 angstroms produces three principal known effects on human skin: erythema (sunburn), tanning, and ergosterol irradiation. The peak effectiveness of ultraviolet for erythema is at 2967 angstroms, which is also the approximate maximum for tanning and ergosterol irradiation. After the skin has been sunburned, it tans, and this prevents further injury. Meanwhile vitamin D is produced through the action of rays of the same wavelength band on ergosterol, and rickets is prevented. Since the pigment produced by tanning lies deeper in the skin than the level of irradiation, a tanned or black skin does not impede this vital physiological process.

Melanin, which is human pigment, prevents repeated erythema, and also hyperemia, a disorder of the blood produced by the penetration of visual and infra-red radiation. Black skin, then, protects naked human beings in regions where ultraviolet is a problem. Such regions are characterized by having the sun nearly overhead much of the year, few cloudy days, and high temperatures. A low angle of the sun and cloudiness both reduce the amount of ultraviolet that reaches the surface of the earth. High temperatures and the wetness produced by sweating increase the vulnerability of the skin to erythema.

In contrast to the genetic capacity for change inherent in skin that tans, black skin is constant. In the distant and naked past, it must have had a clear advantage over tannable skin. That advantage remains to be discovered experimentally. Geographically speaking, people with black skin, who are known to have lived in their present habitats since the rather mobile dawn of history, live in regions close to the equator where ultraviolet is most critical. They inhabit the forests of central Africa and the adjacent grasslands. The second great center is Melanesia, including Papua and northern Australia. They also included the extinct, in the full-blooded state, Tasmanians. In between Africa and Melanesia fringes of land and islands hold connecting links; Southern India, Ceylon, the Andamans, the Malay Peninsula, and the Lesser Sundas contain black-skinned peoples, as do some of the islands of the Philippines.

Except for Tasmania, whose inhabitants obviously migrated there from a region of lower latitude, these areas are all within 20 degrees of the equator, and most of them are within 10 degrees. In all of them there is little seasonal change. Aside from these uniformities, they represent a variety of environments, including shady forests, grasslands, deserts, and coastlines. Since we have a good idea what black skin is good for, we observe that there is no particular reason for it in the forests. Bright equatorial sun is, however, a problem in grasslands, deserts, and on the water.

Returning to the rest of the animal kingdom, we find that grassland and desert mammals are generally light or tawny colored.[18] This is true of animals whose skins are protected by hair. A few animals, however, are naked like man, and these are black or dark gray. They include the elephant, rhinoceros, hippopotamus, buffalo, and certain types of pig. These animals reach their peak of numbers and development in the grasslands or desert fringe; except for the rhino, they also enter the forest, where they are fewer and less favored. Their color, carried in from the sunlight, is neither an advantage nor a disadvantage in the shade.

In Africa the blackest Negroes live in the grasslands. In the forest we find two kinds of people: pygmies, who are not completely black, and Negroes. The pygmies hunt, and the Negroes farm. The two exchange products. Since the Negroes make the arrowheads and nets with which the pygmies hunt, the latter would have a hard time living without either these implements or the plantains that the Negroes give them for food. Furthermore, the food plants that the Negroes cultivate are of Southeast Asiatic origin, and they could hardly have been introduced later than the first millennium B.C. Since southern India got iron about this time, and the motive that brought people across the Indian Ocean to Africa was a search for iron, it is unlikely that the Negroes entered the forest to live much before the time of Christ.

If we look at Melanesia we see again that the forest is poor in game, the principal animal being the pig, escaped from domestication. The pig came in with agriculture, and neither can have been introduced much before the first millenium B.C. Therefore the present black-skinned populations of these two tropical forest areas must be historically recent; black skins in general go with grasslands or deserts, and have entered forests in numbers only with agriculture. In the Belgian Congo, the forest Negroes are decreasing in numbers while the pygmy population remains constant. If we look back to the Pleistocene, we see that the glacial advances and retreats in the north were accompanied by a succession of pluvial and interpluvial periods in the tropics. This is now an interstadial, halfway between. At least once the Sahara was blooming with grass and flowers, and at other times the forest was reduced to a fraction of its present area.

Why, one may ask, did not black skins develop in the Americas, where land within 10 degrees of the equator runs along a course of 4000 miles? The answer, which is geographical, confirms our interpretation of black skins in the Old World. The coast of Ecuador is heavily forested. Open country begins at the Peruvian border, 4 degrees south of the equator, whence it continues to the forest zone of Chile. The coastal desert averages only 20 miles wide. Owing to the combination of the mountains behind and the cold Humboldt current in front, the air is cool, the humidity high, the sky usually overcast, and little solar radiation gets through. Moving up into the highlands, we should expect a double concentration of ultra-violet at 10,000 feet, where one-sixth more solar radiation penetrates the atmosphere than at sea level. However, the region of Kuito, which is on the equator, is frequently cloudy; the year has two rainy peaks. Thunder, Brooks says,[19] is heard on 99 days each year. Since the air is also cold, the Indians cover up as much of their skin as possible. At 17 degrees farther south, on the shores of Lake Titicaca, less rain and fewer clouds appear, but the humidity is moderately high. Americans with untannable blond skins suffer intensely. The Indians, who wear broad-brimmed hats as well as the usual heavy clothing, tan to a deep reddish-brown on exposed parts.

Moving eastward we find most of the Amazonian countryside heavily forested. Indians, Negroes, whites, and all shades between get along with equal ease as far as ultraviolet is concerned. However, between the great river systems in Brazil, the Guianas, and Venezuela are patches of savannah, precisely the kind of country in which black-skinned animals and men luxuriate in Africa. But these patches are small, and not long ago may have been smaller. They support no tempting animal life as in Africa, and the few Indians who go out there are refugees from the forests that line the streams. There is no evidence of any earlier population in this region at all. From all of these considerations, no reason appears for a black-skinned population to have developed in the Americas. The relative antiquity of man in the two hemispheres is therefore beside the point.

While Gloger's rule appears to cover variations in the response of the human skin to ultraviolet, both Bergmann's and Allen's rules are cut to fit the other end of the scale, radiant heat. Unlike ultraviolet, radiant heat both enters and leaves the body, which is physiologically well adapted to maintain an even temperature under extreme environmental conditions. Clothing, shelter, and fire also help, but not to the exclusion of physiological adaptation.

Bergmann's rule, that animals of a warm-blooded species will be larger in the colder and smaller in the warmer portions of its ecological range, is based on the physical fact that the larger a body, all else, including shape, being equal, the smaller the ratio of skin surface area to bulk, since the first varies as the square, and the second as the cube. Small animals have more skin per pound. Since most of the heat loss is through the skin, the smaller the animal, all else being equal, the easier the process of keeping it cool. Other factors, some of which will be dealt with presently, modify this simple picture; if they and others still to be determined did not enter, it would be more than a rule.

As far as man is concerned, most of the measurements that we anthropologists take are of little use in testing Bergmann's rule. The two principal criteria used in the past are stature and the cephalic index. Stature is a composite of head height, neck length, trunk length, and leg length. It makes as much sense in the total measure of man as it would be to measure a rabbit from his hind leg to his left ear. The cephalic index is about as important in this respect as the width between the rabbit's eyes. Weight, trunk length, and chest circumference are our most useful criteria for testing the rule.

In general, weight works.[20] In Europe the Irish have a mean of 157 pounds, the Finns of 154, and so on down the temperature cline to the Spaniards with 132 and the racially white Berbers of Algeria with 124 pounds. In Asia the Mongoloid peoples are graded from the North Chinese with 142 to the Annamites with 112 pounds, and the Siberian peoples of the far north are probably heavier than the North Chinese, although no figures are easily available. Their neighbors across Bering Strait, the Eastern Aleuts, run to means of 150 pounds. In the consideration of these arctic peoples lies the fallacy of using stature as a criterion of total size exposed, for the Aleuts' stature means vary from 159 to 164 centimeters, which puts them in the short category. This shortness is due to reduction in leg and neck length, while the trunk is both long and bulky. In South America there is every evidence that the rule holds true, with bulky Indians at the cold end, and smaller ones in the forests, while up in the chilly altiplano they again grow bulky. In Central America we find a mean of 119 pounds for the Maya of Yucatan, which rises as one goes northward into the United States and Canada to a peak in the 160's.

Low figures are obtained from people like the Andamanese, whose male population averages only 98 pounds, and the Bushmen of the Kalihari, with 89. Even the Baluba, an equatorial Negro tribe, weigh only 118 pounds, and the Australian aborigine around the Gulf of Carpentaria, 123. In Polynesia, where offshore breezes make heat loss no problem, peoples of tropical provenience, the Hawaiians and the Maori, living at 20 and 40 degrees from the equator respectively, weigh from 140 pounds upward, much more than the means for the inhabitants of Java and Sumatra, whence their ancestors are said to have come. Their islands are larger and hotter.

The explanation of Bergmann's rule is far from simple. While light weight would be advantageous in hot places, since there is little that man can do culturally to mitigate the effects of the heat except to stay inside air-conditioned houses, modern conditions make it possible for small people to survive as well in cold places as large people, and yet we change. One clue comes out in the fact that thermal equilibrium is most effective in the prime of life, so that babies and the very old are more likely than adults to suffer from extremes of temperature. Another is that if baby animals are born in the cold, the larger ones are the more likely to escape freezing. This explanation leaves me as cold as the baby, since changes in body size can take place in a single generation, and under nonselective conditions. Man's size is as plastic as his tannable skin color, and as automatic. Anyone who has visited the Lower Amazon country has seen that the Brazilian citizens in that tropical forest are of one size, whatever their color, hair form, or cast of facial features. At least three racial stocks are concerned, the Mediterranean, the Negro, and the American Indian. All come out the same. Farther south, representatives of these three stocks are much larger.

The question of thermal control, affecting shape even more than size, will be discussed presently. At the moment, one nonthermal factor that affects size may be discussed, namely, nutrition. In my North Albanian [21] series I found that the tribesmen living on food raised on granitic soil were significantly smaller than those who walked over limestone, thus confirming the results of French investigators more than half a century earlier. Trace elements are important, and so are feeding habits. In a Moroccan village studied by Schorger [22] the boys were given almost no meat until they reached the age of 14, at which they were expected to work. From then on they ate with the men, whose diet included animal proteins. At that point their growth was relatively rapid. A main diet of polished rice goes with small people; how big they would have been if they had eaten other foods in a hot climate is open to question.

Most striking of all the size differences in man are those between the pygmy peoples of Africa, Indonesia, and Melanesia, and normal human beings. However, the pygmies are not much smaller than some of the people of the Amazon valley. In all these selvas the leaching of the soil through excessive rainfall is held responsible, through the agency of washing out of trace elements, and it may be interesting to note that man is not the only pygmy in the forest. In Africa the elephant, hippopotamus, buffalo, and chimpanzee all have pygmy counterparts. What affects man there cannot be cultural; it is of universal mammalian application, since the animals mentioned eat the whole range of available foodstuffs, and are exposed to the same range of temperature, humidity, and solar radiation.

Along with size comes the question of basal metabolism.[23] Although questions have arisen about coördinating techniques, still the geographical distribution of the results follows a Bergmann pattern. The norm is set for Europe and the northeastern United States; rates more than 10 percent above normal are found among the Eskimo, who go up to 30 percent of excess, the Ojibwa Indians of the Great Lakes region, and the Araucanians of southern Chile. Rates 10 percent and more below the norm are found among Australian aborigines and inhabitants of the hotter parts of India, Australia, and Brazil. Americans in New Orleans are also below par. This investigation needs a lot of checking and controlling, but despite two exceptions,[23, 24] the trend is clear. Furthermore, like alternations of pigment and gross size, changes in basal metabolism can in some cases be acquired.

That basal metabolism should change with climate makes sense, as does the whole mechanism of heat control in man. Here we enter a field where many physiologists have brutalized themselves and their friends for the sake of science. One investigator writes that he and his team even took the rectal temperatures of porcupines in the Talkeetna Mountains of Alaska at 22°F.[25] Others thrust thermocouples into their flesh, piercing their palms and wrists to the depth of the bone. Still others consented to be locked in sealed chambers from which alternately heat and oxygen were withdrawn, while a select few pedaled themselves on bicycles nearly to death. As a result of this self-sacrifice, we are in a position to evaluate Bergmann's rule in man.

Being a warm-blooded animal is a great advantage. It permits one to move and act at nearly all times in nearly all places, instead of scampering feverishly for shade or waiting for the chill to burn off before moving. However, the process of keeping the internal organs at a temperature of 98.6° F has its problems too. This temperature can fall to 77°F or rise to 110°F before death intervenes, but variations of half these magnitudes are serious, particularly on the high side, for man can lose heat more safely than he can gain it. Even when he is trying to keep warm, man loses a certain amount of heat functionally in evaporation of moisture through the palms, soles, axillae, and pubic regions, just to keep tactile and hinge areas ready for action.

As long as the temperature of the outside environment is below 81°F, the body normally loses heat by radiation and convection. At 81° it begins to sweat, and the surface of the body grows increasingly moist, until at 93°F, in a saturated atmosphere, the whole body is covered, water is dripping off the surface, and the perspiration fails to do its work, which is to cool the surface of the skin by evaporation. At this point, if the temperature rises without a drop in humidity, trouble is near. However, in dry air only 40 percent of the body surface is normally wet at 93°F; at blood temperature the ratio is 50 percent, and a complete coverage, in the American human guinea pig, is not attained until 106°F.[26]

The evaporation of sweat is the principal means by which the body loses its heat. Experiments have shown that a resting man at 122°F and a humidity of 44 percent will lose 1798 grams of sweat per hour; a working man, in a humidity of 35.6 percent saturation, will lose 3880 grams per half hour, or half his normal blood volume, at a cooling potential of 25 to 30 times the normal resting metabolism. Needless to say, such a liquid turnover requires him to drink gallons of water, and also taxes his heart. It is greatly to the advantage of human beings living under conditions of extreme heat to avoid this circumstance as much as possible.

Such heat is found largely in the deserts of the world,[18, 19, 27] which lie on either side of the equator, on the tropics of Cancer and Capricorn. Chief among them are the Sahara, Arabian, Persian, Turkestan, Thar, Gobi, Kalahari, Australian, Argentine, Chilean, and Colorado deserts. Of these the Turkestan, Gobi, Argentine, and Colorado deserts lie farther from the equator. Characteristic of deserts is a great diurnal variation in temperature, and often a seasonal one as well. On a hot day the mercury may fall to 71°F at 5 A.M., reach the critical sweating point of 93°F at 10:15 A.M., hit a peak of 108° at 2 P.M., and fall to 93°F again at 7:45 P.M. A hunter, who has nothing to work with but his own body and a bow and arrows or a handful of spears, will be up before daylight, and he will be on his way by the time the coolest point of the daily cycle has been reached. He will be able to go out to his hunting ground before the heat bothers him, and if he is lucky he can make his kill early and take his time on the way home before or during the heat of the day. If he is on a two- or three-day hunting trip, he can snooze under a bush in siesta-time, and return on another morning.

An Arab who is herding camels, or conducting a caravan, will travel by the light of the moon and stars, and sleep under a lightproof black tent in the middle of the afternoon. Such a man if forced to it can walk all day in the heat, but if he travels only at night he can get three times as far without water before collapsing. Even truck drivers work at night, to save their tires as well as their own systems.

Animals that live in the desert belong to two classes, those that can do without water, and those that use it to cool the body through evaporation. The first category includes especially a number of rodents, which derive water from desert vegetation, and can even extract it metabolically from dry seeds. Such animals have no water to spare; they hide behind or under rocks or bushes during the heat of the day, or burrow far underground, in some cases pulling stoppers of earth in behind them. When the ground temperature is 122°F, it may be only 83°F at a depth of 1 foot 3 inches, while at 6 feet it may fall as low as 68°F with considerable humidity. Animals that hide during the day to save water will die when forced to spend a few hours in the bright sun in the heat of the day.

The other class of animals is composed of larger forms, such as the camel, oryx, and addax, which are able to hold up to a fifth of their body bulks in water, and utilize it gradually. In this sense they are no better off than a man of 120 pounds weight carrying two 5-quart canteens. In cool spring weather they are at an advantage over the man, however, for they can derive their moisture from herbage; only in the hot and barren season do they depend on their speed to carry them to water. In addition to their water-holding capacity, these animals have something else in common. They all have long legs and necks, and are extremely gracile for their weight. Their bones are long, fine, and hard, their musculature light. In treeless terrain they can make high speeds. Even the cat family has its desert representative, the long-legged cheetah, which is said to be the fastest runner of living things.

Man in the desert is also light and gracile. He too needs to be able to travel far on a small heat load. But his animal companions have buff-colored hairy coats, which reflect solar light; it is unlikely that they lose their heat in his fashion. He must lose it through his skin surface, and the more surface he has per unit of weight the better. The more he can lose through radiation and convection the less he has to sweat; the more skin surface he can use for evaporation, the higher the temperature he can stand. The smaller his bulk, the less the load on his heart. The shape of his body takes on added importance as we realize that all parts of its surface do not lose heat equally. The back of his hand has about 400 sweat glands to the square centimeter, the forehead 200, and the cheek as few as 50. The hands, which comprise 5 percent of the body surface on normal Americans, lose 20 percent of the heat of the body by evaporation.[28]

When a man begins to perspire, moisture appears first on his forehead, his neck, some of the larger areas on the front and back of his trunk, the back of his hands, and the adjacent part of his forearms. The head and neck must lose heat rapidly for they have the brain to keep in thermal equilibrium, and the head is globular in form, the worst possible shape for heat loss. After this, the cheek, the lateral surfaces of the trunk, and the rest of the extremity surfaces begin, but these regions sweat much less. Sweating is always slight to moderate on areas rich in subcutaneous fat, such as the cheek and the gluteal and mammary regions. The inside of the thighs and armpits sweat even less, since they face in and not out, and are in a poor position for heat loss. The palms and soles, which perspire at lower temperatures, lose the least of all in periods of stress.

The chief burdens, then, fall on the neck and head, which have purely local duties to attend to, and on the hands and forearms, which serve as radiators for the whole body. From the engineering standpoint, the body consists of a collection of cylinders of various diameters, of which the arms and fingers are among the narrowest. When two bodies that have the same volume consistently vary in the diameters of the cylinders of which each is composed, the heat loss is greater for the consistently narrower body than for the thicker one.[29] Hence the relatively great survival value of long, tapering forearms and fingers in a dry, hot place become self-evident.

One of the racial peculiarities of Negroes is long arms, with particular emphasis on the length of the forearm, and large hands, with long fingers. Forest negroes often have relatively short legs, but we have seen that the legs have much less to do with heat regulation than the arms. The Nilotics, Somalis, Masai, and other black-skinned peoples of the Sahara, Sudan, and the Horn of Africa, have long skinny legs as well, and long gracile necks; no case of adaptation to a given environmental situation could be clearer. The same is true of South Indians, the Ceylonese Vedda, most Melanesians, and the Australian aborigines of the desert, as well as white Australians from Queensland. The Bushman of the Kalahari is extremely slender. On the inhabitants of the American deserts information is defective. At any rate, as far as we know, the desert portion of Allen's rule holds for man, for obvious reasons. The mechanism of change is less obvious. If it is Darwinian selection, it is hard to see how it applies to white Australians.

The other end of Allen's rule applies to adaptation to cold. Naked savages can live without much clothing in temperatures down to the freezing point. Several technical experiments have been performed on Australian aborigines sleeping naked in the desert when the night temperature fell to the frost point.[30] These people keep rows of small fires burning, and sleep between rows. Parts of their skin surface become quite cold, others hot. They seem to be able to absorb radiant heat from the fires on some parts of their skin surface, in all of which the venous blood flow is at a minimum. Thus they survive until morning. In the day time the air temperature rises rapidly.

The Yaghans, [20, 30] canoe Indians of Tierra del Fuego, paddled nearly naked in their boats in foggy channels, in an environment where year-round temperatures hover above and about the freezing point. Darwin saw a naked woman nurse a naked baby while sleet melted on her body, and a group of Yaghans who drew up to the outer glow of the explorers' fire sweated profusely. The Ona, foot Indians of the plains on the northern part of Tierra del Fuego, wore guanaco-skin robes and moccasins, and slept behind skin windbreaks in the snow. The Chukchi of Siberia, who wear Eskimo-style clothing, like to remove their shirts to cool off, and Bogoras saw Chukchi women thrust lumps of snow between their breasts for the same purpose.

The mechanism of heat loss in cold conditions will explain all this. When the environmental temperature falls, the body stops sweating at 83°F, and heat loss is accomplished wholly by radiation and convection. Venous blood that has been returning from the back of the hand through superficial blood vessels on the arm is rerouted; vasoconstriction shuts off this road, and vasodilation opens alternate channels through deeplying veins that surround the artery. The chilled venous blood returning to the heart cools the arterial blood, so that it will have less heat to lose, and the heat gained by the venous blood is carried to the heart. Thus heat loss through the hand and arm is reduced to but 1.5 percent of the body's total loss at higher temperatures. The amount of blood that flows through 100 cubic centimeters of fingertip tissue falls from a maximum of 120 to 0.2 cubic centimeters per minute.[31] The arm itself becomes an insulator in depth.

At an air temperature of 73°F a naked American with a rectal temperature of 97° will show the following skin temperatures: head, 94°; trunk, 93°; hands, 86°; feet, 77°. Deep thermocouple work has shown that the hands and wrists chill to the bone, literally. However, when the temperature of the extremities falls below a point between 41°F and 50°F, vasoconstriction ceases, and peripheral blood flow is accelerated and keeps the extremities from freezing.[32] What this means racially is that a person of North European ancestry can afford to have big bony hands which help keep him cool in hot weather, because at the winter temperatures at which he operates, particularly when clothed, the size of his hands makes no difference in heat economy; they are simply shut off from the heat system, like an empty room.

It is a matter of casual observation that most Mongoloids have small and delicate hands and feet and short distal segments of both upper and lower limbs. Furthermore, their necks are short. However, recent work on the Eskimo has shown that despite expectation these people have hands as large as ours.[33] It is believed, although the material to prove this has not yet been published, that racial differences in blood-vessel patterns exist, which would account for the Eskimo hand as well as for the ability of the Australian aborigine to sleep in the cold without clothing.

Turning to the Eskimo foot, which is small, as expected, it is common knowledge that his excellent boot keeps his foot warm, and so it does as long as it is dry. Water can leak in through the stitch holes if the sinew is not preswollen,[30, 34] and it can also come from sweat induced through exertion. A wet boot affords little insulation, and some Eskimos freeze their toes. Similarly, the hand is here a liability; as Quartermaster Corps researches have shown, it is almost impossible to keep a hand warm in the best of mittens when the body is at rest out of doors in very low temperatures.[35] Eskimos bring their arms and hands in next to the body skin, leaving sleeves dangling, when they can.

Ears, nose tips, and other protrusions need special protection; with the fall of the thermometer the amount of blood sent to the ears increases greatly, and a relatively great loss of heat occurs at this vulnerable point. Polar and subpolar peoples are invariably described, in the prime of the individual, as well equipped with subcutaneous fat. This fat is especially developed on critical spots, such as the cheek, wrists, and ankles. One centimeter of fat is given the same insulation rating as a complete suit of winter clothing.[36] The healthy Negro living in a hot country carries almost no subcutaneous fat. His superior performance in the desert, compared with that of whites of the same age and weight, has been demonstrated.[37]

In summary, adjustment to the cold requires large body mass, short extremities, much fat, deep vein-routing, a high basal metabolism, or some combination of these five features. Adjustment to the heat requires small body mass, attenuated extremities, little fat, extensive superficial vein-routing, a low basal metabolism, and a greater number of sweat glands per unit of surface area. Possibly the role of melanin in starting the skin to sweat at a lower threshold by conversion of ultraviolet to radiant heat may be added. Any combination of these seven may be involved. The type or types of physique which are most suited to cold resistance are those which, the doctors tell us, are most likely to suffer from heart trouble, so it is a lucky thing that adjustment to the cold does not place an extra load on the heart. Heat-adapted physiques are those best calculated to stand the extra heart load which they receive.

So far we have been thinking about heat loss from the skin, but calories also leave the body through the lungs. In hot weather the heat loss from the lungs through respiration is negligible, and of little help to the suffering organism, but as the mercury drops this source of leakage becomes serious, reaching 50 kilogram calories per 1000 liters of expired air in extreme cold.[38] Not only does this affect the total heat load of the body, but it subjects the nasal passages to heavy chilling. To what extent the Mongoloid face, inside and out, may compensate for this by its special architecture remains to be discovered.

One other climatic hazard which human beings have faced and overcome is that of reduced oxygen at high altitudes. Dill [39] and his associates have found that the inhabitants of the Andes have become able to live and work at an altitude of 17,500 feet and more, through the fact that their blood carries a much higher concentration of red corpuscles than is the case with people at sea level. At the same time they need more air, which they obtain through more efficient automatic breathing control as well as with larger lungs. The requirements for physique in high altitudes resemble those for cold. Perhaps it is no coincidence that the two great plateaus of the world, the Andes and Tibet, are inhabited by Mongoloid peoples.

This paper does not cover, even in outline, all of the more obvious adaptive variations in man, in the fields of color, size and form. No attempt has been made to deal with the eye or the hair. Physiology has been mentioned only where it affects color, size, and form. Little attention has been paid to genetics, since I believe that a functional description is the first step in the study of heredity. If this paper will rouse a controversy, and start a few more natural scientists, anthropologists included, thinking along ecological lines, I shall be happy. These ideas,[40] right or wrong, appear to make sense as a small sequence of the over-all picture of climate and life on earth, so ably presented in the other papers of this conference.

REFERENCES

1. J. A. Allen, "The influence of physical conditions in the genesis of species," *Radical Review 1*, 108–140 (1877); reprinted in *Smithsonian annual report for 1905* (Washington, 1906), p. 399.

2. Carl Bergmann, "Ueber die Verhältnisse. . . ," *Göttinger Studien 3*, 595–708 (1847).

3. Bernhard Rensch, "Some problems of geographical variations and species formation," *Proc. Linn. Soc.* (London), 149th Session, pp. 275–285 (1936–37).

4. Ernst Mayr, *Systematics and the origin of species* (Columbia University Press, New York, 1949), p. 93.

5. C. S. Coon, S. M. Garn, and J. B. Birdsell, *Races* (C. C. Thomas, Springfield, Ill., 1950).

6. M. T. Newman, *Bol. Bibl. de Antropologia Amer. 13*, 189–192 (1951), review of Coon, Garn, and Birdsell, *Races*.

7. Th. Dobzhansky, *Genetics and the origin of species* (Columbia University Press, New York, ed. 3, 1951), p. 152.

8. Mayr, reference 4, p. 90.

9. Mayr, reference 4, p. 283.

10. Bernhard Rensch, *Das Prinzip geographischer Rassenkreise und das Problem der Artbildung* (Berlin, 1929).

11. A. H. Schultz, "The specializations of man and his place among the catarrhine primates," *Cold Spring Harbor Symposium 15* (Cold Spring Harbor, New York, 1950), 37–53; deduction from breakdown of graph on p. 45.

12. G. W. H. Schepers, "The endocranial casts of the South African apemen," Part 2 in R. Broom and G. W. H. Schepers, *The South African fossil apemen* (Transvaal Museum Memoirs No. 2, Pretoria, 1946); Franz Weidenreich, *The skull of Sinanthropus Pekinensis* (Lancaster, Pa., 1943), No. 127 of *Palaeontologia Sinica, The National Geological Survey of China*.

13. S. T. Bok, "Cephalization and the boundary values of the brain and body size in mammals," *Proc. Koninkl. Nederland. Akad. Wetenschap., 42*,

515–525 (1939); Gerhardt von Bonin, "Brain weight and body weight of mammals," *Jour. Gen. Psych. 16*, 379–389 (1937); "The cerebral cortex of the cebus monkey," *Jour. Comp. Neurol. 69*, 181–227 (1938); "On encephalometry," *Jour. Comp. Neurol. 75*, 286–314 (1941); *Essay on the cerebral cortex* (C. C. Thomas, Springfield, Ill., 1950); B. Danilewsky, "Die quantitativen Bestimmungen der grauen und weissen Substanzen im Gehirn," *Centralblatt für die medicinischen Wissenschafter*, (1880), p. 241; Eugene Dubois, "Ueber die Abhängigkeit des Hirngewichtes von der Körpergrosse beim Menschen," *Archiv für Anthropologie 25*, 423–441 (1898); W. N. Kraus, C. Davison, A. Weil, "Measurement of cerebral and cerebellar surfaces, III: Problems encountered in measuring the cerebral cortical surface in man," *Archives Neurol. & Psychol. 19*, 454–477 (1928); D'Arcy W. Thompson, *On growth and form* (Macmillan, New York, 1945). Our figures were derived from the foregoing sources with the help of Dexter Perkins, Jr. Constants used were: cubic capacity in cubic centimeters, visible cortical surface area, extent of sulci as seen from original specimens and endocranial casts, and a sulcal factor by which the visible cortical surface area is to be multiplied in order to obtain the total or extended cortical surface area. The sulcal factor is 4.5 in modern man, while in Sinanthropus-Pithecanthropus it is estimated as 3, in the Plesianthropi as 2.5.

14. M. Van Dilla, R. Day, and P. A. Siple, "Special problem of hands," in L. H. Newburgh, *Physiology of heat regulation* (Saunders, Philadelphia, 1949), pp. 374–386.

15. A. H. Schultz, "The specializations of man and his place among the catarrhine primates," *Cold Spring Harbor Symposium 15*, 35–53 (1950).

16. *Ibid.*, p. 49.

17. Matthew Luckeish, *Applications of germicidal, erythemal, and infrared energy* (Van Nostrand, New York, 1946), pp. 59–72.

18. R. A. Buxton, *Animal life in deserts* (Arnold, London, 1923).

19. C. E. P. Brooks, *Climate* (Scribner, New York, 1930).

20. C. S. Coon, *The races of Europe* (Macmillan, New York, 1939); E. A. Hooton, "Notes on the anthropometric characters of the Yaghan and the Ona," in S. K. Lothrop, *The Indians of Tierra del Fuego* (New York, 1928); W. W. Howells, "Anthropometry of the natives of Arnhem Land and the Australian race problem," *Peabody Museum Papers 16*, no. 1 (1937); Rudolph Martin, *Lehrbuch der Anthropologie* (Jena, 1928), 3 vols.; G. D. Williams, "Maya-Spanish crosses in Yucatan," *Peabody Museum Papers 13*, no. 1 (Cambridge, Mass., 1931).

21. C. S. Coon, "The mountains of giants," *Peabody Museum Papers 23*, no. 3 (1950).

22. W. D. Schorger, doctoral dissertation, Harvard University, 1952, unpublished.

23. E. A. Wilson, "Basal metabolism and race," *Amer. Jour. Phys. Anthrop. 3* (NS), 1–20 (1945).

24. Italians and Somalis in Italian Somaliland.

25. Laurence Irving, "Physiological adaptation to cold in Arctic and tropic animals," *Federation Proc. 10*, 253 (1951).

26. H. C. Bazett, "The regulation of body temperature," in Newburgh, *Physiology of heat regulation*, pp. 109–192; C. H. Best and N. B. Taylor, *The human body and its functions* (Holt, New York, 1948); Richard Day, "Regional heat loss," in Newburgh, *Physiology of heat regulation*, pp. 240–261; J. D.

Hardy, "Heat transfer," *ibid.*, pp. 78–108; L. P. Herrington, "The range of physiological response to climatic heat and cold," *ibid.*, pp. 262–276; Sid Robinson, "Physiological adjustments to heat," *ibid.*, pp. 193–231; C. R. Spealman, "Physiologic adjustments to heat," *ibid.*, pp. 232–239.

27. E. F. Adolph, *Physiology of man in the desert* (Interscience Press, New York, 1947).

28. Bazett, reference 26, p. 131.

29. Hardy, reference 26, p. 97.

30. F. R. Wulsin, "Adaptations to climate among non-European peoples," in Newburgh, *Physiology of heat regulation*, pp. 3–69.

31. Day, reference 26, p. 243.

32. Spealman, reference 26, p. 236.

33. Kaare Rodahl and James Edwards, Jr., "The body surface area of Eskimos as determined by the linear and the height-weight formulas," USAF Arctic Aeromedical Lab., Ladd Air Force Base, Alaska, Project 22–1301–0001, Part 1 (1952).

34. C. R. Spealman, "Wet cold," in Newburgh, *Physiology of heat regulation*, pp. 367–374.

35. H. S. Belding, "Protection against dry cold," *ibid.*, pp. 351–367; Van Dilla, Day, and Siple, reference 14, p. 384.

36. Bazett, reference 26, p. 145.

37. P. T. Baker, "The effects of a hot-dry climate on gross morphology," OQMG R&D Environmental Protection Branch, Report No. 197 (Lawrence, Mass. 1953); see also R. W. Newman, "Measurement of body fat," *ibid.*, Report No. 193, and "Weights of army personnel," Report No. 194 (1952).

38. Day, reference 26, p. 259.

39. D. B. Dill, *Life, heat, and altitude* (Harvard University Press, Cambridge, Mass., 1938).

40. For help in the collection of data and formulation and evaluation of ideas, I wish to thank Dr. W. H. Crozier, Dr. Stanley M. Garn, Dr. A. Kidder, II, Dr. W. M. Krogman, Dr. Marshall T. Newman, Dr. Herbert J. Ratcliffe, Dr. Wm. L. Strauss, Mr. Fred Ullmer, Jr., and three of my students, Jerry Epstein, Joseph Leschik, and Dexter Perkins, Jr.

ADDITIONAL REFERENCES

H. F. Blum, *Photodynamic action and diseases caused by light* (American Chemical Society Monograph No. 85, New York, 1941).

W. C. Boyd, *Genetics and the races of man* (Little Brown, Boston, 1950).

E. W. Count, *This is race* (Schuman, New York, 1950).

J. B. D'Avila, "Anthropometry of the Indians of Brazil," in *Handbook of South American Indians*, U. S. National Museum Bull. 143, vol. 6 (Washington, 1950), pp. 71–84.

S. Q. Duntley and E. A. Edwards, " 'Melanoid' a skin pigment," *Science 90*, no. 2330, suppl. p. 7 (1939); "An analysis of skin pigment changes after exposure to sunlight," *Science 90*, 235–237 (1939); "The pigments and color of living human skin," *Amer. Jour. Anatomy 65*, 1–33 (1939).

W. H. Flower and Richard Lydekker, *Mammals living and extinct* (London, 1891).

R. R. Gates, "Studies of interracial crossing, I. Spectrophotometric measurements of skin color," *Human Biology 24*, 25–34 (1952).

W. K. Gregory, *Evolution emerging* (Macmillan, New York, 1951), 2 vols.

R. Hesse, W. C. Allee, and K. P. Schmidt, *Ecological animal geography*, (Wiley, New York, ed. 2, 1951).

Hydrographic Office, *Sailing directions for the Persian Gulf*, H. O. No. 158 (Washington, D. C., 1944).

Immanuel Kant, "Von den verschiedenen Racen der Menschen" (On the distinctiveness of the races in general), in E. W. Count, *This is race*, pp. 16–24.

Helmut Landsberg, *Physical climatology* (School of Mineral Industries, Pennsylvania State College, State College, Pa., 1947).

Edward Loth, *Anthropologie des parties molles* (Warsaw and Paris, 1931).

Carlos Monge, *Acclimatization in the Andes* (Johns Hopkins University Press, Baltimore, 1948).

L. H. Newburgh, *Physiology of heat regulation* (Saunders, Philadelphia, 1949).

Jones Quain, *Elements of anatomy* (London, 1909).

G. G. Simpson, *Tempo and mode in evolution* (Columbia University Press, New York, 1944); *The meaning of evolution* (Yale University Press, New Haven, 1949).

E. H. Starling, *Principles of human physiology* (Lee and Febiger, Philadelphia, ed. 6, 1933).

Morris Steggerda, "Anthropometry of South American Indians," *Handbook of South American Indians*, U.S. National Museum Bull. 143, vol. 6 (Washington, 1950), pp. 57–68; "The pigmentation and hair of South American Indians," *ibid.*, pp. 85–90.

T. D. Stewart and M. T. Newman, "An historical résumé of the concept of differences in Indian types," *Amer. Anthropologist 53*, 19–36 (1951).

Walter Stiles, *Trace elements in plants and animals* (Macmillan, New York, 1946).

T. W. Todd and L. Van Gorder, "The quantitive determination of black pigment in the skin of the American Negro," *Amer. Jour. Phys. Anthrop. 4*, 239–260 (1921).

F. A. Ulmer, Jr., "Melanin in the felidae, with special reference to the genus Lynx," *Jour. Mammalogy 22*, 285–288 (1941).

F. R. Wulsin, "Responses of man to a hot environment," OQMG Military Planning Div., R & D Branch, EPS Report no. 139 (Washington, 1939).

3

CLIMATE AND CIVILIZATION

Paul B. Sears

THE MOST CURSORY KNOWLEDGE OF such traits as the use of fire, clothing, shelter, and diet makes it clear that climate is an implicit function of the process we call culture. Since civilization can be defined as an advanced manifestation of culture, it seems reasonable to infer that the relation persists at the advanced level. The issue is clouded, however, because the techniques of civilization seem at times to have emancipated it from the controls that operate under more primitive conditions.

So far as the genesis of civilization is concerned, we do not have to rely solely upon inference. Civilization did not begin until men had surcease from the endless quest for nourishment. Such respite can come only from an efficient agriculture. The classic cradles of that art are also those of civilization — the now semiarid Middle East with its wheat, Latin America with maize, India and Indo-China with rice are examples. In none of these areas was temperature unfavorable to human comfort or to the growth of crops. In all of them adequate moisture was available, directly by rainfall or through drainage from higher lands.

This is not to say that climate alone was involved. But in each instance it has been an indispensable element in a matrix that included favorable conditions of topography, mineral nutrients, and the indigenous fauna and flora. None of these is really independent of climate. Even in the sophisticated food production of today these factors continue to operate, and the existence of an optimum climate for staple crops is a major economic fact. The problem is not whether climate is involved, but the manner and degree of its involvement.

We encounter a difficulty at the outset. Even the best of our present climatic classifications are somewhat arbitrary, provisional, and empirical. Aside from the technical difficulties of the standardizing of observations over long periods of time, it is possible to subdivide climates to almost any degree of refinement — for example, to conditions on opposite sides of a house, or to the interior and exterior of a hedge. Little is on record about one of the most important factors of climate, that is, evaporation, which has had to be treated as a derivative from other, measured factors.[1] In consequence, the reliability of existing classifications can be tested only by comparing them with such geographical phenomena as natural vegetation and soils, which are regarded as an integral expression of climate. It is with these reservations in mind, then, that the following discussion is presented.

So far as I know, no single species of plant or animal can transgress very far beyond its characteristic climatic range, unless it undergoes evolutionary changes that in turn set new limits. For this phenomenon there are good and sufficient reasons to be found in physiology, which finds for each species its range of tolerance in respect not only to the several factors of climate but to their combinations and rhythmic patterns.

The striking exception is man, with a relatively small group of organisms that accompany him and thrive, so to speak, in the shadow of his presence. This does not mean that man lacks physiological limits. Rather he enjoys the benefits of that vicarious and cumulative experience which we call culture, and by means of it can adjust himself, often with great advantage, to almost any type of climate the earth provides. By cultural traits such as clothing, shelter, irrigation, diet, and regimen, man, without evolutionary physical changes, has broken through what must have been his original climatic limits.

That such limits once existed seems reasonable enough, despite the scanty fossil evidence. It is true that man's range during the prehuman stage may have been fairly extensive, for the geological climate in general was milder than it became after the human adventure began. If man became man during the late Pliocene period or early Pleistocene, the human stage appears to have begun in an environment in which species ranges were shrinking, owing to expansion of polar climates.

For simplicity of discussion, and for other reasons, I shall assume that we are still in the Pleistocene, which I shall equate with the Human period. On that basis, the development of human culture has occurred in the face not only of strongly marked climatic zones but of strongly marked climatic pulsations, accompanying repeated advances and retreats of continental ice. Some of these events are conveniently summarized in our long pollen records from Mexico and New Mexico, which show at least three intervals during which climate has been as warm and dry as it is now (Fig. 1).

Thus man, in the early stages of his culture, was doubtless obliged to move at times, and at other times he had excellent opportunities to do so.

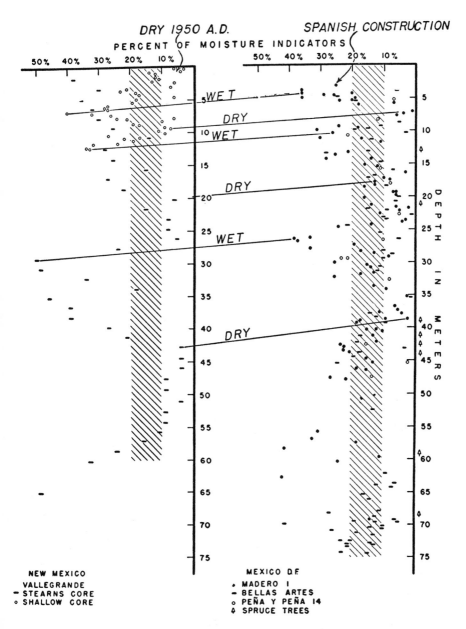

Fig. 1. Diagram showing alternating periods of prolonged moist and dry conditions, revealed by pollen analysis of deep cores (65–75 meters deep) at two stations approximately 1,600 miles apart.

Presumably he made appropriate cultural adjustments under both conditions.

The real questions as to the relation of climate to civilization are two, as I see them. First, to what extent does climate set limits to the process of civilization? Second, to what extent is the *quality* of civilization an expression of climatic influence? The first of these questions has been a challenge to technology, the second a source of lively controversy.

Of the approximately fourteen acres per capita of land surface available to the present world population, nine are reckoned as either too dry, too cold, or too rough to be productive. Of the remaining five, slightly more than three, for a variety of reasons, are substandard for the production of food. This leaves only a little more than one acre of land per capita to carry the burden of feeding the world's population.[2] The bulk of good land lies in those areas of the temperate zones where the balance between rainfall and evaporation is such as to give optimum mineral nutrient cycles for high protein production (Fig. 2). Speaking generally, here are the grain belts of the world. Probably these regions must continue to bear a large share in the feeding of the world. They also contain the soils most responsive to further improvement. In other words, each increment of capital investment in these regions will yield the highest return.

Another interesting possibility has been suggested by Firman Bear, who maintains that to keep such soils from deteriorating, they must be held at the highest level of production. The responsibility of those who control these lands, for the continuing support not only of their own civilizations, but of civilization everywhere, is in any event impressive.

In the present state of technology, civilization is no longer limited to those areas that can underwrite the adventure in terms of their own food production. The tentacles, or if you prefer, the benevolent hands of civilization now stretch past the most formidable climatic barriers into outposts where mineral wealth, military considerations, scientific curiosity, or the mere sense of adventure may justify the effort. But the metabolic centers of civilization remain where there is control of nutrient sources sufficient to provide energy for more than bare subsistence. And the location of those centers is certainly an expression of climate. It is in this sense that we answer our first question — the extent to which climate sets limits to the process of civilization.

This brings us to the intriguing and controversial problem of the relation of climate to the quality of civilization. By the book (for it is necessary now to see what assumptions are involved), civilization has been defined as "an advanced state of human society, in which a high level of art, science, religion, and government has been reached."[3]

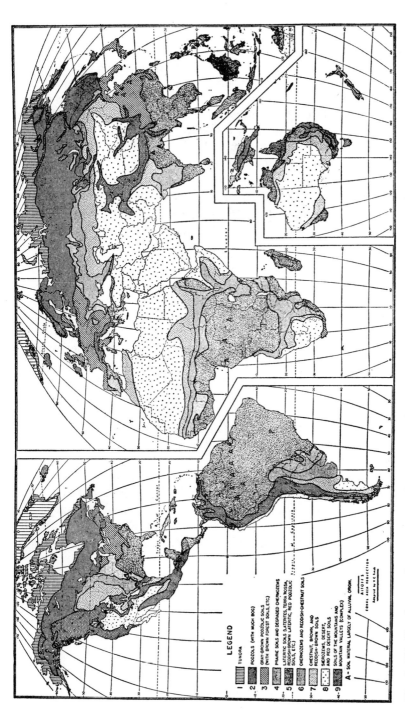

Fig. 2. World soils map showing restricted occurrence of soils (types 4, 6, 7) best suited to high protein production. These soils, which are an expression of climate, play a major role in world food production and must continue to do so. [From U.S. Department of Agriculture, *Climate and man*, *Yearbook of agriculture* (Washington, 1941).]

LEGEND

1 – TUNDRA

2 – PODZOLS (WITH MUCK BOG)

3 – GRAY-BROWN PODZOLIC SOILS (WITH BROWN FOREST SOILS, ETC)

4 – PRAIRIE SOILS AND DEGRADED CHERNOZEMS

5 – LATERITIC SOILS (LATERITE, TERRA ROSSA, REDDISH-BROWN LATERITE, RED PODZOLIC SOILS, ETC)

6 – CHERNOZEMS AND REDDISH-CHESTNUT SOILS

7 – CHESTNUT, BROWN, AND REDDISH-BROWN SOILS

8 – SIEROZEMS, DESERT, AND RED DESERT SOILS

9 – SOILS OF THE MOUNTAINS AND MOUNTAIN VALLEYS (COMPLEX)

A – SOIL MATERIAL LARGELY OF ALLUVIAL ORIGIN

Philosophy is not included in this particular definition; nor is there any mention of the joy of living, which certainly is not a negligible consideration. Of the four elements listed, only one, science, can be measured with some degree of objectivity. Even science is not immune to the charge of prejudiced judgment, as certain recent events show. These events include not only the attacks on Morganism in genetics, but also the resolutions [4] condemning, on the basis of the world-view of dialectical materialism, the "sterile, idealistic" theory of Linus Pauling of resonance in organic reactions. There are also the accounts by elderly colleagues of their experiences when visiting continental European laboratories and attending international scientific congresses a generation or more ago, which indicated that chauvinism in science is not exactly new.

> For each, with profound satisfaction
> > Which our speeches and writings attest,
> Beholds other cultures in action
> > And pronounces his culture the best.

Yet I doubt that the problem is quite as hopeless as it sounds; for there are plenty of competent people, willing to lay aside prejudice and preconception to the best of their ability and consider the evidence. The difficulty of consensus as to the rating of civilizations in terms of quality is less among such individuals than is the technical obstacle, now becoming clear as a result of recent advances in cultural anthropology. Simply stated, each culture (hence each civilization) possesses its own internal logic, which must be evaluated from the inside, so to speak. It is only after a sympathetic participation in more than one culture that any fair comparison can be drawn.

The physical limitations of this method are obvious. Meanwhile, any respectable comparison must be confined to those aspects of civilization that have been established as a kind of international currency. This procedure, I suppose, was the intention of the late Ellsworth Huntington, who attempted his own rating of civilizations.[5] His check list is as follows:

> Power of initiative,
> Inventiveness and capacity for formulating new ideas,
> Ability to develop philosophical systems,
> Ability to carry out far-reaching enterprises covering long periods
> > and areas,
> Power to lead and control other races,
> Highly developed system of education,
> Application of principles of hygiene,
> Standard of honesty and morality,

Degree of personal safety,
Sense for beauty in art (architecture included),
Sense for beauty in literature (belles-lettres),
Sense for beauty in nature (scenery, flowers, etc.).

Whatever reservations we have as to his method, I am inclined to accept the notion that the capacity for sustained, creative (as opposed to destructive) energy lies close to the heart of the problem. A high level of nutrition is, of course, involved in supplying energy, but gives no guarantee that it will be creative. The followers of Malan in South Africa appear to be well nourished. The problem is one of values and direction, and I am unable to see where climate has much bearing on either, with this possible exception: if climate is such as to create a steady supply of problems that must be solved while holding also the promise of rich returns for maintenance of a satisfactory social system, then climate may influence both values and direction of effort.

Huntington's thesis, however, is more physiological than this. He saw in the cool temperate regions, with their frequent cyclonic disturbances, a kind of perpetual system of stimuli to high creative effort (Figs. 3 and 4). But something more than stimulus is needed. The physiological aspects, apart from nutrition, deserve to be thoroughly explored. We have studies on the combined effects of temperature and humidity on productivity, and numerous others on illumination, fatigue, rhythm, and morale. There is also a growing volume of research on human development, on human relations, and on the cultural process itself, all of which bear upon our problem.

The thermal economy of the animal body, certainly an important factor, has its analogy in the internal-combustion engine. Heat is an inevitable concomitant of the oxidation of food, as of fuel, in accomplishing work. Whatever heat is not required to maintain the system and supply the energy for work must be disposed of through radiation. This idea has been advanced by Brody[6] and others in breeding livestock for warm climates. Varieties like the Brahma cattle, which present the largest radiating surface through bodily contour and skin folds, are considered the best.

Mills[7] also has studied the radiating surfaces of various animals — the ears of rabbits and the tails of rats, for example — and lays great stress on the heat economy of the human body as a factor in achievement. He is inclined to write off the cold and hot climates as assets for civilization. In the former too much energy must be used in maintaining a working temperature, in the latter necessary radiation is too much of a burden.

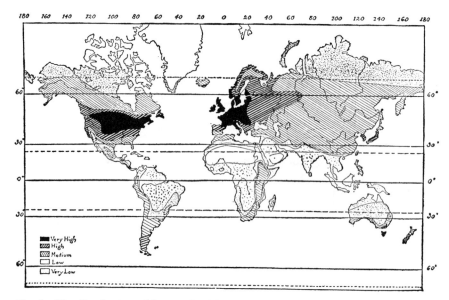

Fig. 3. The distribution of human health and energy on the basis of climate. [From E. Huntington, *Civilization and climate* (Yale University Press, New Haven, ed. 3, 1924), p. 295.]

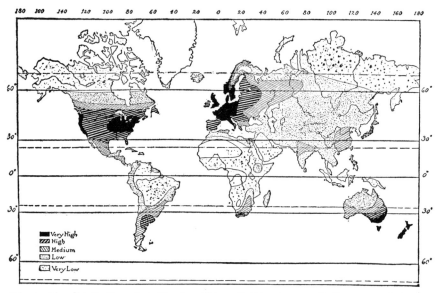

Fig. 4. The distribution of civilization. [From E. Huntington, *Civilization and climate* (Yale University Press, New Haven, ed. 3, 1924), p. 295.]

Conceding that we may have to regard the colder portions of the planet as outposts of its core civilizations, we come to the question of the tropics. Although the tropical rain forest is a tremendous producer of organic material, it is a meager source of human subsistence. Equally serious is the problem of the human thermal budget in the tropics. Neither problem is entirely hopeless, provided we do not expect the people of the tropics to lift themselves by the straps of their own sandals. They must utilize a great deal of the knowledge and skill developed in existing civilized centers as a nucleus on which to build. I agree whole-heartedly with Bates [8] that mere transplantation is not enough; there must be developed within the tropics an endemic culture, based primarily on a new body of scientific research.

One more point remains to be discussed — the challenging notion of Huntington that climatic change has been a major factor in the geography of civilizations.[9]

Whatever one's judgment of various past civilizations may be, there is no question that the centers of civilization have shifted with the passing of time, with respect not only to political power, but to general creative activity. And the direction of movement has generally been away from the tropics, although the decline of Icelandic greatness and the abandonment of Greenland are exceptions. Many of the remains of former glory certainly lie in areas that are now inhospitable desert, or, like Ankgor and the Mayan cities, humid tropical woodlands.

Huntington suggested that climatic change has been a paramount factor in the destiny of these ancient lands, and to support that idea he advanced many interesting arguments. Certainly there have been changes, and they have affected human activity. There is abundant evidence, not only from fossil shore features, but from sediments of once deep lakes in many now dry basins in our own Southwest and Mexico. It is now known that the retreat of continental ice from its extreme position has been a vacillating process, marked by several advances and retreats — a process not yet stabilized. Several lines of evidence indicate that the past two centuries have been marked by rising temperature.[10]

The number, intensity, and duration of these late-glacial phases is still under study,[11, 12] and so is their exact chronology.[13] Yet even when these problems are much better understood than they now are, immense difficulties will remain in the way of knowing to what extent and in what ways climatic change has been involved in the rise and fall of civilizations. In fact the life history of civilizations, apart from possible environmental influences, is still a knotty problem for scholars, who are likely to offer explanations as numerous as their various backgrounds. Did Rome fall because of moral corruption, economic weakness, geographic de-

terminism, or a kind of inevitable senescence through which all civilizations must pass? Did she ever fall? Or has she expanded her culture
throughout the world, with accretions from many sources and under new
political forms?

The civilization of Babylon, as far as economy is concerned, apart
from its efflorescence in empire and the arts, endured for a much longer
period than the time that has elapsed since the final destruction of its
irrigation system by the Mongols. But some of the events preceding that
destruction should be noted. For centuries the operation of agriculture
had been increasingly burdened by heavy loads of silt in the life-giving
canals. So much labor was required for their annual cleaning that little
leisure remained for anything else, and the long piles of silt beside the
canals grew steadily in height and volume. Presumably this was due to
increasing pressure, through cutting and grazing, upon the vegetation of
the highlands whose run-off supplied the water. Under those conditions,
the landscape became increasingly vulnerable to the effects of climate
with its infrequent but violent rains and dry-season winds.[14]

In all of the great Mediterranean civilizations, even Egypt, similar
symptoms of environmental disintegration are found, with economic
decline and a decrease in creative activity that we may concede without
any question as to what constitutes civilization. That there has been no
decline of innate capacity in the people themselves is suggested by the
recent achievements of native leaders, trained at Beirut and abroad. But
everywhere the primary evidence is that of human pressure on a vulnerable landscape, aided and abetted by that at once most useful and
most noxious of animals, the goat.

It is a weakness of Huntington's argument that he did not reckon with
man-accelerated erosion and other cultural influences. In the judgment of
the late Dr. Jacob Lipman,[15] eminent student of soils, the erosion in
Palestine far exceeded in its disastrous effects any real or supposed
changes of climate since the days of milk and honey. This view is
supported by the observations of Lowdermilk, and by those of the late
Dr. F. W. Oliver, who retired to Egypt and spent his final years in the
study of wind erosion and the process of desertization.[16] I had occasional
letters from him during this time, which, with his published papers,
showed clearly the power of vegetation to stabilize environment, even in
that dry region, and the disastrous effects of human pressure.

There is, in fact, early contemporary evidence to the same effect in a
striking quotation from Plato, recently unearthed. It might have become
well known earlier if his readers had not been preoccupied with lin-
guistics and metaphysics. Critias, speaking of the ancient kingdom of
Attica, states: "What are now her mountains were lofty, soil-clad hills;

her so-called shingle-plains of the present day were full of rich soil; and her mountains were heavily afforested — a fact of which there are still visible traces. There are mountains in Attica which can now keep nothing but bees, but which were clothed, not so very long ago, with fine trees producing timber suitable for roofing the largest buildings; and roofs hewn from the timber are still in existence. There were also many lofty cultivated trees, while the country produced boundless pasture for cattle. The annual supply of rainfall was not lost, as it is at present, through being allowed to flow over the denuded surface into the sea, but was received by the country, in all its abundance, into her bosom, where she stored it in her impervious potter's earth and so was able to discharge the drainage of the heights into the hollows in the form of springs and rivers with an abundant volume and a wide territorial distribution. The shrines that survive to the present day on the sites of extinct water supplies are evidence for the correctness of my present hypothesis." [17]

Equally convincing is the testimony of that remarkable engineer Henrico Martinez,[18] who wrote less than ninety years after the Spanish Conquest of Mexico of the increasing downwash of mud and the stripping of soil from the uplands due to cutting of the forests and the unrestricted grazing of Christian cattle.

If I seem to have made a bad case for the influences of climatic change, I have done so only to clear the air. I must confess that the idea has always intrigued me, even though the years have brought an increasing appreciation of the difficulty of the problem. After it had been fairly well established that a period of post-Wisconsin climate warmer and drier than the present might explain the numerous prairie relicts in forested Ohio, and that such a climate had existed, as shown by pollen analysis, I ventured to apply this information to a curious problem in Indian cultural migration.

A map that shows the prairie relicts of the upper Mississippi Basin outlines also the archeological remains of the group of cultures known as Mound Builders, which exhibit definite southwestern affinities. By the time of the first European settlement, these cultures had been replaced by types which, while maize growers also, were essentially forest dwellers. The evidence for this development led me to suggest that the flowering of the Mound culture had been encouraged by a northeastward shift in the maize optimum.[19] Lest this idea seem far fetched, let it be remembered that our modern economy is deeply affected not so much by the limits in which a given crop can possibly be grown as by the area of its optimum climate. What applies now should have applied a fortiori to a simpler technology.

It was with considerable comfort that I learned later of good evidence in Europe that Neolithic culture had moved northwestward into the Baltic area by virtue of just such a warm-dry climate as that postulated for the advance of the Mound Builders.[20] Moreover, recent carbon 14 datings place much of the activity of the latter group in the period of desiccation that marked the end of the Late Archaic in Mexico and the establishment of the Teotihuacan culture (500 B.C.–A.D. 800).[21] That the Mound culture continued on for a time during the ensuing moister period serves to confirm the reasonableness of the general idea. It is certainly not to be expected that such a solid development would crumble at once.

The influence of even brief climatic fluctuations, where climate is a limiting factor, is no longer in dispute. Migration in our own Great Plains has shown that a drouth of only a few years' duration can profoundly affect segments of our own culture, despite our technological resources.[22]

The Bat Cave discoveries, on the shores of a dead and desert lake bed in western New Mexico, exhibit the stark operation of climatic factors.[23] Here the Indians grew maize for some thousands of years before they abandoned the site. When a lake dries up, those dependent upon it for their economy have only one direction to go — that is up. The not-too-distant uplands abound in archeological sites, where either springs or brooks occur, but all such sites contain artifacts of more recent date than those of the Bat Cave site. Incidentally, the sediments of this ancient lake contain much pollen, and even the shallow borings we have made to date reveal climatic fluctuations of considerable magnitude, and present consistent evidence as yet unpublished, of a present-day climatic trend toward warmth and desiccation.

It is in the Basin where Mexico City is located, however, that we have the most dramatic evidence of climate as a limiting factor.[24] Here the Bat Cave theme is repeated on a grand scale, with variations. Our evidence of climatic change as indicated by the fossil-pollen profile is sustained not only by known lake levels but also by a thorough study of some 70 meters of sediment. Briefly, the Archaic culture, which flourished from about 2000 to 500 B.C., did so by virtue of an initial period of moist climate and high lake level. About 500 B.C., at a time of extreme desiccation and low lake level, the Late Archaic culture became early Teotihuacan. It then moved up to high ground at the northern end of the Basin — some 30 meters higher and 30 kilometers away — where, evidently, were sources of ground water, doubtless supplemented by trapped rainfall.

The end of the Teotihuacan culture was as sudden as the beginning and took place during a moist period, about A.D. 800. Vaillant suggested that deterioration came because the protecting forests had been destroyed to make fuel for the extensive burning of lime. Cook [25] later found evidences of extensive erosion during the Teotihuacan interval. It may be that the destructive effects of cultural activity were great enough to offset the blessings of returning moisture.

At any rate, the lakes presently filled up and a lacustrine culture returned to the Basin below, developing to full flower by the time of the Spanish invasion in 1521. Artificial drainage since that time has largely canceled the advantage of more favorable climate. Even this moister, more favorable climate was not permanent. During the summer of 1952 pollen profiles from Los Lagunas de Zempoala in the high-altitude conifer forest revealed the recent warm-dry trend, confirming similar evidence already in hand from New Mexico. We had been unable to secure adequate evidence from material collected in the Basin of Mexico, where there has been much recent disturbance, nor does it appear in the pioneer study by Deevey [26] made at Lake Patzcuaro. It is safe to say that the drainage of the Basin of Mexico comes at a particularly bad time in the climatic sequence.

Deevey, in addition to showing the possibility of pollen analysis in Mexican lake sediments, and indicating its importance, found evidence of human activity in the form of a few grains of maize and agave pollen.[26] Maize is not today known to survive without the aid of man, and geneticists agree that its pollen does not travel far from the source. In addition, the place and time of origin of maize have been the subject of much consideration.

No maize pollen was found in our ten archeological cores in the Basin.[24] One station has since shown it, but some of the others were probably too far from the ancient corn gardens. However, in examining two deep cores obtained within the present City of Mexico, my associate, Mrs. Kathryn Clisby, found maize pollen to a maximum depth of 9 meters. This takes maize back at least 4000 years, to the Early Archaic. Within the past few months, on completing her analyses, she found grass pollen of unusual size, matched only by that of maize and its relatives teosinte and tripsacum, at the depth of 70 meters, or well back into the Pleistocene.

This material was submitted to Dr. Barghoorn and Miss Wolfe at Harvard, who, with Dr. Mangelsdorf, have given us generous collaboration. While the identity of the pollen cannot be confirmed without further rigorous study, the most likely possibility is that maize is represented. Evidence from sediments and pollen indicates deposition under conditions of climate similar to those accompaning the maize pollen at 9 meters and above. The long intermediate interval of 61 meters bears evidence of much activity, climatic, volcanic, and topographic.

Meanwhile the evidence for Pleistocene man in Mexico, while not established to general satisfaction, is strengthening.[27] If there, did he know and use maize or a closely related grass? Did he carry either elsewhere and use it as a basis for civilization farther south during the ensuing interval? Or was the grass whose large pollen occurs at 70 meters a temporary intrusion from some other place of origin? These and other important questions may be solved only by the expensive and laborious process of deep drilling in the numerous extinct lake beds that occur from New Mexico through Central America and down into the Andean country, where the records now lie buried. But any prospect of clearing up the origin and movement of maize through a study of cores representing, say, the past 10,000 years now seems much less promising than we had supposed.

Thus have complications been added to one phase of the already difficult but endlessly intriguing problem of the relation of climate to human culture. The only hope lies not in isolated studies but in the fullest coöperation of many disciplines and laboratories. In this instance, we are indebted not only to generous Mexican colleagues but to the resources of Oberlin, Yale, Harvard, Ohio State, and the University of Massachusetts, with support from the Geological Society of America and the Wenner-Gren Foundation, and more recently, the National Science Foundation.

SUMMARY

Climate and civilization are both complex phenomena, whose analysis and evaluation present many technical difficulties. Their relation is complicated by the fact that man, through cultural processes, can transgress climatic boundaries such as limit the ranges of other species.

That climate affects civilization profoundly is not questioned. The relation, however, is not simple. Stimulus to activity and favorableness for sustained effort have been suggested as keys. So has the moisture budget, but this last has often been more seriously affected by cultural practices than by climatic change. On the other hand, soils capable of high protein production are an expression of climate and are essential to sustained civilization.

Civilization (relatively speaking) has been affected by climatic changes that shift the areas of optimum production of basic food plants. This is established for Neolithic migration into the Baltic region at the time of the Thermal Maximum, and probably is true for advanced maize cultures in the Upper Mississippi drainage. Drying and renewal of lakes in the Basin of Mexico have caused important cultural shifts, as has the disappearance of lakes in the Southwest. Drouths of even a few years' duration have been factors in internal migration within the United States.

The problem can be dealt with only by coöperative research on a wide front — research that takes account of the many respects in which climate can affect civilization, of the cultural process itself, and of the often drastic effects of land use on the environment.

Because of the critical role played by maize in American civilizations, that plant serves to illustrate some of the complexities to be met. Its pollen has been recovered to a depth of 9 meters in Mexican sediments that date back into Archaic cultural levels. But an apparently identical pollen is preserved at depths of 70–75 meters, certainly well back in the Pleistocene. Modern maize is dependent upon man, and the evidence for Pleistocene man in Mexico is increasing; nevertheless, the whole question now appears to be much more difficult than had been supposed.

REFERENCES

1. C. W. Thornthwaite, "Problems in the classification of climates," *Geogr. Rev. 33*, 233–255 (1943).
2. L. D. Stamp, *Land for tomorrow* (Indiana University Press, Bloomington, 1952).
3. C. L. Barnhart, ed., *The American college dictionary* (Random House, New York, 1947), p. 221.
4. A. E. Stubbs, trans., "Moscow conference on the theory of chemical structure in organic chemistry," *Nature 169*, 92–94 (1952).
5. E. Huntington, *Civilization and climate* (Yale University Press, New Haven, ed. 3, 1924), p. 252.
6. S. Brody, *Bioenergetics and growth* (Reinhold, New York, 1945).
7. C. A. Mills, *Climate makes the man* (Harper, New York, 1942).
8. C. Bates, *Where winter never comes* (Scribner, New York, 1952).
9. E. Huntington, *Climatic change* (Yale University Press, New Haven, 1922).
10. K. Faegri, "On the variations of western Norwegian glaciers during the last 200 years," *Proc. Oslo Assembly (19–28 Aug. 1948) Union Géodésique et Géophysique International* (Louvain, 1948), pp. 293–303.
11. P. B. Sears, "Forest sequence and climatic change in northeastern North America since early Wisconsin time," *Ecology 29*, 326–333 (1948).
12. E. S. Deevey, Jr., "Paleolimnology and climate," the concluding article of this volume.
13. R. F. Flint and E. S. Deevey, Jr., "Radiocarbon dating of late Pleistocene events," *Amer. Jour. Sci. 249*, 257–300 (1951).
14. E. B. Worthington, *Middle East science* (H. M. Stationery Office, London, 1946).
15. J. G. Lipman, personal communication.
16. F. W. Oliver, "Dust-storms in Egypt and their relation to the war period, as noted in Maryut, 1939–45," *Geogr. Jour. 106*, 26–49 (1945); *108*, 221–226 (1946).
17. A. J. Toynbee, *Greek historical thought from Homer to the age of Heraclius* (Beacon Press, Boston, 1950), pp. 169–170.

18. Henrico Martinez, *Reportorio de los tiempos e historia natural de Nueva España (1606)* (Secretaria de Education Publica, Mexico, 1948).

19. P. B. Sears, "The archeology of environment in eastern North America," *Amer. Anthropologist 34*, 610–622 (1932).

20. J. Iversen, "The influence of prehistoric man on vegetation," *Danm. Geol. Undersg.* IV. 3, 6, 5–22 (1949).

21. P. B. Sears, "Climate and culture – new evidence," *Science 114*, 46–47 (1951).

22. C. W. Thornthwaite, *Study of population redistribution of the Great Plains. Migration and economic opportunity* (University of Pennsylvania Press, Philadelphia, 1934).

23. P. C. Mangelsdorf and C. E. Smith, Jr., "New archaeological evidence on evolution in maize," *Botanical Museum Leaflets, Harvard University 13*, 213–260 (1949).

24. P. B. Sears, "Palynology in southern North America. I. Archeological horizons in the basin of Mexico," *Bull. Geol. Soc. Amer. 63*, 241–254 (1952).

25. S. F. Cook, "Soil erosion and population in central Mexico," *Ibero-Americana 34*, 1–86 (1949).

26. E. S. Deevey, Jr., "Pollen analysis and Mexican archeology," *Amer. Antiquity 10*, 134–149 (1944).

27. Luis Aveleyra Arroya de Anda and Manuel Maldonado-Koerdell, "Asociacion de artefactos con mamut en el Pleistoceno superior de la Cuenca de Mexico," *Rev. Mex. de Estudios Antropologicos 13*, 1–29 (1952).

4

ATMOSPHERIC AND OCEANIC CIRCULATION AS FACTORS IN GLACIAL-INTERGLACIAL CHANGES OF CLIMATE

Hurd C. Willett

THERE IS NO POSSIBILITY WITHIN THE limitations of the present discussion of treating with adequate completeness such a vast subject as atmospheric and oceanic circulation. It is necessary at the outset to delimit specifically and radically the scope of the discussion in such a manner that the more essential facts and deductions are stressed. The necessary curtailment of the scope of the present discussion is effected primarily along the following three lines.

(1) *By generality of statement and omission of proof.* There are very few facts or deductions relative to details of the climatic conditions that have prevailed during historical and geological time, and even fewer relative to the probable causes of their considerable changes, that can be presented as rigorously established or universally accepted. Statements of fact or deduction concerning these conditions and causes of changes must be offered for the most part in generalized form without conclusive proof. However, such statements are qualified according to the author's best judgment of their reliability, and in cases of highly controversial opinion, the source of the opinion and of the evidence supporting it is indicated.

(2) *By restriction of the discussion to the Pleistocene Glacial Epoch.* There is little doubt but that the essential features of both the normal seasonal patterns of the general circulation of the atmosphere and the mean pattern of the oceanic circulation are largely determined in both hemispheres by the topography of the continents and the oceans. During the million years, more or less, of the current Pleistocene Epoch there have occurred no large-scale changes of this topography sufficient to alter significantly the primary pattern of the general circulation of the earth's atmosphere and oceans. Consequently by restricting the discussion to the

Pleistocene Epoch we can treat this important topographic factor as constant in its present well-known pattern, and thus avoid unending and probably fruitless speculation as to the causes of the radically different and relatively unknown glacial pattern of the preceding Permian, or Permo-Carboniferous, glacial epoch.

(3) *By relegation of the oceanic circulation to a position of secondary importance.* It has been generally accepted as fact by both meteorologists and oceanographers that the latitudinal transport of heat by oceanic circulation plays a relatively minor role in the heat balance of the earth compared with the latitudinal heat transport effected by the circulation of the atmosphere. Certainly this assumption is justified with respect to the relatively well-known wind-driven surface currents, which include among many others the warm Gulf Stream and Japanese current, and the cold Greenland Current and Humboldt Current of the southern hemisphere. The volume and heat transport of most of these surface wind-driven currents is approximately known. Furthermore, under the assumption of the essential constancy of the topography of the continents and oceans — an assumption that is applicable to the Pleistocene Epoch — these surface ocean currents can change only in response to changes of the circulation and climatic pattern of the atmosphere. Consequently they can be neglected as a primary cause or initiating factor of important climatic change.

With respect to the thermal circulation of the deep ocean between polar and tropical latitudes, little is known because the current velocities are far too small to measure directly. One recent estimate [1] based on dating by radioactive carbon indicates that the period of such deep ocean circulations probably is to be expressed in millenniums rather than in centuries. Further confirmation of the necessarily utterly slow motion of the deep ocean circulations is furnished by the application of continuity considerations to the characteristic conservatism and the thermal and saline stratification of the deep ocean water masses. Certainly it is reasonably safe to assume that the deep oceanic circulation is extremely slow to respond to any changing conditions, either atmospheric or extraterrestrial in origin. Presumably it functions essentially as a vast inertial flywheel in any pattern of climatic change, acting always as a stabilizing or delaying factor, never as a primary cause or an initially or directly responsive element of change of circulation or climate. In view of the probable insignificance, and our rather complete ignorance, of the quantitative contribution of the deep ocean circulation to the poleward heat transport, and in view further of the almost certainly essentially inertial and indirect character of its response to the primary causes of climatic change during Pleistocene time, the deep ocean circulation, like the wind-driven surface circulation, is given no primary consideration in the present discussion of the glacial-interglacial changes of climate.

The first point to be stressed in relating changes of the pattern of the general circulation of the atmosphere to the Pleistocene glacial-interglacial cycle of climate is the fact that we have no a priori basis for drawing conclusions as to the changing character of the general circulation during Pleistocene time other than the geological evidence as to the corresponding changes of climate. In other words, with reference to geological time, our estimate of the changing pattern of the general circulation must be derived from the evidence of the changing pattern of climate, and not the reverse. However, in so far as it may be possible to demonstrate from historical and observational records that a similar pattern of change of climate and atmospheric circulation is occurring postglacially and currently, then the recent changes should prove useful in the interpretation and explanation of the greater changes during Pleistocene time. Since there appears to exist a striking similarity of pattern between the great Pleistocene climatic cycles and the smaller postglacial and current cycles, the present discussion is concerned with a brief treatment in turn of the following three topics:

(1) Essential features of the Pleistocene glacial-interglacial cycles of climate and atmospheric circulation.

(2) Essential features of the postglacial historical and observational cycles of climate and atmospheric circulation,

(3) Possible explanations of climatic cycles.

1. Essential Features of the Pleistocene Glacial-interglacial Cycles of Climate and Atmospheric Circulation

A variety of geological evidence [2-5] has established with a fair degree of probability, but by no means finally or completely, a number of facts of basic importance about the large-scale features of the pattern of climatic change, and consequently also of change of atmospheric circulation, between the periods of minimum and of maximum glaciation during the Pleistocene Epoch. The more important of these facts may be summarized briefly as follows:

(a) All of the evidence indicates that these major glacial-interglacial cycles of change of climate and atmospheric circulation are in phase, rather than in opposition, on the northern and southern hemispheres of the earth. This in-phase relation apparently holds also for the secondary cycles of eight to ten thousand years' duration which are superposed on the primary glacial-interglacial cycle, as evidenced by the two or three peak points of glaciation, with temporary intervening recession, which characterize each of the four primary glacial maximums of the Pleistocene Epoch.

(b) The present pattern of terrestrial climate, and the corresponding pattern of atmospheric circulation, lie somewhere between the extreme of a maximum of glaciation and the extreme of an interglacial minimum, probably approximately two-thirds of the way from the glacial to the interglacial extreme. The glacial climatic pattern, in contrast to the present condition, is characterized by a considerable expansion of the polar cap zone of glaciation and by a corresponding equatorward shift and latitudinal compression of the present zonal pattern. The middle-latitude belt of maximum cyclonic rainfall probably extends its influence 15° farther equatorward into the present subtropical high-pressure belt of relatively dry and settled weather, which in turn is compressed toward the equator. The equatorial belts of heavy tropical rainfall are restricted to a zone in rather close proximity to the equator.

The glacial pattern of the general circulation corresponds to the pattern of climate.[5] The zonal westerlies, including the jet stream of the upper troposphere, are considerably expanded and also intensified in comparison with their present state, and with them the prevailing storm tracks of middle latitudes are displaced to lower latitudes, with increased storminess. In fact, along with equatorward expansion, the primary characteristic of the glacial circulation pattern is one of increased intensity and steady storm activity, including in particular a marked acceleration of the condensation cycle. This acceleration is manifested not only in the precipitation of higher middle latitudes that builds the ice sheets, but also in the extremely pluvial conditions that prevail in the lower middle latitudes (which today experience semiarid subtropical conditions), and in the greatly increased rainfall in the belts of equatorial convergence between intensified tropical easterlies. Undoubtedly increased subsidence and divergence in the narrowed and intensified subtropical high-pressure belts result in clear skies and extremely hot dry conditions in which the evaporation phase of the accelerated condensation cycle must be maintained at high efficiency. Hence the glacial circulation pattern on either hemisphere is characterized by equatorward expansion and intensification of the major zonal wind systems, with increased storminess and rainfall in all principal zones of convergence and frontal activity, maintained by a greatly accelerated functioning of the condensation cycle between a dynamically intensified hot, dry, subtropical, high-pressure belt and cool zones of convergence and storminess in close proximity on either side.

(c) The interglacial pattern of climate and of atmospheric circulation, in comparison with that of today, departs in the opposite sense from

that of the glacial extreme.[3] Apparently the polar-cap circulations contract and disappear so completely that no permanent glaciation remains
on the surface of the earth. This disappearance of the polar-cap circulation
is accompanied by a displacement of the zonal westerlies and cyclonic
storminess of middle latitudes into the higher latitudes, with a great
increase of warmth and precipitation in the polar latitudes. The subtropical high-pressure belts extend through the middle latitudes, producing
generally settled, mild, stormfree conditions, with rather widespread
deficiency of rainfall, most noted in the zones of the present more
southerly storm tracks. With this contraction of the zonal pattern of the
general circulation toward the poles, the intensity of the over-all circulation relaxes and the functioning of the condensation cycle is slowed, so
that the entire zonal pattern of climate is diffused and weakened, particularly with respect to the present contrast between the conditions of
the equatorial rainfall belts and the hot, dry conditions of the subtropical
high-pressure belts of subsidence.

2. Essential Features of the Postglacial Historical and Observational
Cycles of Climate and Atmospheric Circulation

The end of the most recent (Würm) major glacial period of the
Pleistocene Epoch is usually placed at approximately 6500 B.C. It was
the time at which the ice boundaries and climatic conditions in Europe,
at least, had returned essentially to those of today. In North America,
apparently, the larger ice sheet lagged somewhat in its recession, so that
following the Climatic Optimum there occurred one minor glacial
readvance, the Cochrane, before the ice sheet was finally eliminated.
This readvance had no counterpart in Europe. Climatic changes since
6500 B.C. are known with increasing detail and accuracy as we approach
the present, first by the changing distribution of plant and animal species,
the numerous remains of which are widely distributed, second by the
historical record of racial and cultural developments and migrations, and
finally, during the recent two or three centuries, by an increasing amount
of accurate observational record. The essential features of the climatic
changes during this postglacial period may be summarized briefly as
follows: [3, 4, 6]

(*a*) There is continually in progress an entire spectrum of cyclical
fluctuations of climate, cycles of shorter period and smaller amplitude
being superposed on those of longer period and larger amplitude. These
cycles include one whose half period, at least in Europe, extends from
the Climatic Optimum at about 3000 B.C. to the peak glaciation from A.D.
1600 to 1900, a second cycle of smaller amplitude and a period of some

2000 years, cool-wet from 500 B.C. to A.D. 100, warm-dry from 400 to 1000, and cool-wet from the thirteenth century to the present, and shorter and smaller cycles, from a few centuries in period to the 80-year, the double sunspot, and the single sunspot cycles observed during the past two centuries.

(*b*) The major climatic cycles of postglacial time apparently have occurred in phase on the two hemispheres and followed a pattern of climatic change identical in form to that of the typical glacial-interglacial cycle. At the time of the Climatic Optimum from 4000 to 2000 B.C. most glaciers disappeared, at least in Europe, and even the Greenland and Antarctic ice caps decreased several hundred feet in thickness. Deciduous forests spread northward in North America and northern Europe into many regions too cold or too stormy to permit their growth today, while the same period was one of warmth and desiccation in many of the lower-latitude border areas of present wintertime cyclonic activity. On the other hand, the Little Ice Age of recent centuries, from which perhaps we have just started to emerge during the past half century, marks an all-time peak of glaciation since the termination of the last ice sheet, some 8500 years ago in Europe, and probably 4000 years ago in North America. Nearly all of the glaciers in middle latitudes today are new formations, developed since the postglacial optimum of climate, not remnants from the last ice sheet. In other words, in postglacial time we have experienced a climatic cycle, identical in form to and probably of roughly one half the amplitude and one tenth the period of a major Pleistocene glacial-interglacial cycle. It doubtless is identical with the secondary climatic cycles of eight to ten thousand years' duration that appear in superposition on all four of the Pleistocene glacial maximums, and which presumably have occurred without leaving permanent record throughout the Pleistocene Epoch.

(*c*) The short-period climatic fluctuations of small amplitude during recent observational time have also followed, in essential form, the same basic glacial-interglacial pattern of change. The changes are observed to be strictly in phase on the two hemispheres, even to the predominant advance or recession of glaciers in all parts of the world. The cycle is one of alternate expansion and contraction of the circumpolar vortex with equatorward or poleward displacement of the prevailing storm tracks. Periods of expansion of the circumpolar vortex tend to be cool in middle latitudes, accompanied by increased rainfall in lower middle latitudes and decreased rainfall in the highest latitudes, but with general advance of glaciers in all zones. This advance of glaciers in the higher latitudes must reflect primarily summer rather than winter conditions. Periods of contraction of the circumpolar vortex are marked by warm characteristics, particularly in the higher latitudes, and by generally increased rainfall, at least on the Northern Hemisphere poleward of latitude 50°N, and decreased rainfall equatorward of this latitude.[7, 8, 9] These conditions, which have characterized the past 30 years, are ones of predominant glacial recession in all latitudes on both hemispheres.

3. Possible Explanations of Climatic Cycles

A great variety of explanations have been offered to account for the cyclical fluctuations of terrestrial climate. These explanations have utilized every possible factor, terrestrial and extraterrestrial, that might conceivably affect the terrestrial heat balance and the general circulation of the atmosphere and oceans. At the present time authorities who have studied this problem are far from agreement, even as to the primary factors involved. The mounting evidence of recent years, however, appears to point with increasing conclusiveness to one specific primary factor of climatic control, namely, variable solar activity. The following discussion presents a brief summary of some of the evidence and reasoning that favor this conclusion, which is far from general acceptance at the present time.

Two facts of observation which emerge clearly from the preceding brief summary of the characteristic descriptive features of all cyclical fluctuations of climate must be emphasized:

(1) All climatic fluctuations, both long and short, appear to run closely in phase on the Northern and Southern Hemispheres;

(2) All climatic fluctuations, from the very long to the short, appear to follow essentially the same geographical pattern of change, differing only in period and in amplitude.

The first of these two facts precludes the possibility of the acceptance of any explanation of the glacial-interglacial climatic cycles that operates essentially in opposite phase on the Northern and on the Southern Hemisphere. The second fact makes it at least philosophically desirable, if not physically necessary, to develop a hypothesis for the explanation of climatic cycles that can apply in its essential form to cycles of every observed period and amplitude.

Of the infinite variety of combinations of possible causative factors that have been constrained to account for the glacial-interglacial cycle of climate, those which today still find wide acceptance of the primary causative factors fall into three quite distinctive categories:

(a) Terrestrial factors, primarily continentality and volcanology;

(b) Geometrical variability of insolation, represented by the effects of variable eccentricity of the earth's orbit, of precession, and of variable inclination of the earth's axis of rotation to the plane of the ecliptic.

(c) Variability of the intrinsic output of solar energy, either in the total effective black-body radiation, or, more probably, in the selective emission by the sun of short-wavelength ultraviolet or corpuscular (charged particle) radiations.

The argument [6] for basing the occurrence of a glacial epoch primarily on the terrestrial factors stresses the importance of continental uplift in blocking the circulation of atmosphere and oceans, thus leading to a relative cooling of the higher latitudes — an effect that presumably is further intensified by the reduction of insolational heating caused by the frequent ejection of fine volcanic ash (dust) into the higher atmosphere. Glaciation then presumably starts on favored elevated land areas in higher middle latitudes on the poleward side of the prevailing storm tracks. As the glaciers expand they lead to intensified local cooling, which forces the prevailing storm tracks equatorward, and concentrating the poleward thermal gradient and maximum storminess in lower middle latitudes. Presumably there exists an inherent thermodynamic instability in the glacial circulation pattern, in the sense that when the ice sheets become overextended they fail to receive sufficient nourishment in their central and poleward portions, where they start to waste away, eventually leaving the equatorward peripheral portions stranded and isolated from any immediate supply of cold air. These peripheral glaciers are then rapidly liquidated, the glacial phase of the cycle thus is terminated, and the whole process may start over again in the manner of the major cycles of the Pleistocene Epoch.

The principal arguments against the explanation of a Pleistocene glacial-interglacial cycle based on continentality and volcanology as the primary control factors may be summarized in the following points, several of which appear to be fatal to this hypothesis:

(1) The present contours of continents and oceans, probably even a slightly greater elevation of land masses, were present for some millions of years before the comparatively recent Pleistocene glaciation appeared. There is no evidence that volcanic activity increased recently; and there is evidence that some geological periods of extreme volcanic activity were not accompanied by glaciation.

(2) The concept of the termination of a glacial pattern of climate and circulation by its own inherent instability cannot be sustained by reasoning that is even qualitatively strict, much less quantitatively so. Furthermore, all of the geological evidence indicates that the last ice sheet, and probably others before it, receded progressively step by step in the same manner that it advanced, and not by any interior disintegra-

tion. If such a possibility is removed, nothing remains in this terrestrial hypothesis by which to account for the successive relatively short glacial-interglacial cycles of the Pleistocene Epoch.

(3) Neither continentality nor volcanology has anything to offer by way of an explanation of the considerable cycles of climate and glaciation that have occurred during postglacial time, apparently identical in form to the Pleistocene cycles of greater amplitude and longer period. Even proponents [6] of the terrestrial hypothesis of glaciation accept irregular solar variability as the most plausible explanation of the secondary postglacial cycles.

(4) Comparison [10] of present climatic patterns in relation to continentality on the Northern and the Southern Hemispheres establishes the fact that, far from being the favorable factor that it is assumed to be, the relatively high degree of continentality of the northern hemisphere in higher middle latitudes produces a substantial unfavorable effect on the climate as far as the possibility of glaciation is concerned. A certain degree of continentality presumably is a necessary condition for glaciation, in that it doubtless offers the necessary base for and thus determines the geographical pattern of development of an ice sheet, but in no sense whatsoever can it be the primary cause of the Pleistocene glacial-interglacial cycles of climate.

The argument for basing the explanation of the Pleistocene glacial-interglacial cycles of climate primarily on the geometrical variation of the distribution of insolational heating over the surface of the earth was given quantitative form by the computations of Milankovitch.[11] Assuming changes of mean temperature to be based on simple radiational equilibrium with respect to changing insolation, he laboriously computed the changes of mean temperature on selected latitude circles of the Northern and of the Southern Hemispheres at 5000-year intervals, at the times of winter and of summer solstice — changes that would have occurred during the past 600,000 years as a result of the combined effects of precession, of cyclical variations of the eccentricity of the earth's orbit around the sun, and of minor variations of the inclination of the axis of rotation of the earth to the plane of the ecliptic. On the assumption that Pleistocene glacial chronology was determined primarily by summer coolness in the higher latitudes of the Northern Hemisphere, Zeuner [12, 13] compared Milankovitch's computation of the changes of mean temperature at the summer solstice at 65°N during the past 600,000 years with the chronological sequence of Pleistocene glaciation. He believes that he finds an almost perfect correspondence, even to the detail of the secondary peaks of each of the four glacial maximums of the Pleistocene Epoch, between Milankovitch's computed curve of summer mean temperature at 65°N and our best understanding of the Pleistocene glacial sequence. On this basis Zeuner prepares what he believes to be an absolutely dated chronology of the Pleistocene Epoch, a chronology that has been widely accepted by many geologists and other scientists (cf. Gamow [14]).

The following objections, however, appear to make this geometrical variation of insolation untenable as a hypothesis by which to account for the glacial sequence of the Pleistocene Epoch:

(1) Apart from a superficial resemblance in the sequence of cool periods in Zeuner's curve of summer temperature to the Pleistocene sequence of ice sheets, there is nothing to relate the two chronologies. Zeuner's chronology reduces the length of the Pleistocene Epoch to only a fraction of the time usually assigned to it; it offers no reason for the Ice Ages starting only at the beginning of the recorded glacial epoch, for it extends the glacial-interglacial cycle back indefinitely in time; it permits a time interval of five to fifteen thousand years for each secondary glacial peak, but with much longer intervening periods of nonglacial climate, a sequence that does not correspond at all to the apparent structure of the four primary glacial periods; and finally it places the peak of the post-glacial climatic optimum some 11,000 years ago instead of the 5000 years or less that is now rather definitely assigned to it.

(2) Zeuner's chronology, by the nature of the controlling factors, requires essential opposition of phase of the glacial-interglacial cycle on the Northern and on the Southern Hemisphere, in direct contradiction to the evidence.

(3) The geometrical solar hypothesis offers no explanation whatsoever for any climatic cycle of period less than 20,000 years, thus contributing no more than does the terrestrial hypothesis to the explanation of postglacial climatic cycles.

(4) Although Milankovitch's computations yield rather large departures of mean temperature, in the higher latitudes at time of solstice, from present normals (up to 7°C at 65°N), negative summer departures are compensated by positive winter departures, so that the total insolation incident on either hemisphere in the course of a year is completely unchanged by the geometrical variation of insolation. Furthermore, Simpson [10] points out that by assuming gray-body rather than selective transmission of solar radiation by the atmosphere, and by neglecting effects of atmospheric circulation, Milankovitch computes temperature departures that probably are three to four times too large. Simpson's considered opinion is that not only is the geometrical variation of insolation not the primary cause of climatic variation, but that it does not contribute even perceptibly to it, and that any superficial resemblance between the

Zeuner chronology and Pleistocene chronology is purely accidental. In this conclusion Flint [2] concurs fully, as does the author.

The hypothetical possibilities of variable solar activity as the primary cause of climatic cycles are numerous. [4, 5, 15, 16] Until quite recently the discussion of irregular solar variability as the primary cause of glacial-interglacial cycles of climate was concerned almost exclusively with variation of the total effective black-body radiation of the sun. From the point of view of the geologist it is comparatively simple to assume that an over-all lowering of the sun's effective radiation of heat energy by 5 or 10 percent should lower the mean temperature of the earth by so many degrees, thus permitting glaciation to start in favored locations in the higher-latitude belt of storm activity and precipitation. Once started in the higher latitudes, glaciation tends to extend toward lower latitudes, compressing the prevailing storm tracks and climatic zones equatorward, thus causing intensified poleward temperature gradient and storminess in lower middle latitudes in a pattern similar to that outlined above under the terrestrial hypothesis.[16] This concept satisfies also the geologist's requirement of a substantial lowering of the mean temperature of the globe at time of maximum glaciation.

Simpson [17] first pointed out the impossibility of accounting for the glacial pattern of climate and circulation by a general decrease of solar heating. The essential effect of such a decrease must be to lower the mean temperature of the earth's surface primarily in the tropics, to decrease the poleward temperature gradient, and to lower substantially the water-vapor content of the atmosphere. The inevitable result of these effects is to weaken the general circulation of the atmosphere and to decrease storminess and precipitation in all latitudes, conditions directly opposed to those of a glacial climate. It is obviously paradoxical to expect to maintain an intensified poleward temperature gradient and storminess, with its inevitable increase of the poleward transport of heat and water vapor in lower middle latitudes, from a tropical zone which is cooler, receiving less heat, and evaporating less water vapor than at the present time.

Simpson demonstrated rather conclusively that if the glacial circulation pattern is to be accounted for by an over-all change of the solar constant, it can be effected only by an increase, not by a decrease, of insolational heating. The difficulty in this proposal of Simpson's lies in the possibility of maintaining sufficiently low temperature in the poleward zones of increased cyclonic activity and precipitation to permit the growth of vast ice sheets and extension of glacial climate. Simpson maintains that the necessary initial glaciation is accomplished by the greatly intensified storminess with its heavy accumulation of winter snow and the protection against melting by the summer sun that is offered by the extended cloud cover. However, Simpson [18] recognizes that if the solar constant increases beyond a certain limit, the increased heating must abruptly reverse the process of glaciation, leading directly into an extremely pluvial interglacial period with a strong glacial pattern of the general circulation, an occurrence for which there is no geological evidence.

Some of the difficulties of Simpson's hypothesis are eliminated, and much additional evidence is obtained in favor of irregular solar activity as the primary cause of all climatic cycles, if we consider irregular emissive activity of the highly selective sort that accompanies sunspot disturbances, rather than variation of the effective black-body radiation of the sun, as the controlling factor. In other words, it is proposed to discuss as the primary cause of all climatic cycles the type of solar activity of which sunspots, chromospheric eruptions, solar coronal disturbances, ionospheric and geomagnetic disturbances, etc. are indices, but are not direct measurements. The physical causative agency that presumably acts directly on the upper atmosphere must be short-wavelength ultraviolet radiations, emissions of charged particles, or a combination of these agencies. But neither these agencies, nor their immediate thermal, kinetic, or electrochemical effects in the higher atmosphere, are directly measured at present, nor do they find any expression in the Smithsonian determinations of the solar constant. Consequently the argument for this hypothesis is perforce essentially statistical at the present time.

The remainder of this discussion is devoted to a brief summary listing of the arguments, admittedly highly controversial in character, which may be presented in favor of the hypothesis that irregular solar activity of the selective variety controls the entire complex of climatic cycles, including the major Pleistocene glacial-interglacial cycles.

(1) In that it necessitates no over-all heating of the atmosphere the hypothesis eliminates the primary objection to Simpson's hypothesis. Whether the direct effects in the higher atmosphere of the selective solar emissions are thermal, kinetic, or electrochemical of a sort which rearranges heat and cold sources in the lower atmosphere, they apparently can modify the circulation pattern of the lower atmosphere without producing over-all heating.

(2) The irregular variations of these highly selective emissions from the sun are constantly undergoing fluctuations which relatively are very great, with maximum activity for short periods a hundred or a thousand-times minimum activity. This high degree of variability is in direct con-

trast to that of the effective solar constant measured by the Smithsonian Institution, which reflects very slight, if any, solar variability. Furthermore, to judge by sunspots, which consitute the only available long-term index of the highly selective solar activity, this activity undergoes extreme long-term variations of a cyclical complexity which is very similar to that of terrestrial climate, and which during the past thousand years strikingly parallels the climatic cycles at many points. There is no reason to suppose that during geological time solar irritation, like terrestrial climate, has not suffered correspondingly greater cycles of fluctuation. Hence this is the only possible factor of climatic control among all of those considered that can reasonably be made to account for the entire spectrum of climatic cycles, current, historical, and geological.

(3) Without any question the long-term effects of variable selective solar activity should be in phase on the two hemispheres, as all climatic cycles appear to be.

(4) The essential statistical test of the justification of the assignment of a primary role to irregular solar variability of the selective type in climatic changes lies in the degree to which suitable responses of the general circulation pattern to the proper solar stimuli are observed. From the foregoing discussion it is evident that the characteristic of the general circulation of foremost importance to climatic fluctuation is that of the poleward contraction or expansion of the zonal wind systems and prevailing storm tracks, in the sense that rising pressure in polar latitudes and falling pressure in lower middle latitudes represent a trend toward a more glacial climate, and vice versa. It is further apparent from recent studies by Rex [19, 20] and Willett [8, 21] that, at least under present-day conditions of the general circulation, the predominance of a more zonal pattern of the circulation favors cool and wet (more glacial) conditions in middle latitudes, while the predominance of a more cellular pattern (presence of blocking anticyclones in the higher middle latitudes) favors warm dry conditions in middle latitudes and warm wet conditions in high latitudes (interglacial characteristics). The rapid recession of all glaciers during the past 30 to 40 years was caused by a strong trend of the general circulation pattern in the latter direction.

In the light of these facts a number of statements may be made concerning significant responses of the general circulation pattern, primarily as expressed by the distribution of atmospheric pressure at sea level, to irregular solar stimuli. The relative sunspot number, as the only solar index of long record, has been related to atmospheric circulation in a multitude of statistical studies during the past half century, many of them of doubtful statistical soundness. However, there can be no doubt at the present time but that changes of the world weather patterns are significantly related to sunspots, to the 11-year cycle, to the Hale or double-sunspot cycle, and to longer cycles. Only a few significant facts concerning these relations, facts that emerge as reasonably well established, are noted briefly in the following points:

(*a*) During the past two centuries sunspots have varied in a rather pronounced cycle of roughly 80 years, in alternating 40-year periods of high and of low activity. The periods of high activity have tended definitely toward the interglacial in climatic pattern, those of low activity toward the glacial. In particular, the rather abrupt transition from very high to very low solar activity, following major sunspot maxima in 1787, 1871, and 1947 (1957?) are followed by most pronounced reactions from exceptionally mild to exceptionally severe climatic conditions in middle latitudes.[7]

(*b*) World weather patterns change more markedly during the period of increasing sunspots, between minimum and following maximum of the 11-year cycle, than at any other phase, but the characteristic change of circulation pattern is shown during the past century to be quite different at alternating maxima of the double sunspot cycle.[22, 23] The change of pattern before a minor maximum is one of pressure rise in middle latitudes and fall in higher latitudes, or increasingly zonal circulation, favoring glacial advance. The change of pattern before a major sunspot maximum is one of pressure rise at selected points in the higher latitudes (predominance of blocking anticyclones) which favors glacial recession, and which characterizes markedly the pronounced warming of climate with increased storminess in the higher latitudes of the northern hemisphere, and the rapid recession of all glaciers, during the past 30 to 40 years of rapidly increasing sunspot activity.

(*c*) Thorarinsson's [24] detailed study of the year-to-year advance or recession of major glaciers in the Scandinavian area during the period of general recession from 1900 to 1940 shows that the two periods of most rapid recession were centered squarely on the major sunspot maxima of 1917 and 1937, extending roughly from the preceding to the following minima. Two periods of cessation of recession and temporary mild re-advance were centered on the two minor sunspot maxima of 1905 and 1928, extending roughly from the preceding to the following minima.[8]

(*d*) A recent study by Bodurtha [25] of wintertime polar anticyclogenesis in the Alaskan area, which is the one seat of development of blocking anticyclones for which adequate aerological data are available, confirms earlier studies indicating that in this area both the mean winter pressure and the frequency of strong anticyclogenesis in winter increase in a highly significant manner with increasing sunspot number. A recent breakdown of the occurrence of strong anticyclogenesis in this area [26] indicates that the anticyclogenesis occurs asymmetrically with respect to the sunspot maximum during the years of increasing rather than those of decreasing spots, and that the years of the major sunspot maxima contribute two to one, compared with the years of the minor sunspot maxima, to the high frequency of anticyclogenesis.

A vast amount of additional work might be referred to in citing studies of sunspot-to-weather relation, but that already cited indicates sufficiently the nature of the more significant recent evidence in this field. However, one additional and highly significant line of evidence to support the thesis of immediate atmospheric response to solar disturbance has been developed. This evidence is the result of the pioneer work of Duell and Duell,[27] recently extended and confirmed by Craig,[28] concerning the immediate response of the sea-level distribution of atmospheric pressure to sudden solar emissions of charged particles and ultraviolet radiation, as indicated, respectively, by the observation of geomagnetic disturbances and chromospheric eruptions on the sun.

Craig, following the lead of Duell and Duell, proves beyond any reasonable statistical doubt that on the Northern Hemisphere during the days immediately following geomagnetic disturbance, as opposed to the days of minimum disturbance, there is a definite tendency for pressure to rise in the higher latitudes, and to fall slightly in the lower latitudes. The maximum contrast is experienced from 4 to 6 days after the initial day between latitudes 70°N and 40°N, with a relative mean increase of pressure of 2.2 mb at the higher latitude. This corresponds definitely to a slight shift of the general circulation toward a glacial pattern. The effect was found clearly only for the winter months (December to March) and for years of relatively undisturbed solar conditions (average number of sunspots less than 40).

Owing to the shortness of the adequate record of observation of chromospheric eruptions, only a relatively short period (statistically insignificant) could be analyzed for this index. However, the effect seems to be independent of season and level of solar disturbance (sunspot number). The effect which Craig finds, and which will be of great interest if it receives further confirmation, is essentially that of a tendency toward a leveling of cellular pressure differences, that is, filling of cyclonic cells and weakening of anticyclonic cells, following chromospheric eruptions, or presumably active ultraviolet emission. This change corresponds to the strengthening of a zonal circulation pattern, or weakening of an anticyclonic blocking pattern, and represents essentially progress of the pattern toward glacial characteristics.

In view of the facts presented in the preceding discussion, however unproved and doubtful some of them may be considered, the following highly tentative suggestions are offered as to the probable relation between solar disturbance and atmospheric circulation:

(*a*) The extreme poleward contraction and typically settled steady state of the general circulation during a period of true interglacial climate probably is conditioned by a highly undisturbed state of the sun, with an absolute minimum of selective emission of short-wavelength ultraviolet and of corpuscular radiation.

(*b*) The steady expanded zonal state of the general circulation with maximum equatorward displacement of storm tracks, which characterizes a period of true glacial climate, probably is conditioned by a steady moderately disturbed state of the sun, with high ultraviolet emission and relatively steady but not excessive emission of charged particles — a state which at the present time appears to be most closely associated with a minor sunspot maximum. Presumably ultraviolet rather than corpuscular radiation is predominant.

(*c*) The highly chaotic periods of climatic stress, with markedly contrasting extremes of storminess, rainfall, and temperature in middle latitudes, accompanied by anticyclonic blocking of the circulation pattern and by the rapid glacial recession probably occasioned by the widespread occurrence of hot dry summers, presumably are conditioned by an extreme degree and variability of solar disturbance, particularly by intermittently intense emissions of corpuscular radiation. This state of the sun at the present time appears to be most closely associated with a major sunspot maximum, primarily on the side of increasing sunspots. Presumably the effects of corpuscular rather than ultraviolet invasions are predominant.

In conclusion, we remark again on the misfortune, for investigations of this type, occasioned by the lack of direct observation of either the amount and character of the critically variable solar emissions, or the direct effects that they produce in the higher atmosphere. Since some conceivable *modus operandi* should be ascribed to the types of emissions that are assumed to produce substantial effects in the atmosphere, a suggestion is offered, again highly tentatively, as to the most plausible realm of action of each type of solar emission.

The primary effects of the short-wave length ultraviolet emission are presumably electrochemical. They are largely responsible for the maintenance of the ionized layers of the higher atmosphere, but it seems most probable that they affect the lower atmosphere by direct or indirect thermal effects. Direct thermal effects are doubtless found in the higher atmosphere, but indirect effects on the heat balance of the lower atmosphere may be important, in the sense probably of increasing the greenhouse effect by the formation of ozone, or possibly by increasing the numbers of condensation nuclei and cloudiness of the higher troposphere. An increased greenhouse effect probably would reduce monsoon thermal gradients, and weaken any cellular features of the sea-level atmospheric-pressure distribution that are dependent on them.

Undoubtedly the direct effects of the charged-particle emission are kinetic or kinetic-thermal. Presumably these particles are focused toward the magnetic poles of the earth by its magnetic field, thus accounting for the immediate response of rising pressure in the higher latitudes, or at least in selected regions in high latitudes. There is no basis at the present time on which to estimate the ultimate effects of such invasions.

ADDENDUM

One remarkable bit of direct evidence confirming the author's point of view regarding the immediate response of atmospheric circulations to solar corpuscular invasions was called to his attention by Dr. E. Wahl at the Symposium on Climatic Change, after the completion of the preceding manuscript. This bit of evidence is important to the thesis of this paper, first because it is the first instance of the measurement of the direct thermal effect produced in the higher atmosphere by a sudden solar disturbance, and second, because the reaction of the circulation of the lower troposphere was prompt, of considerable amplitude, and strikingly toward the expected pattern. For this reason the following brief discussion of the event, its consequences, and a few interpretive remarks are appended.

During a 24-hour period, from February 24 to 25 (1952), the regular twice-daily high-altitude atmospheric soundings taken by Scherhag in Berlin [29] recorded a rise of temperature at the 20- to 10-mb levels in the stratosphere of 40°C. This sudden heating effect diffused slowly downward, a peak increase of about 12°C being reached at the 50-mb level a few days later, while in the course of the following week a slow return to near-normal temperatures occurred at all levels. No similar sequence of events has been noted before, but it must be remarked that very few series of soundings to such high altitudes have been made, and they have not been analyzed for this type of occurrence.

The solar source of this extreme heating of the stratosphere from February 24 to 25 is implied almost beyond any doubt by the fact that in the forenoon hours of February 24 (GMT) an exceptionally strong solar flare (chromospheric eruption) was observed, followed closely by radio fadeout. At the same time the K_p index of geomagnetic activity rose to 7.0, the sum for the day being 44+, up from 15 on the previous day, while the international character figure for the day was 1.7, up from 0.6 the previous day. This was the most extreme geomagnetic disturbance that had occurred since the previous October. It had been closely approached on only one intervening day, December 27, when the K_p sum and the character figure C increased, respectively, to 42^+ and 1.8 from values of 20^- and 0.9 on the previous day. Thus the various indices indicate that there occurred on February 24 probably the strongest invasion of solar ultraviolet (solar flare and radio fadeout) and solar particle emission (geomagnetic indices) of the current (1951–52) winter season. Since February was a relatively inactive sunspot month (relative sunspot number, 21) it may be assumed that the effect of this solar outbreak should be of the type established by Craig for geomagnetic disturbances during winters of low sunspot number, that is, an effect of strong pressure rise in the high latitudes centered at 70°N.

Inspection of the circulation patterns shows that just this development took place to an extreme degree. From the 5-day period ending on February 24 to the period ending one week later, from the Greenwich meridian westward to 180°, the polar easterlies increased from 2.1 to 6.3 m/sec, the highest value of the 1951–52 winter season, while the subtropical easterlies fell from 1.3 to −1.1 m/sec, the lowest value of the season. The zonal westerlies remained weak (sea-level, 0.8 to 1.6 m/sec; 700 mb, from 7.5 to 8.3 m/sec), while two very intense Atlantic storms developed and remained nearly stationary for days, one off the northeast coast of the United States and the other in the central Atlantic just north of the Azores. At the same time strong polar anticyclogenesis started over Greenland and extended westward to Alaska, in one of the most extensive polar anticyclones of this winter season. These changes represent an extreme shift of the circulation pattern of the northern hemisphere toward low-latitude storm activity.

If it is assumed that the atmospheric reaction outlined above, including the extreme heating of the stratosphere, is a reaction primarily to solar corpuscular invasion, as is indicated by the pattern of the circulation change that developed, then tentative explanations may be offered for two observational facts concerning the atmosphere. The peak frequency of polar anticyclogenesis of the extreme blocking type that occurs during winters of increasing solar activity, primarily at the major sunspot maximum, is almost exclusively a phenomenon of the north American continent, and not of the Asiatic. This selection can be explained by the location of the north magnetic pole northwest of Greenland, so that the corpuscular radiation tends to be directed toward the western side of the Arctic regions. The anticyclogenetic effect of extreme solar corpuscular activity apparently is felt upstream (westward) from the magnetic pole.

The location of the center of this peak frequency of polar anticyclogenesis in the vicinity of the Yukon Valley was attributed by Bodurtha [25] to strong cyclogenetic activity in the Gulf of Alaska or along the Aleutians to the west, but the recent analysis [26] of cyclogenetic frequencies in the Aleutian area does not confirm this explanation, in that there is no increase but rather a slight decrease of strong cyclogenetic activity in this area during the periods of peak anticyclogenetic activity in eastern Alaska. This evidence points toward direct solar incitement as being the primary cause of the anticyclogenetic activity.

The second observational fact which may be explained tentatively by the distribution and direct thermal effects of solar corpuscular radiations is that of the seasonal differences of temperature of the Arctic and Antarctic substratosphere. On the basis of recent balloon radiosonde data, which are comparatively few in number from the Antarctic, Rubin [30] finds that in winter the atmosphere at the 16-km level in the Antarctic may average as much as 30°C colder than at the same level in the Canadian Arctic in winter, whereas summer temperatures at the same level in the Antarctic are some 6°C warmer than in the Arctic. Rubin attributes these differences primarily to stronger insolational heating during the Antarctic summer, and to stronger meridional circulation during the Northern than during the Southern Hemisphere winter. This latter fact can be established only very uncertainly under the present lack of aerological data from the Southern Hemisphere.

It is quite probable, however, that, depending upon the polarity of the earth's magnetic field and the prevailing charge of the solar corpuscular radiation (presumably largely negative electrons), one pole or the other tends to be strongly favored. If the north magnetic pole is favored by the corpuscular invasions, and if they are capable of producing heating effects such as those recently observed over Germany, then the high winter temperature of the Arctic stratosphere — a temperature that it is very difficult to account for by any consideration of atmospheric circulation or radiational equilibrium — would be explained. The production of ozone by ultraviolet should be essentially the same in the two hemispheres. This hypothesis can be further tested by a simple comparison of the frequency and intensity of auroral displays in the Arctic and in the Antarctic, if comparable observational data are obtainable. Furthermore, the warmth of the polar atmosphere and the active recession of glaciation that accompany periods of extreme solar activity, and the polar anticyclonic blocking pattern of climatic stress, may also be attributed in part to direct heating of the higher atmosphere by excessive solar corpuscular radiation.

REFERENCES

1. Technical Report No. 4 (Contract N6onr, Task Order 18) 1952, Lamont Geological Observatory, Columbia University.

2. R. F. Flint, *Glacial geology and the Pleistocene Epoch* (Wiley, New York, 1947).

3. H. C. Willett, "Long-period fluctuations of the general circulation of the atmosphere," *Jour. Meteorol.* 6, 34–50 (1949).

4. H. C. Willett, "Solar variability as a factor in the fluctuations of climate during geological time," *Geografiska Annaler, Glaciers and Climate*, häfte 1–2, 295–315 (1949).

5. H. C. Willett, "The general circulation at the last (Würm) glacial maximum," *Geografiska Annaler*, häfte 3–4, 179–187 (1950).

6. C. E. P. Brooks, *Climate through the ages* (Benn, London, ed. 2, 1949).

7. H. C. Willett, "Extrapolation of sunspot-climate relationships," *Jour. Meteorol.* 8, 1–6 (1951).

8. H. C. Willett, "Solar influences on the weather," *Trans. New York Acad. Sci.*, Ser. II, *13*, 277–280 (1951).

9. L. Lysgaard, *Recent climatic fluctuations* (Danish Meteorological Institute, Copenhagen, 1949).

10. G. C. Simpson, "Possible causes of change of climate and their limitations," *Proc. Linnean Soc.* 152, 190–219 (1940).

11. M. Milankovitch, *Kanon der Erdbestrahlung und seine Anwendung auf das Eiszeitproblem* (Royal Serbian Academy, Belgrade, 1941).

12. F. E. Zeuner, "The Pleistocene chronology of central Europe," *Geol. Mag.* 72, 350–376 (1935).

13. F. E. Zeuner, *The Pleistocene period* (Ray Society, of London, 1945).

14. G. A. Gamow, *Biography of the earth, its past, present and future* (Viking Press, New York, 1948).

15. R. A. Craig and H. C. Willett, *Compendium of meteorology* (American Meteorological Society, Boston, 1951), pp. 379–390.

16. von G. Viete, "Ueber die allgemeine atmosphärische Zirkulation während der diluvialen Vereisungsperioden," *Tellus 2*, 102–115 (1950).

17. G. C. Simpson, "Further studies in terrestrial radiation," *Memo. Roy. Meteorol. Soc. 3*, 1–26 (1930).

18. G. C. Simpson, "World climate during the quaternary period," *Quart. Jour. Roy. Meteorol Soc.* 60, 425–478 (1934).

19. D. F. Rex, "Blocking action in the middle troposphere and its effects upon regional climate, Part I, An aerological study of blocking action," *Tellus 2*, 196–211 (1950); "Part II, The climatology of blocking action," *ibid.*, 275–301.

20. D. F. Rex. "The effect of Atlantic blocking action upon European climate," *Tellus 3*, 100–112 (1951).

21. H. C. Willett, "Temperature trends of the past century," *Centennial Proc. Roy. Meteorol. Soc.*, 195–206 (1950).

22. H. C. Willett, *Report of the Weather Bureau – Massachusetts Institute of Technology extended forecasting project* (Cambridge, July 1, 1949).

23. S. Hanzlik, "Der Luftdruckeffekt der Sonnenfleckenperiode für die Monate Dezember . . . " II Mitt. *Gerlands Beitr. Geophys.*, *29*, 138–155 (1931).

24. S. Thorarinsson, "Present glacier shrinkage, and eustatic changes of sea level," *Geografiska Annaler 22*, häfte 3–4 (1940).

25. F. T. Bodurtha, "An investigation of anticyclogenesis in Alaska" (doctoral thesis, Massachusetts Institute of Technology, 1951).

26. H. C. Willett, *Final report of the Weather Bureau – Massachusetts Institute of Technology Extended Forecasting Project for the fiscal year July 1, 1951 – June 30, 1952* (Cambridge, 1952).

27. B. Duell and G. Duell, "The behavior of barometric pressure during and after solar particle invasions and solar ultraviolet invasions," *Smiths. Misc. Coll.*, Vol. 110, No. 8 (1948).

28. R. A. Craig and D. Hawkins, "Atmospheric pressure changes and solar activity," Special Report No. 38, A. M. C. Contract W19-122ac-17 (1951).

29. H. Schweitzer, "A brief report on some high-altitude observations taken by Scherhag in Berlin," *Umschau 52*, 247 (1952).

30. M. Rubin, *Seasonal variations in the antarctic troposphere* (M. S. thesis, Massachusetts Institute of Technology, 1952).

5

RADIATION BALANCE OF THE EARTH
AS A FACTOR IN CLIMATIC CHANGE

H. Wexler

Radiation from the sun is practically the sole source of energy for atmospheric processes and therefore it seems reasonable to examine variations in radiation received and emitted by the earth and its atmosphere as a possible cause of climatic variations. Changes in quantity and quality of solar radiation and variations in composition and albedo of the earth's atmosphere could conceivably modify world climate, and it is the purpose of this paper to examine briefly these variations in an attempt to estimate the magnitude of the resulting modifications. Particular emphasis will be placed on climatic fluctuations in recent decades because of a belief, first stated by Willett, that recent climatic fluctuations differ only in degree but not in kind from the great fluctuations of the past, and also because the availability of meteorological and other data permit the testing of some proposed theories of climatic change.

ENERGY BALANCE OF THE EARTH AND ITS ATMOSPHERE

Each minute nearly 2 gram calories of solar radiant energy fall on 1 square centimeter of area exposed perpendicularly to the sun's rays outside the earth's atmosphere. This means that, averaged over the whole earth, each square centimeter of the outer surface of the atmosphere receives 700 langleys/day. (One langley (ly) = 1 gram calorie/cm^2). If we set this energy income equal to 100 units (1 unit = 7 ly/day), then the average radiation budget over the earth for all seasons, as computed by Möller,[1] is given in Fig. 1.

Of the 100 units of solar radiation (of wavelength 0.2 μ to 3 μ) impinging on the top of the atmosphere, 35 units (the earth's albedo) are reflected to space by air, clouds, and earth, and therefore do not contribute to the energy of the atmosphere; 14 units are absorbed by clouds, dust particles, and various gases in the atmosphere (principally water vapor and ozone), leaving 51 units to arrive at the earth's surface, 34 units as direct solar radiation and indirect clear sky radiation that results from the scattering of the direct solar rays by air molecules and other small particles in the atmosphere, and 17 units as indirect solar radiation transmitted and scattered by clouds.

The earth, radiating as a black body at its observed average surface temperature of 287°K, sends up 113 units of long-wavelength ($4\,\mu$ to $100\,\mu$) radiation. Because water vapor strongly absorbs radiation in most of these wavelengths, the atmosphere is very nearly opaque to the terrestrial

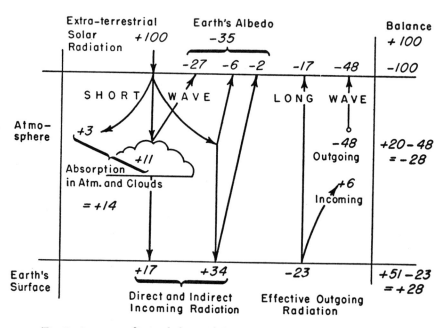

Fig. 1. Average radiation balance of the earth's atmosphere (after Möller[1]).

radiation. Only 17 units escape directly to space unhindered by the atmosphere; the atmosphere, absorbing 96 units, returns 90 units to earth, thus leaving only 23 units to comprise the "effective outgoing radiation" as it would be measured by a radiation instrument located at the earth's surface. The atmosphere gains 6 units of the terrestrial radiation and emits 48 units to space. Totaling the various incoming and outgoing radiations, there is an over-all balance at the top of the atmosphere, a net loss of 28 units in the atmosphere, and a net gain of 28 units at the earth's surface. The net energy gain at the surface is mostly utilized in evaporating water, which rises as vapor and is condensed into clouds and precipitation, releasing the heat of condensation, and thus making good the deficit of energy in the atmosphere.

Thus, it is seen that as far as the earth-atmosphere system is concerned, there is balance of the incoming and outgoing radiation. The intensity of the outgoing radiation depends on the average temperature of the earth's surface, which at a value of 287°K may be considered as an equilibrium temperature. What radiative changes can affect this equilibrium temperature? First, changes in the amount and kind of energy received from the sun. Second, quantitative changes in those atmospheric gases which absorb solar and terrestrial radiation. Third, changes in the albedo of the earth and its atmosphere caused by variations in cloud type and amount, presence of air-borne particles such as fine dust in the atmosphere, and changes in reflectivity of the earth's surface. Each of these phenomena will be examined in turn, with respect to both their possible occurrence and their estimated effects on surface temperature or other climatic elements.

VARIATIONS IN AMOUNT AND KIND OF SOLAR RADIATION

In the absence of direct measurements of amount and spectral distribution of solar radiation impinging on the atmosphere, reliance must be placed on indirect means. For 50 years the Smithsonian Institution has extrapolated radiation measurements made on high, cloudless mountain tops to obtain values of the "solar constant." These values at first showed day-to-day variations of several percent, but as more and more corrections were introduced, presumably to reduce effects of variations in atmospheric transmission, the measured fluctuations of the solar constant decreased, until today they average less than 1 percent. There is still lack of general agreement as to whether the presently observed small changes are true variations in the solar constant, changes in transmission of the earth's atmosphere, or random errors of observation.

With regard to changes in spectral distribution of solar energy, there is quite convincing evidence from ionospheric observations that there exists considerable variation in the ultraviolet, presumably including also the region from 2000 to 2800 A. Radiation in this band is important since it is absorbed by atmospheric oxygen and ozone. According to Menzel,[2] during periods of sunspot maxima there is 20 times as much energy in certain ultraviolet bands as during sunspot minima. This will increase the value of the solar constant by a few percent which, however, could not be detected from ground measurements. The enriched ultraviolet radiation is not continuously present in the sun's radiation during sunspot maxima, but comes in rather short-lived bursts of energy, probably associated with solar flares. These cause the sudden ionospheric disturbances (SID's) which last for minutes or hours, and create high-frequency radio fade-outs.

Changes in the Solar Constant. Arbitrarily varying the solar constant has exerted a special fascination on those who like the direct and supposedly simple approach to the explanation of climatic changes, particularly of the ice ages. Thus, Simpson [3] has invoked a 10-percent *increase* in the value of the solar constant and Flint [4] and Viete [5] have invoked a substantial *decrease* as a condition necessary to explain the same periods of glaciation. If the atmosphere-earth system responded as a black body to ± 10-percent changes in solar radiation changes in the average temperature of the system of ± 6°C would result.

Briefly stated, Simpson's increased solar radiation heats lower latitudes more than higher latitudes, increases the equator-to-pole temperature gradient, which in turn increases the intensity of the circulation. The greater wind speed and higher temperature increase evaporation, and the greater storminess and moisture content increase the amount of cloudiness and precipitation. The increased cloudiness, by reflecting much of the increased radiation, does not permit the earth and its atmosphere to respond as a black body and thus prevents the temperature from rising proportionately; in fact, in certain regions the temperature may be lower than before. The increased precipitation, largely in the form of snow at high latitudes and altitudes, encourages the winter build-up of glaciers, which do not melt much in the cloudy, cool summers, and so allows an annual accumulation of snow and ice. As the sun's output increases to near its maximum value, the increased radiation succeeds in so heating the atmosphere that increased melting and evaporation cause the glaciers to diminish and thereby create the warm interglacial periods. As the sun's radiation decreases to normal again, the cycle is repeated, and another ice age is born. Simpson attaches great importance to the necessity for an increase in the solar radiation (to create initially an ice age), because he wants increased evaporation, moisture transport, and storminess — conditions which he believes necessary for the initiation of an ice age. On the other hand, according to Simpson, a 10-percent *decrease* in radiation would cool the air, lower the equator-to-pole temperature gradient and decrease the moisture content, transport, and storminess to such an extent that the precipitation, even if all in the form of snow, would be insignificant.

The first and most important objection to Simpson's theory is that there is no evidence, observational or theoretical, which would account for the sun's energy output increasing and decreasing significantly in the time intervals required for the explanation of the ice ages; in fact, current theories as to maintenance of the sun's energy argue against such large variations in solar energy. Second, even if a large solar increase did occur, then it leads to an apparent paradox of "hotter sun, cooler earth."

Changes in Ultraviolet Radiation. To get around this paradox, Haurwitz [6, 7] suggested a theory linking sudden outbursts of ultraviolet radiation with a sudden heating of the ozone layer, deployment of this layer poleward from the subsolar point, and consequent increase of pressure at 30° latitude. Rough calculations indicated that the pressure rise at sea level at this latitude might be as large as 20mb, or 2 percent of the sea-level value. Such large changes in pressure would materially change the weather over large portions of the earth's surface. But there are some basic weaknesses in Haurwitz' admittedly rough calculations which the present writer has attempted to remove. [8] Computing the readjustment of atmospheric mass after short-period (of the order of one-half a pendulum day) meridional oscillations resulting from an ultraviolet impulse, we found, in agreement with Haurwitz, that there is a decrease in sea-level pressure at the subsolar point; however, this decrease extends to 40° latitude, poleward of which there exists a pressure rise that reaches its maximum near or at the geographical pole. Assuming that, as a result of increased absorption of ultraviolet radiation, the temperature in the ozone layer (comprising the top 5 percent of mass of the atmosphere) increases suddenly by 10°C, the resulting maximum surface pressure change is less than 0.01mb, or less than 0.001 percent of atmospheric pressure. This is much too small to be of meteorological significance unless repeated ultraviolet impulses occur in such a way that their effects on atmospheric pressure are additive, and can mount up to the order of 1 percent of atmospheric pressure. Since solar ultraviolet impulses are more numerous during periods of sunspot maxima than sunspot minima, we decided to summarize sea-level pressure data according to maxima and minima of the sunspot cycle. The period 1899–1939, comprising nearly four sunspot cycles, was used since for that interval daily northern-hemisphere sea-level weather maps are available, from which pressures at 5° or 10° latitude and longitude intersections were abstracted and placed on punch cards. For each cycle the maximum and minimum sunspot periods were determined by taking those three consecutive years showing the greatest and least accumulated total of sunspot numbers. Differences were taken by subtracting the average sea-level pressures during the periods of sunspot minima, thus defined, from those of the following sunspot maxima and averaging for the four cycles.

The pressure differences, separated for winter (October through March) and summer (April through September), and averaged around latitude circles, are shown in Fig. 2. The abscissa of this figure is the sine of the latitude so that the areas are proportional to earth areas. The two curves are quite similar and show maxima of 0.75 mb at 70° latitude and minima of 0.25 mb at 30° to 40° latitude. Because of scarcity of pressure data in the tropics, the curves south of 25° or 20° latitude are uncertain. The individual cycles, when plotted in a similar manner, reveal a good deal of variation as to location of maxima and minima, but in general the maxima are found in middle or higher latitudes, and the minima at lower latitudes. These results, average for both seasons, are shown in Fig. 3, together with Clayton's earlier results [9, 10] for comparison. Clayton based his work on data from some 200 stations over the world for the period 1860 to 1917, covering five sunspot cycles. Clayton's curve is similar to

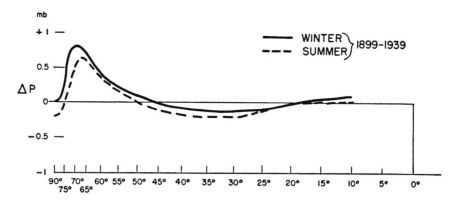

Fig. 2. Average pressure-difference profiles, sunspot maxima minus sunspot minima, winter and summer, 1899–1939, Weather Bureau analysis.

the Weather Bureau curve, but its maximum and minimum points are displaced southward. The Weather Bureau and Clayton curves for the same sunspot cycle of 1910–1920 also display similar differences. The Weather Bureau January 1900–1939 curve is also shown in the same figure.

In a previous paper [11] the author showed for the winter and summer half-years the geographical distribution of sunspot maxima minus sunspot minima pressures for the Northern Hemisphere for 1899–1939. We found that the regions which made the principal contributions to the positive area at higher latitudes are the polar anticyclonic source regions in northwestern North America and central Siberia; and we also found that during sunspot maxima the average pressures in these regions were as much as 2.5 mb higher than at sunspot minima, while most of Europe, the Norwegian Sea, and adjacent portions of the Arctic Ocean had lower pressure during sunspot maxima than at sunspot minima, with differences as large as 1mb. The summer pattern is quite similar to that of winter, the correlation between the two being 0.53. But the winter and summer

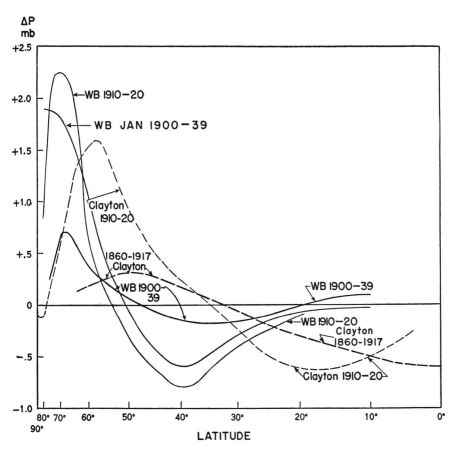

Fig. 3. Average pressure-difference profiles, sunspot maxima minus sunspot minima. Weather Bureau and Clayton results compared.

half-years, as here defined, are too broad to be representative of each of the respective seasons. We therefore decided to compute the sunspot maximum minus sunspot minimum pressure differences for January and July. January will be discussed first, and the geographical distribution of the differences is shown in Fig. 4. Here, as in the winter half-year, the contributions to the positive difference at high latitudes are located over the Gulf of Alaska, Greenland, and north-central Siberia. Intervening negative regions are found over Hudson Bay, northeastern Siberia, and southern Scandinavia. Note that in this three-cell pattern of positive and negative differences as one proceeds from east to west, starting at Hudson

Fig. 4. Average pressure difference, sunspot maxima minus sunspot minima, January 1900–1939.

Bay for the negative areas and in north-central Siberia for the positive areas, the absolute magnitude of each successive difference of like sign increases. Farther south the cellular pattern and the magnitudes are not so well marked. Although the January pattern has features similar to those of "winter," the symmetry and magnitudes of the former are much more striking. An interpretation of this cellular pattern in terms of "blocking" and a suggested explanation will be the subject of another paper.

Up to now the discussion has been concerned with pressures summarized annually, semiannually, or monthly in accordance with the

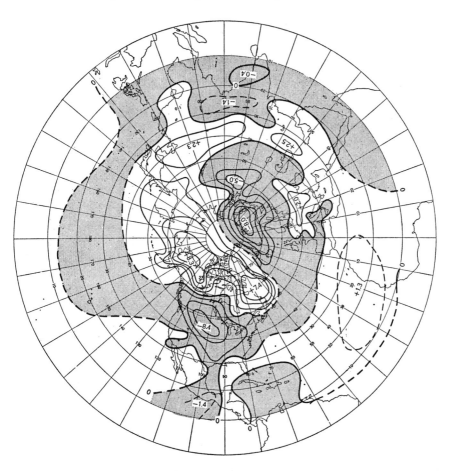

Fig. 5. Average temperature difference (°F), sunspot maxima minus sunspot minima, January 1900–1939.

periods of maxima and minima of the sunspot cycle. With the exception of Clayton's data, the source of the material has been the 40-year series of the daily Northern Hemisphere sea-level charts. Now we shall see the results of similar computations when we use independent temperature and precipitation data for January, taken from individual stations listed in Clayton's *World Weather Records*. In Fig. 5 we see the average

January difference of temperature, sunspot maxima minus sunspot minima; and in Fig. 6 is indicated a similar difference in precipitation, expressed as percentage of the average January 1899–1939 precipitation for each station.

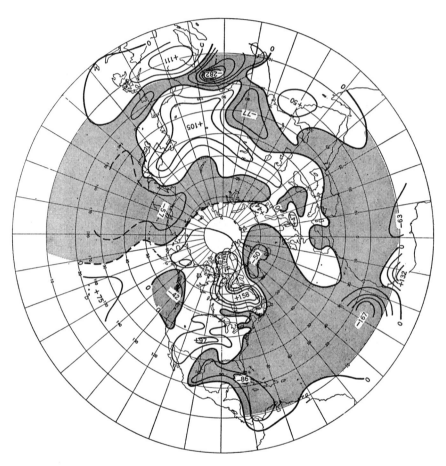

Fig. 6. Average precipitation difference, sunspot maxima minus sunspot minima, expressed as percentage of the average (normal) precipitation, January 1900–1939.

If we translate the pressure difference pattern in Fig. 4 in terms of a wind-flow difference pattern, following the usual rule in the Northern Hemisphere of clockwise flow about positive (high) differences and counterclockwise flow about negative (low) differences, then the temperature and precipitation difference charts for the most part can be readily interpreted. For temperature, one should keep in mind the normal

January surface temperature picture, and let the difference winds move the isotherms. For precipitation the interpretation must be based on the wind and temperature difference patterns and is somewhat more complicated: up and down motions over topographical features and domes of cold air, and displacement of storm tracks and presence of increased maritime air flow into continental regions are some of the elements to be considered.

Using all these criteria, we find the sea-level pressure, temperature, and precipitation difference patterns at middle and high latitudes for the most part surprisingly consistent. For example, we see in the Dakotas and Montana that the average January is 7°F to 8.5°F colder during sunspot maxima than during sunspot minima. This, and the remainder of the negative difference area are readily explained by the increased wind motion from the cold source region in Canada. The positive temperature difference area in Alaska and northwest Canada is explained by increased flow of warmer air aloft from the Pacific Ocean, while the positive temperature difference area in northeastern Canada and western Greenland is explained by increased air motion from the Atlantic Ocean. The increased precipitation during sunspot maxima in northern North America also owes its origin to increased flow of unstable maritime air into regions usually covered by dry stable polar continental air masses and to their resulting uplift. The increased precipitation over the central United States is explained by displacement southward of tracks of storms coming from the Pacific Ocean, and by the increased flow and greater uplift of maritime air over the thicker domes of polar air in the central United States. The lesser precipitation in the Canadian and northern United States Pacific coastal areas is due to the displacement of the storm tracks south of their normal position in the eastern Pacific Ocean, and to the foehn or chinook effect of the increased flow of continental air westward to the Pacific Coast.

It is similarly possible to explain in terms of the wind difference pattern the negative temperature difference in northern Europe and the region to the north, as well as the positive temperature difference in central Europe. The precipitation difference patterns in these regions can for the most part also be related to the wind and temperature difference patterns. No attempt will be made to explain the temperature and precipitation patterns in other regions, partly because the lack of sufficient data renders uncertain the reality of the patterns shown in the figures.

Thus far, comparison of Figs. 4, 5, and 6 has revealed a remarkable consistency of the pressure, temperature, and precipitation difference patterns found by subtracting Januarys of minimum sunspot number from Januarys of maximum sunspot number. A total of 12 January pairs was used in this compilation, and the difference values shown in the figures are the *average* differences, not the accumulated total of the differences, for three successive pairs of Januarys, each comprising the three years of a sunspot maximum and three years of the previous sunspot minimum. The consistency is all the more remarkable when it is realized that the data are from different sources, the sea-level pressure data being taken from interpolated grid points on analyzed daily Northern Hemisphere weather charts, while the temperature and precipitation data are taken from actual records at a few hundred individual stations.

There is as yet no proof that these particular pressure, temperature, and precipitation difference patterns are uniquely determined by taking differences between sunspot maxima and minima. Nor can such proof be readily produced. It may well be that similar patterns can be obtained by selecting comparable groups of years at random, without any regard to sunspot number, and taking differences. When, in fact, such a random experiment was performed for the winter and summer half-years, the patterns and magnitudes of pressure differences were remarkably similar to those of sunspot maxima minus sunspot minima found earlier.[12]

Much more work remains to be done before a sunspot control of large-scale pressure and weather patterns can be established. The small number of sunspot cycles for which data for the whole Northern Hemisphere exist is a severe handicap. Nevertheless, there are enough promising clues, both theoretical and observational, to keep at a high pitch the interest of the investigator. For example, if one should be so bold as to consider the pressure, temperature and precipitation difference patterns of Figs. 3, 4, and 5 as suggestive of the response of the earth's atmosphere to differences in solar activity for periods much longer than an 11-year sunspot cycle, and, furthermore, if one should assume, as Willett once did,[13, 14] that prolonged periods of high solar activity (maximum sunspots) favored glaciation, then the January difference patterns certainly would support this hypothesis, at least qualitatively. The increased precipitation over most of North America would still be in the form of snow in northern regions, despite the higher temperatures there, and would also be in the form of increased snowfall over the north-central portion of the United States where the January 32°F and 20°F isotherms would be shifted several hundred miles south of the positions they held during sunspot minima. Similarly, January temperature and precipitation conditions over Scandinavia and adjacent regions would also favor glaciation. So, according to the hypothesis, winter (January) conditions during periods of greater solar activity would favor increased solid precipitation in regions where glaciers were known to have existed in the past.[15] The favorable winter conditions, however, are only a *necessary* and not a

sufficient condition for glaciation, since the winter snow and ice accumulation might well disappear in the summer. It has been generally
recognized that cool, cloudy summers would also be required to preserve
the winter snow and ice. Are the summers in the critical areas where

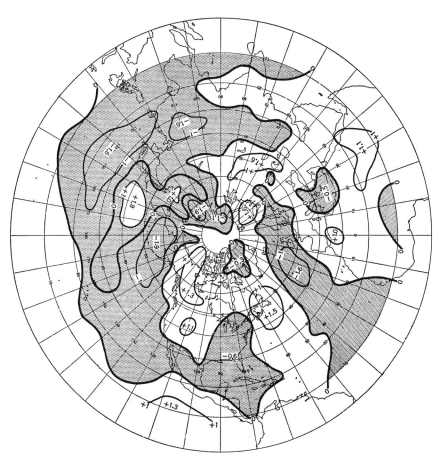

Fig. 7. Average pressure difference, sunspot maxima minus sunspot minima, July
1900–1939.

extensive glaciation once was found cooler and cloudier during periods
of sunspot maximum?

To examine this question there are presented in Figs. 7, 8, and 9 the
July 1900–1939 average difference charts, sunspot maxima minus sunspot
minima, for sea-level pressure, temperature and precipitation.

Not much can be said about the pressure difference chart in Fig. 7

except that the magnitudes of the pressure differences are smaller than those in January, but at high latitudes there still seems to be some sign of the 3-cell pattern found in January.

The explanation of the July positive and negative temperature

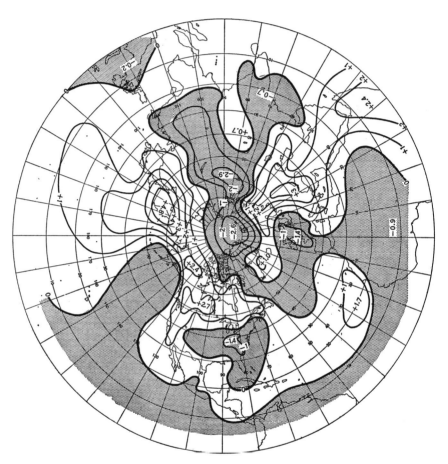

Fig. 8. Average temperature difference (°F), sunspot maxima minus sunspot minima, July 1900–1939.

differences in Fig. 8 in terms of a wind flow difference pattern as deduced from Fig. 7 is not so clear-cut as in January; the lower temperatures in southern Alaska, the British Isles and most of northwestern Europe might be associated with an accentuated flow inland of cooler maritime air during sunspot maxima. The cooler area over the eastern two thirds of the United States is difficult to explain by advection and it is possible that increased convective cloudiness caused by more cyclonic circulation might be more important. This supposition is supported by the precipitation difference chart in Fig. 9, where during sunspot maxima more precipitation is seen to occur over essentially the same area of the United

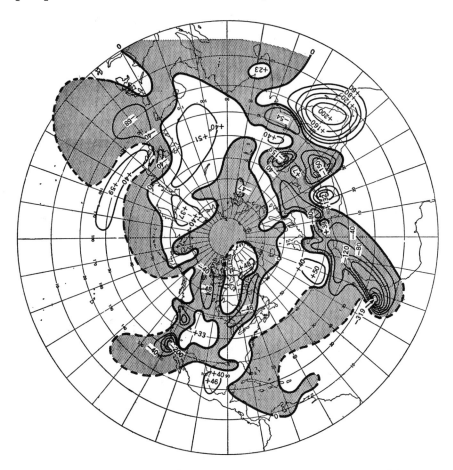

Fig. 9. Average precipitation difference, sunspot maxima minus sunspot minima, expressed as percentage of the average (normal) precipitation, July 1900–1939.

States covered by the temperature deficit. Likewise, most of northwestern Europe has heavier precipitation and presumably more cloudiness, probably as a result of a greater maritime influence during sunspot maxima.

Thus in support of the solar hypothesis of glaciation one might say, on the basis of Figs. 8 and 9, that during sunspot maxima as compared to minima July (and presumably the summer season as a whole) is cooler and wetter in central and eastern United States, the British Isles, northwestern Europe and most of Scandinavia, these regions being critical in the sense that they marked the southernmost extension of the last glacier.[15] The small temperature deficits shown in Fig. 8 by themselves would hardly be sufficient to delay melting and ablation of the winter snow and ice accumulation and one should probably interpret the temperature and precipitation difference patterns found in the period of variable solar activity in 1900–1939 as being geographically similar to those patterns which occurred during prolonged periods of abnormally variable solar activity in the past but of much smaller magnitude.

CHANGES IN COMPOSITION OF THE EARTH'S ATMOSPHERE

Changes in the transmission of solar and terrestrial radiation through the atmosphere can be brought about by changes in the composition of absorbing gases. The important gases that affect both short- and long-wavelength radiation are water vapor, ozone, and carbon dioxide. Keeping in mind that changes of about 10°C in surface temperatures averaged over the earth are believed to be necessary to account for the difference between glacial and interglacial periods, let us see how large a temperature change can result from varying the amount or temperature of these gases.

The importance of atmospheric absorption of radiation to the earth's temperature is illustrated by the well-known "greenhouse effect" of water vapor, which is nearly transparent to the short-wavelength solar radiation, but nearly opaque to the long-wavelength terrestrial radiation. An increase in the amount of water vapor in the atmosphere might accentuate the "greenhouse effect" and thus raise the temperature of the earth's surface. However, the water-vapor content of the air is dependent on evaporation and precipitation, which themselves are functions of temperature, wind speed, and storminess. Thus, changes in these last three elements will influence the water-vapor content, which in turn can change the surface radiative-equilibrium temperature. For example, decreasing the relative humidity from 100 to 50 percent throughout a sounding typical of polar maritime air, and allowing the moist and drier types of air to seek a quasi-radiative equilibrium over a snow surface during sunless, windless, cloudless conditions, will result in a surface equilibrium temperature about 6°C cooler for the drier atmosphere.[16] Thus, if some condition causes the atmosphere to lose one-half of its moisture content, this would permit the average surface temperature to fall by more than one-half of the amount required to bring on an ice age. The effects of a water-vapor decrease of this magnitude would then be of climatic significance, but the question what caused the moisture drop in the first place would be unanswered.

The ozone content of the atmosphere varies seasonally, geographically, and interdiurnally, the last variation depending on the prevailing weather type. Since ozone absorbs strongly in a narrow band centered about 10 μ, located in the important "window" region of the water-vapor spectrum, changes in ozone content and vertical distribution would be expected to have some effect on the outgoing radiation from the earth's surface. Since ozone owes its origin to the disassociation of oxygen molecules by certain ultraviolet radiations, it is conceivable that changes in these radiations might lead to changes in the ozone content. However, since other radiations decompose the ozone, it might well be that a large increase of ultraviolet does not change the original equilibrium vertical distribution of ozone, but would increase the air temperature, especially by absorption at the top of the ozone layer. According to a calculation made by my colleague, Dr. L. D. Kaplan, an increase of 10°C in the temperature of the ozone layer would increase the downward radiation by about 10^{-3} ly/min, which, other things being kept equal, would increase the surface temperature by 0.2°C — a value much too small to account for surface temperature variations required to produce the major climatic changes observed in the past.

Changes in the carbon dioxide content remain to be considered. Carbon dioxide absorbs strongly in a band from 13 μ to 17 μ — a region of rather weak water-vapor absorption. For large CO_2 content, one wing of this band extends into the water-vapor absorption window; changes in CO_2 content might therefore conceivably affect the outgoing radiation. Carbon dioxide occupies about 0.03 percent of the atmosphere by volume and, in contrast to ozone, is believed to be distributed rather uniformly throughout most of the troposphere and lower stratosphere. An increase in CO_2 content brings closer to the earth's surface the "effective layer" that is the source of CO_2 earthward emission. If there exists a temperature decrease with height above the earth's surface, then the increased CO_2 content might lead to an increased downward flux of radiation in the CO_2 band, not only because of the larger CO_2 content but because the radiation originates at a higher temperature. Other things being equal, the increased downward radiation might conceivably increase the temperature of the earth's surface. Callendar has collected measurements of CO_2 content made over the past 70 years, and finds that it has increased by 10 percent, from 0.029 to 0.032 percent, in 40 years,[17] the change being caused by increased combustion of fuels in recent years. Callendar has also computed the surface temperature increase caused by the CO_2

increase and finds that, for an atmosphere of "normal" decrease of temperature with height, the temperature increase amounts to 0.003°C a year, or 0.09°C in 30 years. This amount would be too small to account for the estimated 0.33°C warming of the earth's surface in the last 30 years, as given by Lysgaard.[18] Callendar's estimate of warming by increased CO_2 would be reduced, and perhaps changed in sign, if the computations were carried out in an atmosphere possessing a temperature *increase* with height instead of a *decrease* as Callendar assumed, since the lowering of the "effective layer" of CO_2 radiation in the former case results in a decrease in the radiation because of the lower temperature at which it originates. Such temperature increases with altitude, called "inversions," are found almost everywhere over land at night and over polar regions in winter, day and night.

CHANGES IN ALBEDO

Changes in albedo of the earth and its atmosphere may influence greatly the radiation received at the earth's surface. The amount and type of clouds, the state of the earth's surface, and the amount and type of solid particles in the atmosphere may each alter the albedo materially. Each of these phenomena, but especially the first, also affects significantly the return to space of the long-wavelength radiation emitted by earth and atmosphere.

Cloudiness and Radiation Balance. On the basis of an average cloudiness of 54 percent and a few reflectivity measurements of overcast (stratus) clouds measured at Mount Wilson, California, by Aldrich,[19] an over-all earth's albedo of 43 percent was computed, and accepted for many years. Recently, however, from Danjon's measurements of earthlight reflected from the moon,[20] Fritz estimated the earth's albedo to be 35 percent.[21] Before proceeding with a discussion of variations of amount and reflecting properties of cloud as a primary cause of albedo changes, it might be of interest to see what effect a *real* reduction of the earth's albedo from 43 to 35 percent might have on the radiation balance and equilibrium temperature of the earth-atmosphere system.

Simpson [22] studied the effect of cloudiness on radiation balance, using zero earth albedo for clear skies and Aldrich's value of 78 percent for overcast skies. Using a solar constant of 1.95 ly/min, he finds the average insolation of the earth's surface to be 0.488 ly/min. In Fig. 10 this point is plotted on the ordinate and is signified by the legend "A = 0%" in recognition of the fact that Simpson ignored any reflection of solar radiation from the atmosphere and earth during clear weather. For overcast skies, the incoming radiation absorbed will be $0.488 \cdot 0.22 = 0.108$

ly/min. This point is marked by "A = 78%." In the absence of further information, a straight line connecting these two points is probably the best approximation to the relation of incoming radiation to cloud amount. The two additional straight lines flanking this line represent radiation

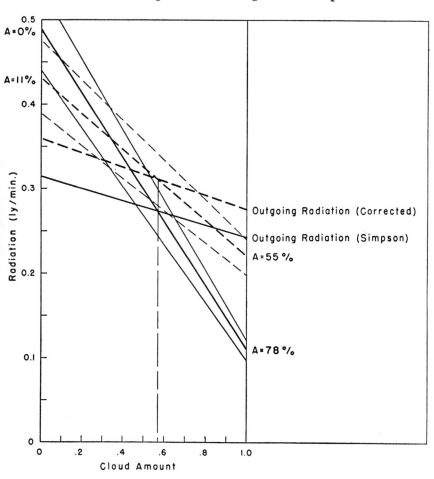

Fig. 10. Radiation as related to cloud amount (see text).

against cloud amount if the solar constant were 110 percent and 90 percent, respectively, of its accepted value. Using a simplified approximation of Hettner's absorption spectrum of steam (later shown to give too high absorption for atmospheric water vapor [23]) and of the observed temperature, moisture, and cloud distribution over the northern hemisphere, Simpson computed the outgoing radiation from earth and atmosphere as a function of latitude. He found that the outgoing radiation, averaged over the earth, was equal to 0.271 ly/min, or some 3 percent lower than the average incoming radiation of $0.488 \cdot 0.57 = 0.278$ ly/min for an albedo of 43 percent. This remarkable agreement between two figures derived from independent data encouraged Simpson to go on. He found the values of the outgoing radiation for clear and for overcast skies to be 0.307 and 0.235 ly/min, respectively. Note that the arithmetic mean of these latter values is 0.271 ly/min. Implicitly assuming that the average outgoing radiation remains as the arithmetic mean of the values for clear and for overcast skies, Simpson multiplied the latter values by the factor 278/271 to equalize average outgoing radiation with average incoming radiation, and thus obtained 0.314 and 0.242 ly/min for clear and for overcast skies, respectively. The straight line connecting these points is drawn in Fig. 10 and is labeled "outgoing radiation (Simpson)"; it represents a linear approximation of outgoing radiation against cloud amount. The intersection of this outgoing-radiation line with the incoming-radiation line shows that radiative balance is achieved at 0.565 cloud amount and 0.273 ly/min. This derived value of the average cloud amount is in very close agreement with the generally accepted value of 0.54 given by Aldrich [19] and 0.544 found by C. E. P. Brooks.[24] Changing the solar constant from 90 to 110 percent of normal, but keeping constant the average temperature and moisture distribution of the atmosphere, changes the equilibrium cloud amount from 0.46 to 0.65, or an increase of 0.010 for each 1-percent increase in solar constant.

Now using a smaller albedo, 55 percent for overcast skies and an average albedo of 11 percent for the planet earth during clear skies,[21] a new straight line of incoming radiation against cloud amount may be drawn; terminal points of this dashed line are labeled "A = 11%" and "A = 55%". Flanking it are the corresponding dashed lines for 110 percent and 90 percent of the solar-constant value. In drawing the new outgoing radiation curve, we proceed as follows: for an albedo of 35 percent the average incoming radiation over the earth is 0.317 ly/min. Simpson's original value of outgoing radiation for average conditions is 0.271 ly/min, for clear skies, 0.307 ly/min, and for overcast skies, 0.235 ly/min. If the average incoming radiation is 0.317 ly/min, then for radiative equilibrium the average outgoing radiation must be equal to this value, which indicates that Simpson's value of 0.271 ly/min is much too small. Since Simpson used a simplification of the water-vapor absorption spectrum, based on Hettner's measurements of steam rather than on water vapor at atmospheric temperature, and also since decreasing pressure and temperature aloft tends to "open up" the absorption spectrum, the atmosphere is probably much more transparent to long-wavelength radiation on the average than Simpson computed. So far as is known, no computations of the outgoing radiation as a function of cloudiness, based on latest knowledge of the water-vapor absorption spectrum and its changes with pressure and temperature, have been performed. As a rough first approximation to the correct values of the average outgoing radiation during clear and overcast conditions, we shall multiply Simpson's clear and overcast values of the outgoing radiation by the factor 317/271 and so arrive at 0.360 and 0.275 ly/min for the clear and overcast terminal points of the dashed line in Fig. 10 labeled "outgoing radiation (corrected)." This line intersects its corresponding incoming-radiation line at 0.572 cloud amount and 0.311 ly/min, the new radiative-equilibrium values. The value of the equilibrium cloud amount, 0.572, is very close to the value of 0.565 found from Simpson's curves in Fig. 10. Changing the solar constant from 90 to 110 percent of normal, however, changes the equilibrium cloud amount from 0.28 to 0.77, an increase of 0.025 for each 1-percent increase in solar constant. Thus, we see that for a given increase in the solar constant the compensating increase in cloud amount for the smaller albedo will be 2.5 times that for the larger albedo. (This result is contained in an unpublished note by L. D. Kaplan, written in 1950.)

Let us now use the equilibrium radiation values determined by Simpson, 0.273 ly/min, and the new one, found by using different albedos of cloud and earth's surface as described above, 0.311 ly/min, to compute the corresponding radiative-equilibrium temperatures of the earth-atmosphere system, which will be considered to radiate as a black body. These equilibrium temperatures turn out to be 241°K and 249°K, respectively. Thus it appears that an actual decrease in albedo of the earth from 43 to 35 percent might mean an increase in the average temperature of the earth-atmosphere system of 8°C; if this value applies also to the earth's surface, it is near enough to account for the surface temperature change of 10°C which geologists have estimated distinguishes glacial periods from interglacial periods.[4] Apparently, changes in the earth's albedo, no matter how brought about, can be an important factor in changing the mean temperature of the earth and its atmosphere, and consequently world climate.

If one ascribes changes in albedo to changes in cloud amount, it is difficult to see how, keeping constant the land-forms and the radiation received by the earth, significant changes in cloudiness can arise from internal (atmospheric) considerations alone. A possibly important terrestrial influence on cloud amount will be mentioned in the section on atmosphere turbidity, following the next topic. It is recognized that variations in albedo may be caused by changes in reflectivity of clouds, rather than their amount, created by large changes in the prevailing type and thickness of clouds.[25] But again it would be difficult to explain these changes without recourse to external influences.

Changes in Reflectivity of the Earth's Surface. The earth's surface reflects solar radiation by various amounts depending on the type of surface. The largest change in albedo of the earth's surface would be from the normal 3 to 35 percent characteristic of water surfaces and bare and vegetation-covered ground surfaces to the 50 to 85 percent characteristic of a snow-covered surface.[25] Once a snow blanket is laid down, the surface albedo may suddenly increase by a large factor, thus considerably diminishing insolational heating; under these circumstances one might argue that snow cover could conceivably be self-perpetuating. But an extensive snow blanket is laid down as a by-product of certain atmospheric circulation patterns, and if the circulation should subsequently change so as to bring in a warmer regime, the snow cover can disappear very quickly; this sequence is very often observed over extensive snow areas in winter. The unusual persistence of a snow cover is caused primarily by the persistence of abnormal atmospheric circulation patterns. The question still remains — what caused the abnormal circulation pattern to come about in the first place?

Changes in Atmospheric Turbidity. Dust and other foreign particles floating in the atmosphere may have an important influence on the albedo of the atmosphere. Solar radiation is reflected and scattered by these particles and some of it is returned to space without being absorbed by the atmosphere or earth. These particles enter the atmosphere primarily by human activity, wind erosion of desiccated areas, and volcanic action.

It is conceivable that release of particles by human activities has increased the amount of fine particles in the atmosphere. The agricultural cultivation of vast areas formerly covered by stable forest or grass cover has increased the opportunity for dust from the bare ground surface to be blown into the atmosphere when meteorological conditions are suitable. Release of combustion products from industrial, transportation, and space-heating sources has undoubtedly increased the number of foreign particles in the atmosphere. Some evidence for the accumulative effect of air-borne particles in the atmosphere is shown by measurements of electrical conductivity in the atmosphere over the oceans. Measurements made by the *Carnegie* from 1914 to 1928 show a progressive decrease in conductivity over the open oceans, caused presumably by the annulment of small ions by larger ions, which gradually have accumulated through the years by release of smoke and gas from ocean-going vessels, and perhaps also by pollution from nearby continental sources.[26] Whether this increase in the number of larger ions and the consequent decrease of the small ions has had any significant effect on the transmission of solar radiation is not known.

A large contribution to atmospheric dust is that picked up by wind from the earth's surface and held in suspension for long periods of time. Because of the requirements for dry soil and winds of the proper speed, this type of turbidity depends on the weather, and as such cannot be considered a basic or primary cause for climatic changes.

Volcanoes serve as a source for foreign particles whose occurrence is independent of the weather and which therefore may possibly serve as a primary cause for climatic changes. This idea is not new, dating back at least to the time of Benjamin Franklin. W. J. Humphreys [27] has been perhaps the stoutest advocate of the volcanism theory of climatic change and has tried to estimate, by radiation-flux computations and analysis of temperature records, the drop of world temperature that would result from a pall of volcanic dust. He came to the conclusion that a drop of 6°C to 7°C might well result from volcanic dust which increases the earth's albedo. It is difficult to gauge the validity of Humphreys' verification because of the very small area (parts of the United States and western Europe) for which he had temperature observations.

There is still another effect of volcanic dust which may be just as important as its direct screening of solar radiation, and that is its ability to serve as nuclei for ice-crystal formation in the atmosphere. Schaefer has studied the nucleating efficiency of volcanic-ash particles in serving as nuclei for the formation of ice crystals, and has found that as the temperature was lowered Crater Lake ash became effective as sublimation nuclei at temperatures from −17°C to −28°C and Paricutin ash, from −23°C to −30°C.[28] It may thus be possible for those volcanic dusts that are nucleating agents to increase the total cloud cover over the earth after being introduced into cloudless layers supersaturated with respect to ice. That such layers exist was demonstrated during pilot-balloon soundings made by the German *Meteor* Expedition off the west coast of Africa.[29] It was observed that 60 percent of all balloons bursting at heights greater than 10 km created cloud patches similar to cirrus clouds, presumably by release of nucleating material carried inside the balloon. It is thus possible for the solar depleting effect of volcanic dust to be magnified many times over by the property of certain kinds of dust of serving as nuclei for formation of clouds in supersaturated layers of the atmosphere.

Now of all the theories of climatic change that have some degree of physical plausibility, the volcanism theory has the outstanding advantage that the effect of volcanic ash and other particles in reducing solar radiation has been observed and measured in numerous cases. The explosion of

Krakatoa in 1883 and the consequent spread of its ash over the world is the outstanding volcanic eruption for which world-wide observations are available. It took three months for Krakatoa ash to move to western Europe [30] and to decrease the radiation received on a surface normal to the sun's radiation at Montpellier, France (Fig. 11), the only solar observatory known to be in existence at the time. The radiation at this observatory averaged nearly 10 percent below normal for three years. The effects of subsequent less intense volcanic outbreaks have been evident to a lesser extent.

Before continuing with the historic account of volcanoes and radiation, I should like to digress for a moment and report on two recent cases of unusual atmospheric turbidity and the effect on radiation and temperature.

In late September 1950 the eastern United States, Canada, and Europe were covered by a pall of smoke emanating from extensive forest fires in western Canada. On September 25 and 26, when practically no daytime clouds were reported, the solar radiation received on a horizontal surface at Washington, D. C. was 253 ly/day, or 52 percent of normal for clear days. It is estimated that this loss of radiation lowered the maximum temperatures for these days by 5°F to 10°F.[31]

On June 12, 1951 a volcanic eruption occurred on Fogo Island of the Cape Verde group, throwing ash and smoke to an altitude of 25,000 feet. The cloud of ash and smoke traveled westward and entered the central and eastern United States on June 20, producing quite noticeable haziness.[32] Appalachicola, Florida, was under the influence of the ash from June 25 through June 28, and when the volcanic ash moved in, the radiation received on a horizontal surface dropped in three days from 96 to 88 percent of the normal value for clear days. However, because winds were offshore instead of onshore, as normally, the temperature was a few degrees above normal except on the 25th, when it was 1°F below normal. Apparently, this particular volcano was so minor that there was little reference to it in the press.

Returning to the historic account of noteworthy volcanoes, in the lower diagram of Fig. 12 radiation values on a surface normal to the sun's rays, observed at solar-radiation stations in the United States and Europe, are plotted for the years 1900 to 1938. (These data were kindly supplied by Dr. H. C. Willett.) Two large depressions in this curve are evident, in 1903–04 (Pelée, Santa Maria, Colima) and in 1912–14 (Katmai in the Aleutian Islands). Since Katmai, there have been no major volcanic outbursts in the Northern Hemisphere. The effect of Katmai ash on solar radiation was apparent as far away as Algeria, and solar radiation stayed below normal for about three years.

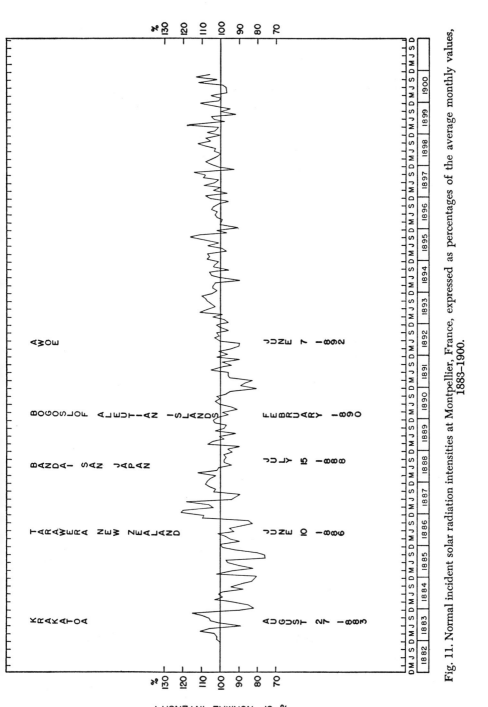

Fig. 11. Normal incident solar radiation intensities at Montpellier, France, expressed as percentages of the average monthly values, 1883–1900.

As may be seen from the upper curves in Fig. 12, there has been an increase in radiation from 1900 to 1938 that is apparent in each month of the year; the correlation of the annual means, 1900–1938, with a linear trend is 0.39, the average increase per year being slightly greater than 0.1 percent. After Katmai, an increasing trend is quite noticeable. From 1915 to 1938, 19 of the 24 years have been above the 39-year normal. It is during the same period of increasing radiation values that temperatures,

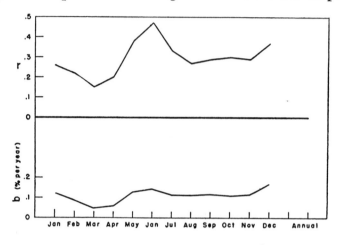

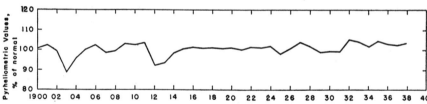

Fig. 12. Variations in normal incident solar radiation observations for stations in the United States and Europe, 1900–1938. *Lower figure,* annual values of radiation expressed as percentages of normal; *top figure,* correlation with a linear trend for each month; *middle figure,* average annual increase in radiation values for each month of the year expressed in percentage of normal.

particularly at higher latitudes, in the Northern Hemisphere have increased so markedly, as may be seen by inspecting Fig. 13, taken from Lysgaard.[18] The increase in average January temperature of the 30-year period 1910–1940 over the 30-year period, 1880–1910 is 3°C in western Greenland and 2°C over a large part of the adjacent area. In general, the Arctic Ocean and continental areas, with the exception of China, show the greatest warming, the Southern Hemisphere less than the Northern Hemisphere, July less than January.

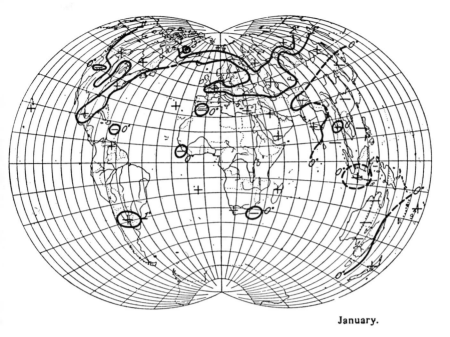

January.

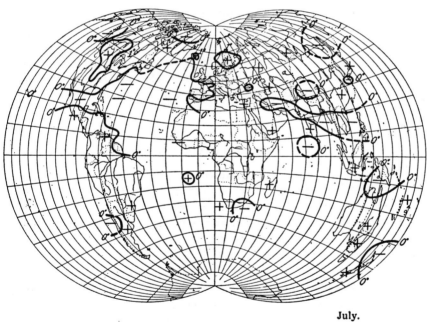

July.

Fig. 13. Average temperature increase from the 30-year period, 1880–1910, to the 30-year period, 1910–1940, January and July (after Lysgaard[18]).

The suggestion made here is that the gradual clearing up of the atmosphere as it rids itself of volcanic dust has decreased the dust albedo and possibly also the cloud albedo, and has enabled more solar radiation to penetrate to the ground. It is significant also that during the 20-year period 1925–1944 the Smithsonian determination of the solar constant at Montezuma, Chile, has increased by 0.25 percent.[33] This increase might well be interpreted as the result of a clearing atmosphere in the Southern Hemisphere, although such has been hindered by two major volcanic outbreaks in the southern Andes, south of 35° latitude, in 1921 and 1932. The floating ash from the latter eruption decreased normal incident solar-radiation values by an average of 3 percent at the Smithsonian station at Montezuma, Chile, 23°S latitude, for 6 months after the eruptions ceased.[34] The ash was observed visually in New Zealand and South Africa, but it did not affect the solar-radiation measurements at Table Mountain, California, 34°N latitude, which indicates that the volcanic ash was confined largely to the Southern Hemisphere.

The prolongation of volcanic activity in the Southern Hemisphere, and the confinement of its ash mostly to that hemisphere, may be a possible explanation of the lesser warming since 1910 in the Southern as compared with the Northern Hemisphere. But how can one explain the fact that the greatest warming has taken place in the Northern Hemisphere at latitudes so far north that darkness prevails during most of the winter? To explain this, a change in atmospheric circulation must be invoked, wherein, under the influence of the increased solar radiation at lower and middle latitudes, there is greater advection of warm air from the south to the Arctic Basin.

APPLICATION TO CLIMATIC VARIATIONS

Theories of climatic variation which appear reasonable to the author are those based on (1) variations of solar radiation as indicated by sunspot cycle, (2) changes in atmospheric transmission of solar radiation caused primarily by variable amounts of air-borne volcanic dust, and (3) changes in transmission of longer-wavelength terrestrial and atmospheric radiation caused primarily by changes in CO_2 content. All three theories suffer from lack of sufficient theoretical and observational support, but contrary to most other suggested theories, they have the advantage that sunspots, volcanic eruptions and atmospheric CO_2 content have undergone significant variations in the past, at least to make possible an attempted correlation with climatic fluctuations of the past few centuries.

During winter increased solar radiation accompanying increased sunspottedness, increased transmission of this radiation because of a clearer atmosphere (see Fig. 14), and greater surface albedo in the northern snow-covered land and ice areas will combine to make the increase in effective insolation larger at lower latitudes than in higher latitudes. Over continents this increased meridional insolation gradient will result in an increased meridional temperature gradient. An increased CO_2 content will probably also contribute to a steepening of the wintertime meridional temperature gradient.

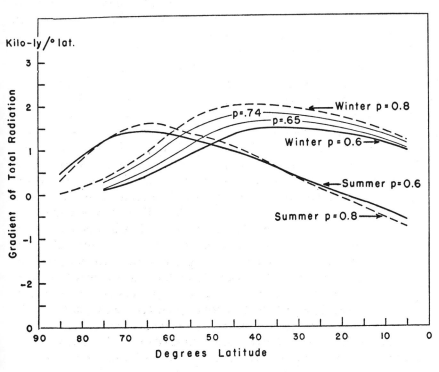

Fig. 14. Meridional gradient of total (sun and sky) radiation against latitude for a clear atmosphere, $p = 0.8$, and for a turbid atmosphere, $p = 0.6$, winter and summer (computed from Milankovitch's data[35]).

Other things being equal, this winter increase in the meridional temperature gradient over the continents will speed up the westerlies aloft over North America, say, and will favor their breakdown eastward over the North Atlantic Ocean in the form of "blocking" cyclonic and anticyclonic eddies,[36] the cyclones being located to the south of the westerlies and the anticyclones to the north. These eddies will increase the poleward spread of heat into the Arctic Ocean and adjacent areas. This increased horizontal "austausch" of heat on a spherical earth from a source at lower latitudes will give rise to greater heating at higher latitudes than at lower latitudes.[37] The pronounced January warming trend of 24°F in the period 1912–1937 at Spitsbergen is an example of such warming induced by changes in atmospheric circulation. Subsidence within the "blocking" anticyclones may also contribute slightly to the warming at high altitudes.

The recent ($\sim$ 50 year) world-wide warming may thus be interpreted as the result of two secular trends — decreasing atmospheric turbidity and increasing CO_2 content — on which is superimposed a cyclic variation of solar radiation associated with the sunspot cycle.

In considering further the turbidity effect caused by volcanic eruptions geologists have pointed out that although some ice ages were preceded by volcanic activity, as indicated, for example, by study of ocean sediments, other ice ages seem to have occurred without preceding or concurrent volcanic activity. Also, the reverse statement is often made, namely, that many periods of intense volcanic activity occurred without an accompanying period of glaciation. Taking up the latter objection first, it should be pointed out that not all volcanoes should produce pronounced and persistent effects on transmission of solar radiation. There are two important conditions that appear to be necessary. First, a catastrophic volcanic explosion is necessary which will eject fine pumiceous material to great heights in the atmosphere where it will persist for many years, and, second, the ash must have high nucleating efficiency. Catastrophic volcanic explosions, releasing the terrific internal pressure, enable the dissolved gases to escape from the magma, which is then permeated by numerous small bubbles, and a portion of it is dispersed in the form of fine light particles to great heights. (According to Pernter,[38] the average radius of the persistently suspended Krakatoa particles, as computed from optical effects, varied from 0.98 to 1.7 microns.) A sporadic emission of heavier volcanic ash to the lower atmosphere by normal volcanic activity appears not to be sufficient. Not all volcanoes will reach the intensity of violence required to permeate the entire atmosphere with the dust, but even if they did, not all materials ejected as volcanic ash would be effective as nucleating agents. The type of material ejected varies not only from volcano to volcano, but from time to time from the same volcano. Hence, if one should desire to explain why some periods of volcanic activity were not followed by ice ages, one might say (a) that although normal volcanic activity was present, no catastrophic explosions took place, or (b) that if violent volcanic explosions took place, the material emitted was not of sufficiently high nucleating efficiency. Regarding oceanic-sediment evidence of ice ages that show no previous deposit of volcanic dust, we should note that, according to

Humphreys,[39] an annual emission of dust necessary to decrease the direct solar radiation by 20 percent would, after 100,000 years, accumulate only to a layer 0.02 in. thick. Such a thin layer would be exceedingly difficult to detect in sediment analysis.

Although some persons might be willing to accept as real the depressed insolation caused by volcanic dust and a consequent tendency of climate to be more wintry, they might well ask how the interglacial periods, which were about 3°C warmer than the present climate, can be explained by the volcanism theory. To meet this very real objection I should like to suggest that in the turbulent atmosphere the fall-out of fine aerosols proceeds extremely slowly, with centuries perhaps being required for the settling out of most of the submicron-sized particles. Since these particles may serve as sublimation and perhaps as condensation nuclei, their screening effects on solar radiation may be magnified many times over by their ability, under favorable conditions, to collect ice or water about them, and so perhaps to extend and intensify the natural cloud cover. After centuries of little or no major volcanic activity, when the volcanic ash finally falls out in its natural state or as a captive of precipitation elements, the atmosphere may have so few nuclei present that cloud cover and precipitation activity are diminished. This would then give rise to the warm and dry climate characteristic of interglacial periods.

In recent centuries there has been violent volcanic activity over large portions of the earth, which terminated, for the time being at least, in Katmai in 1912 and the southern Andes eruptions of 1921 and 1932. The slow clearing of the suspended ash has permitted some warming of the earth, more in the Northern Hemisphere than in the Southern. Perhaps the clearing has not proceeded sufficiently, however, to eliminate completely the positive effects of the residual fine ash on world cloud amount and precipitation.

ACKNOWLEDGEMENTS

The assistance and suggestions supplied by Dr. L. D. Kaplan and Mr. T. H. MacDonald of the Meteorological Physics Section and by Mr. G. W. Brier and Mr. Miles F. Harris of the Meteorological Statistics Section, U. S. Weather Bureau, are gratefully acknowledged.

REFERENCES

1. F. Möller, "Der Wärmehaushalt der Atmosphäre," *Experientia* 6, 361–367 (1950).

2. D. H. Menzel, "Earth-sun relationships," in *Centennial Symposia,*

Harvard College Observatory Monograph No. 7 (Cambridge, 1948), pp. 319–329.

3. G. C. Simpson, "Ice ages," *Nature 141*, 591–598 (1938); also in *Smithsonian Report for 1938*, pp. 289–302.

4. R. F. Flint, *Glacial geology and the Pleistocene Epoch*, (New York, 1947).

5. von G. Viete, "Ueber die allgemeine atmosphärischen Zirkulation während der diluvialen Vereisungs perioden," *Tellus 2*, 102–115 (1950).

6. B. Haurwitz, "Relations between solar activity and the lower atmosphere," *Trans. Amer. Geophys. Union 27*, 161–163 (1946).

7. B. Haurwitz, "Solar activity, the ozone layer and the lower atmosphere," in *Centennial Symposia, Harvard College Observatory Monograph No. 7* (Cambridge, 1948) pp. 353–367.

8. H. Wexler, "Possible effects of ozonosphere heating on sea-level pressure," *Jour. Meteorol. 7*, 370–381 (1950).

9. H. H. Clayton, *World weather* (Macmillan, New York, 1923).

10. H. H. Clayton, "The Atmosphere and the sun," *Smiths. Misc. Coll.*, Vol. 82, No. 7 (1930).

11. H. Wexler, "Possible effects of ozonosphere heating on sea-level pressure," *Trans. New York Acad. Sci.* [2] *13*, 282–287 (1951).

12. Reference 11, Figs. 4a, 4b.

13. H. C. Willett, "Solar variability as a factor in the fluctuations of climate during geological time," *Geogr. Ann. 31*, 295–315 (1949).

14. H. C. Willett, "Solar influences on the weather," *Trans. New York Acad. Sci.* [2] *13*, 277–280 (1951).

15. Reference 4, plate 3.

16. Computed from Fig. 5 of H. Wexler, "Observations of nocturnal radiation at Fairbanks, Alaska and Fargo, N. D.," *Mo. Wea. Rev. Suppl. No. 46* (1941).

17. G. S. Callendar, "The artificial production of carbon dioxide and its influence on temperature," *Quat. Jour. Roy. Meteorol. Soc. 64*, 223–240 (1938).

18. L. Lysgaard, "Recent climatic fluctuations," *Folia Geogr. Danica 5* (1949).

19. L. B. Aldrich, "The reflecting power of clouds," *Smiths. Misc. Coll.*, Vol. 69, No. 10 (1949).

20. A. Danjon, "Nouvelles recherches sur la photométrie de la lumière cendrée et l'albedo de la terre," *Ann. l'Obs. Strasbourg 3*, 139–181 (1936).

21. S. Fritz, "The albedo of the planet Earth and of clouds," *Jour. Meteorol. 6*, 277–282 (1949).

22. G. C. Simpson, "Further studies in terrestrial radiation," *Mem. Roy. Meteorol. Soc. 3*, No. 21 (1928).

23. H. Wexler, "Absorption of radiation by water vapor as determined by Hettner and by Weber and Randall," *Mo. Wea. Rev. 65*, 102–104 (1937).

24. C. E. P. Brooks, "The mean cloudiness over the earth," *Mem. Roy. Meteorol. Soc. 1*, No. 10 (1927).

25. Table 154 in R. J. List, editor, *Smithsonian meteorological tables* (Washington, ed. 6, 1951).

26. G. R. Wait, "Some experiments relating to the electrical conductivity of the lower atmosphere," *Jour. Wash. Acad. Sci. 36*, 321–343 (1946).

27. W. J. Humphreys, *Physics of the air* (McGraw-Hill, New York, ed. 3, 1940).

28. V. J. Schaefer, "The occurrence of ice crystal nuclei in the free atmosphere," *Gen. Electric Res. Lab., Occas. Rep. No. 20*, Proj. Cirrus, Schenectady, N. Y. (1950).

29. E. Kuhlbrodt and J. Reger, *Die aerologischen Methoden und Beobachtungsmaterial*, Bd. XV, *Wiss. Ergeb. d. Deutsch. Atlant. Exped. "Meteor," 1925–27* (de Gruyter, Berlin, 1933).

30. H. Wexler, "Spread of the Krakatoa volcanic dust cloud ase related to the high-level circulation," *Bull. Amer. Meteorol. Soc. 32*, 48–51 (1951).

31. H. Wexler, "The great smoke pall, September 24–30, 1950," *Weatherwise 3*, 129 (1950).

32. W. F. Brown, "Volcanic ash over the Caribbean, June, 1951," *Mo. Wea. Rev. 80*, 59–62 (1952).

33. L. B. Aldrich, "Report of the Astrophysical Observatory," *Appendix 8, Ann. Rep. Smiths-Inst. for 1950* (Washington, 1951).

34. L. B. Aldrich, "Smithsonian pyrheliometery and the Andean volcanic eruptions of April 1932," *Smiths. Misc. Coll.*, Vol. *104*, No. 6 (1944).

35. M. Milankovitch, "Mathematische Klimalehre," in Koppen-Geiger's *Handbuch der Klimatologie* (Berlin, 1930), vol. 1, Teil A.

36. D. F. Rex, "Blocking action in the middle troposphere and its effect upon regional climate, I. An aerological study of blocking action," *Tellus 2*, 196–211 (1950).

37. A. Ångström, "Atmospheric circulation, climatic variations, and continentality of climate," *Geogr. Annaler 31*, 316–320 (1949).

38. J. M. Pernter, "Der Krakatau-Ausbruch und seine Folge-Erscheinungen," *Met. Zeit. 6*, 329, 409, 447 (1889).

39. Reference 27, pp. 599–600.

6

THE INSUFFICIENCY OF GEOGRAPHICAL
CAUSES OF CLIMATIC CHANGE*

John Wolbach

Pᴇʀɪᴏᴅꜱ ᴏꜰ ᴡɪᴅᴇꜱᴘʀᴇᴀᴅ ɢʟᴀᴄɪᴀᴛɪᴏɴ separated by longer periods of mild climate have apparently characterized the climate of the earth for nearly two billion years. The dating of the two principal Post-Cambrian and at least five Pre-Cambrian glaciations suggests a rough periodicity of the order of a quarter billion years in the occurrence of extensive glaciation. Evidence of widespread Proterozoic glaciations has effectively disposed of the once popular hypothesis that recent ice ages arose as a consequence of the gradual cooling of the earth, more or less continuously from the time of its formation. There is no evidence for any unidirectional change in the temperature of the earth, arising from either terrestrial or solar sources. Geological evidence, to be discussed later in this paper, indicates that solar cyclic variations, essentially similar to those now observed, existed in Pre-Cambrian times as well. Earth-sun relations, orbital as well as thermal, in the Proterozoic and Archeozoic, closely resemble those of the Mesozoic and Cenozoic periods.

We may therefore ask whether geographical evolution alone appears sufficient to explain the observed climates of the past, or whether irregular or semicyclic changes in the solar radiation must also be postulated.

From geological evidence the Pleistocene, the Permian, the early Cambrian and late Pre-Cambrian, and the Huronian glaciations were characterized by extensive continental ice sheets. Little information is available on earlier glaciations, but it seems probable that one or more of them were extensive. In addition to the major glaciations, some evidence of glaciation has been found for nearly every geological period since the Cambrian. These glaciers usually were mountain or piedmont types and indicate at most minor climatic variations. However, even

* The research reported in this paper has been sponsored in part by the Geophysics Research Directorate of Air Force Cambridge Research Center, Air Research and Development Command, under Contract No. AF19(604)–146.

these local glaciations seem to be accompanied by variations of the climatic zones.

From the Cambrian to the present, fossils provide sufficient data for the formation of a rough history of climate. These remains and impressions of plants of various times indicate variations in latitude of the climatic zones from one period to another. In general, climatic zones appear to have been more clearly differentiated in the Mesozoic and Cenozoic eras than in the Paleozoic. The evidence may be associated in part with the greater specialization and variety of vegetation in the more recent eras.

C. E. P. Brooks [1] states that a mild nonglacial climate has existed for nine-tenths of the time since the Cambrian, and appears to be the normal climate of the earth. Listing the Eocene and Jurassic climates as typical, he reports that the zone of temperate vegetation then extended 20° farther and that of tropical vegetation 10° farther from the equator than at present.

Brooks considers that climatic conditions result almost entirely from geographical conditions. The principal ice ages have occurred during or immediately following episodes of extensive diastrophism. The continents then stood high with mountain ranges and were free of marine invasions. The normal mild climate of most of geological history appears to have been associated with low-lying flat continents broken by epicontinental seas.

The present low salt content of the ocean supports the idea that low-lying lands are the normal geographical condition of the earth, for the present rate of transportation of salt into the oceans by the action of streams and rivers would provide the oceans with their present degree of salinity in roughly 100 million years. Holmes [2] lists errors of measurement which indicate that this figure is conservative, but his value of 300 million years is only 10 to 15 percent of the time available for the oceans to reach their present condition. The moderate salinity thus suggests that the continents were normally low and presented no sharp relief. The rate of erosion was reduced. In addition, epicontinental flooding reduced the area to be eroded.

Brooks emphasizes the association of normal warm mild climate with the normal geographical conditions mentioned above. If, for example, the Bering Straits were broadened and deepened, the Japanese current would flow into the Arctic Sea and would melt much of the pack ice. Were parts of North America to be submerged, as at times in the past, its climate would become insular, and its cooling action on the North Atlantic would be reduced. Moreover, the persistence of warm moist air over the epicontinental seas would lengthen the melting season of the polar sea until little or no ice persisted through the summer. With these cooling effects reduced, the Greenland ice sheet would almost certainly melt, and the North Atlantic basin climate would indeed be seriously modified.

With widespread land submergence over the globe and low relief of continents, ocean currents circulate freely and warm moist air can travel without much loss of moisture. Once established, a layer of warm moist air, because of a slow reduction of temperature with height, is surprisingly stable, as shown by trade winds. If warm air masses become established at higher latitudes, a meridional circulation and the action of heavy clouds, blanketing the polar regions during the long winter night, may maintain mild temperatures. Extremes of these conditions may explain antarctic coal measures and the growth in some periods of coral reefs at polar latitudes.

Should the marine invasions withdraw from the continents, the supply of warm moist air would diminish, and cooler drier air with less blanketing effect would cover continental areas. This process in turn permits greater cooling by radiation and the cool air further blocks the circulation of warm air until at polar latitudes the sea may freeze.

The presence of large thick polar ice caps or their complete absence is a stable condition, as Brooks has shown. When the ice caps are small and perhaps seasonal, varying from 0° to 20° in diameter, they have a correspondingly varying cooling effect upon upper latitudes. Their action greatly magnifies and tends to prolong into trends what might otherwise be smaller deviations in weather tendencies.

With establishment of continental snow-clad conditions at polar latitudes, the climatic zones are strongly differentiated and intense circulation of air occurs. Arid conditions associated with ice ages suggest barriers in air circulation arising from the sharp relief of continents, with further intensifying of air circulation elsewhere. Vigorous circulation is required to cause the heavy precipitation of snow on cool plateaus that must accumulate for glaciation to occur. The extension of ice sheets further modifies climate, and the contraction of warm regions and evaporation areas, which reduces the available precipitation, seems to be the chief limitation on the growth of ice sheets.

According to Brooks, great continental land masses, particularly those of high latitudes, have great climatic importance. In winter, radiation from the land favors formation of great masses of intensely cold air, which have a cooling effect on the seas, particularly to the south and east. Snow, by reflecting a large portion of incident radiation, has a further considerable cooling action. The glaciated continent of Antarctica is surrounded by thick pack ice the cooling effect of which is comparable to that of land. This icy area probably reduces the temperature of the sea-girded Southern Hemisphere more than the combined continental areas reduce the Northern Hemisphere's temperature.

THE PERMIAN TROPICAL GLACIATION

Let us consider the application of the geographical hypothesis particularly to glaciation in the tropics. The Pleistocene and the Huronian glaciations developed mainly in high and temperate latitudes, while the Permian ice age developed mainly in the tropics. The early Cambrian or late Proterozoic ice age apparently flourished both in temperate zones of North America and in tropical South Africa and in India and China, although less extensively at lower latitudes than the Permian. Traces of still more ancient glaciations in North America and Africa suggest that these continents have always occupied roughly their present positions in relation to the poles. Data on topography prior to late Cambrian times are so scanty that they preclude any attempt to discuss geographical causes of these early ice ages, and we may concentrate on the Permian glaciation.

This series of glaciations began in Carboniferous times, with small ice sheets in Australia and South America. In the Permian period, extensive glaciers developed throughout the tropics and south temperate zones. In Africa ample evidence points to glaciers as extensive as those of North America in the Pleistocene. Over wide areas of South Africa the ice sheets flowed in a poleward direction so that snow accumulation must have begun far inland. Extensive glaciations also took place in Central India, and in regions to the south now submerged by the Indian Ocean. Large ice sheets developed over a wide range of latitude in Argentina and Brazil and in Australia. In contrast, only scattered glaciation, according to available evidence, occurred above latitude 35°. Squantum tillites indicate Permian glaciations around Boston and in areas extending eastward; local glaciers occurred in Alaska and Europe. According to Wright and Priestley, glaciations did not occur on the coast of Antarctica.

The idea of continental drift introduced by Wegener to explain equatorial glaciations seems from many viewpoints an objectionable hypothesis, creating more problems than it solves, especially when applied to more recent geological history. The idea of a change in the position of the earth's axis of rotation is an even less tenable explanation because such a change could be produced only by the action of enormous forces exterior to the earth.

Brooks argues that the extensive glaciations in the tropics could be brought about by the natural evolution of geographic events. We may now examine his explanation of the Permian ice age.

Present evidence suggests that in Permian times the northern continents formed two land masses. North America, Greenland, Iceland, and north-western Europe formed one continent. Northeastern Eurasia formed the other, with a broad epicontinental sea separating the two in the region north of the present Black and Caspian Seas. The tropical continents formed a great land mass, Gondwana land, with South America and Africa probably joined at their bulges by a land bridge. India and Australia formed further portions of the same continental extension. Broad intercontinental seas separated Gondwana from the northern continents. A large Antarctica may for a time have been connected to Australia and perhaps also South America by land bridges. In any case apparently no sea ways existed for warm equatorial waters to reach the almost, or possibly at times completely, landlocked Southern Sea extending from South America eastward to Australia.

These geographical features are basic to Brooks's geographical hypothesis of the low-latitude Permian glaciations. The important conditions are:

(1) That the continent Gondwana direct the entire equatorial ocean current into the Northern Hemisphere, and at the same time shut off the Southern Sea from warm currents. The only Southern Sea currents are cold ones, originating from Antarctica. This pattern of ocean circulation tends to produce perpetual summer in the Northern and perpetual winter in the Southern Hemisphere. Climatic zones are displaced northward.

(2) That the Gondwana continent along the equator be extensively elevated and extend farther into the Southern than the Northern Hemisphere. Such a continent favors coolness of the southern landlocked seas. With the temperature difference existing between the northern and southern shores of the continent, cool trade winds originating just south of the southern shore will blow northward across the elevated continent to the thermal equator in the Northern Hemisphere. High elevation on the southern shore produces cloudiness on the southern coast. With a gradual rise of land northward, a heavy cloud cover will persist because of the cooling of the air with elevation. The clouds will reflect much of the incident tropical solar radiation, preventing the continent from becoming hot. Abundant precipitation should occur at the higher elevations. If at the continental south shore the sea temperature is only 50°F, the snow line may be as low as 6000 feet in the uplands of the far interior.

(3) A general refrigeration, which may have been brought about by volcanic action.

This theory has especial merit in so far as it emphasizes that topography to a very large degree indeed determines where glaciation will occur. On the other hand, while Brooks mentions that a general refrigeration is also necessary, he appears to rest his case on extreme topographic conditions not very well supported by the available evidence.

Brooks postulates that Gondwana extended in many places as far as 40°S. Otherwise the presence of warm equatorial water in the Southern Sea would have made extensive snow accumulation possible only at very high elevation. Even so, he appears to require at least an elevation of 6000 feet. Holmes [2] mentions extensive evidence that the glaciers actually occurred on low-lying terrain. Schuchert [3] gives an elevation of 4000 feet for the snow-accumulation areas of Africa.

A continent extending so far south presents another difficulty in the problem of water transport to the snow accumulation areas 1500 miles inland. If the southern shore had an appreciable elevation, clouds should form and the precipitation fall on the coastal lands. On the other hand, if the southern coast of Gondwana was low and flat, clouds would not form; the air passing over the low tropical lands would be greatly heated by the tropical sun and the snow line would be raised to around 12,000 to 15,000 feet in the glaciated regions. The effects would thus be about the same as if the seas extended close to the equator.

These considerations indicate the paramount importance of a general refrigeration. The refrigeration, by producing large masses of floating ice, would keep the Southern Sea cool relatively near to the equator. Then the evaporation areas may have been cool sea embayments, containing floating ice, and extending up to about 20°S, and reasonably near to the snow-accumulation areas. Further, if in fact Antarctica was not glaciated in the Permian, as the present scanty evidence suggests, we may infer that the refrigeration was associated with too low a level of precipitation for glaciation in polar regions and was favorable only for the formation of large masses of pack ice.

A further problem arises from the observed occurrence of glacial and interglacial periods within the ice age. Five major stages of glaciation were recorded in Australia and three in South America. Coleman [4] reports inconclusive interglacials in Africa and true interglacial periods in India during the most extensive Permian glaciation. These latter substages are of short period, similar to the recurrent Pleistocene glaciation. Only about thirty separate marine invasions and withdrawals are recorded since the early Cambrian, with an average period of about 18 million years. If the glacial cycles are due only to geographical evolution, then uplifts and submergences occurred in the Permian with unusual rapidity, as these topographic cycles are normally much longer than the glacial ones. If the glacial conditions are produced mainly by the peculiar topography of the Permian and the Pleistocene, it is difficult to understand how these geographical conditions can exist without producing ice sheets, and even more difficult to see how the ice sheets could be removed once formed. This problem is especially formidable for the Permian, where minor geographic changes in favor of a warmer climate would tend to raise the level of evaporation and precipitation and to extend the ice sheets into higher latitudes which formerly were cold and dry.

Recognizing the difficulty of explaining the shorter cycles geographically, Brooks himself has admitted that explanation of at least the more rapid glacial and interglacial changes appears to require a variation in solar radiation reaching the earth's surface. Such variation also explains the general refrigeration required for a successful theory. This variation may arise either from an intrinsic change in the solar radiation, or from the loss of solar radiation to the earth by reflection by dust particles in the upper atmosphere. Brooks notes evidence of great volcanic activity in the Permian, and apparently some of this was of the explosive type able to put dust into the upper atmosphere. However, the correlation between glacial advances and volcanic explosions is extremely inconclusive and until many more data are available we can form no opinion on this point.

Dr. Bell, in a later paper in this volume, suggests that ice ages are preceded by reduced solar radiation. The cooling of warm, moist air reduces its water-carrying power and its stability. Consequently its warming action and blanketing effect in high latitudes are reduced. Even more important, a reduced solar radiation persisting over a long period of time would allow the oceans to grow cooler all over the earth, thus producing the required general refrigeration.

Applying Miss Bell's hypothesis to the postulated geographical conditions of the Permian, the writer suggests that with a reduction in the solar radiation the extended Antarctic continent would be the first region to suffer a severe drop in temperature. The Arctic Sea fed by tropical ocean currents might remain unfrozen even while pack ice began to form in the Southern Sea around a snow-covered Antarctica.

Here we note that geologists agree that the early Permian glaciation occurring in Australia and South America was associated with and possibly preceded by severe cold conditions which killed off much of the Paleozoic vegetation in the Southern Hemisphere. The surviving plants evolved into new forms, Glossopteris or Gangamopteris flora. Its variants spread from middle or high latitudes of South America and Australian extensions, and appeared in a short time throughout Gondwana land. In the Northern Hemisphere stunted variants of Paleozoic vegetation survived into the later Permian. Reptile life, persisting in America and Europe, suggests that the climate there was less severe than in the south.

Thus with the peculiar distribution of land and ocean currents of the Permian, a small change in the solar radiation might have produced the observed drastic cooling in southern tropical regions. With different geography the cooling would be more uniform and moderate over the globe.

ASTRONOMICAL AND SOLAR CYCLES AS INDICATED BY VARVES

Extensive geological and especially oceanographic data may soon yield sufficient further evidence of the changes of land and sea temperature to permit us to determine more precisely the solar variation throughout geological time. At present the most specific and detailed geological evidence for solar behavior is to be found in the analysis of varves or annual bands of sedimentary deposits, consisting of laminae of which the composition changes with the season.

Analysis of varves includes studying the thickness and composition of corresponding laminae of successive bands somewhat as in the case of tree rings. The laminae indicate seasonal variation attributed to the 11-year sunspot cycle and to the 26,000-year cycle of the precession of the equinoxes. The so-called period of precession, indicated by varves of differing antiquity, usually averages only 21,000 years. Some geologists, on the basis of astronomical data, find this period to be the resultant of astronomical precession and further variations of the earth's orbital motion. Their explanation is further substantiated by Dr. Brouwer's determination, presented in a later section in this volume. His cycles show striking agreement with the cycles observed in the notable Green River varves.

A few typical results from the analysis of varves may be mentioned. Zeuner [5] reports evidence for approximately an 11-year sunspot cycle, and a 23-year double sunspot cycle in recent and ancient varves. He also lists observations of a 50-to-56-year cycle, roughly corresponding to the weather cycle indicated by some current meteorological observations, and observations of the 21,000-year cycle of precession. In Southwest Africa, Pre-Cambrian varves, 500 to 1000 million years old, show a cyclic variation of 11.5 years. Korn [6] reports layers of slate in Thuringia, Germany, with an age of about 275 million years, according to the radioactivity method of age measurement; cycles of 11.4 years, 23 years, 56.5 years and 21,000 years appear. Korn also lists upper Permian layers, of age 200 million years, of the Harz Mountains in Germany with an observed cycle of about 11 years. Antevs [7] reports prominent cycles of 11 to 14 years in the upper Permian castile formation of Texas, about 200 million years ago.

Bradley [8] describes cycles in the middle Eocene observed in the Green River valley varves of Utah and Colorado. He lists cycles averaging a little more than 11 years, but varying from 7 to 18 years. Also he finds that the average length for the cycle of precession is 21,630 years, but individual cycles vary from 16,000 to 27,000 years. A third cycle of about 50 years is also listed. Antevs, Brooks, Glock, Douglas, and Reed have observed a 10-year cycle more commonly than an 11-year cycle principally in Pleistocene varves, and also in tree rings. The more ancient varves seem to show an 11-year cycle.

Thus one may conclude that during much, and possibly all, of the geological past solar activity varied over a cycle that closely resembles in length the sunspot cycle observed today. Further, the past precession cycles do not badly disagree in length with the variations in the length of the precession cycle presented by Brouwer.

At present, varves provide virtually no evidence for climatic variations beyond those accounted for by the sunspot and precession cycles. The varve records of variation in temperature and precipitation do not yield significant data regarding longer cycles of solar variability. The geological climatic variations give no evidence for any unidirectional change in the earth's thermal relations with the sun, a conclusion completely in harmony with the evidence from varves.

One further result from varves worth mentioning here is the determination of the direction of the geomagnetic axes with respect to true north. Torresson, Murphy, and Graham [9,10] report that magnetic polarization measurements of undisturbed sedimentary rocks, ranging in age from the Pliocene to the Eocene, with a few from the Jurassic, show the earth's magnetic field to have possessed its present polarity. Out of 99 samples, about two thirds indicate that the earth's magnetic field centered closely to true north rather than to the present geomagnetic north. Other samples indicate a variation in declination centering about true north with a maximal departure of about 30°.

From New England varves, 15,000 to 20,000 years old, the same writers measured values of magnetic declination and found a range of values from 35° east and 25° west of present declination. From 5000 years of depositions, they find swings that require 750 to 2000 years from one limit to the other. These figures suggest a cycle ranging from 1500 to 4000 years.

At present, studies of electromagnetic storms and sudden ionospheric disturbances indicate that the electromagnetic relation between the sun and the earth is important. Many of the features of the sun's surface seem to be electromagnetic in origin. Solar activity may have both a direct and an indirect effect on the earth's magnetic field, by the ejected clouds of ions and outbursts of far ultraviolet radiation. Menzel reports in the following paper how the earth's magnetic field focuses streams of ions and corpuscles from the sun into the auroral regions, with sufficient kinetic energy to modify perhaps the atmospheric circulation in these regions. Dr. Bell discusses in her communication the possibility that this corpuscular radiation so focused may have had a considerable effect on climates of the past.

REFERENCES

1. C. E. P. Brooks, *Climate through the ages* (McGraw-Hill, New York, 1949).
2. A. Holmes, *The age of the earth* (Nelson, London, 1937).
3. C. Schuchert, *Textbook of geology, Part II, Historical geology* (Wiley, New York, 1924).
4. A. P. Coleman, *Ice ages, recent and ancient* (Macmillan, New York, 1926).
5. F. E. Zeuner, *Dating the past* (Methuen, London, 1946).
6. H. Korn, "Stratification and absolute time ground building and sedimentation rate in a varied trough from the Thuringian French Lower Carboniferous and Upper Devonian," *N. Jahrb. Min. Geol. u. Pal.* B-Bd. *74A,* 50–186 (1938).
7. E. Antevs, "Retreat of the last ice sheet in Eastern Canada," *Canada Geological Survey Mem.*, Ottawa, *146,* 142 (1925).
8. W. H. Bradley, "The varves and climate of the Green River Epoch," *U. S. Geological Survey Professional Paper* 158E (Washington, 1929), pp. 87–110.
9. O. W. Torresson, Thomas Murphy and J. W. Graham, "Magnetic polarization of sedimentary rocks and the earth's magnetic history," *Jour. Geophys. Res. 54,* 111 (1949).
10. J. W. Graham, "The stability and significance of magnetism in sedimentary rocks," *Jour. Geophys. Res. 54,* 131 (1949).

7

ON THE CAUSES OF THE ICE AGES*

Donald H. Menzel

ONE MAJOR DIFFICULTY WITH THE problem of the ice ages is that we have too many theories, almost any one of which sounds plausible on the basis of qualitative reasoning. Quantitative discussion of the problem proves to be difficult because there are so many unknown factors and uncertain elements.

Even in this modern day, we find that weather is too complicated a phenomenon for us to forecast in detail. We approach the problem with some confidence, but fully realize that an appreciable margin of error may result. Weather arises from a complicated interaction of many variables: the over-all circulation of the air, the distribution of temperature and pressure throughout the atmosphere, geographical factors like mountain ranges and large bodies of water, season of the year, and possibly the state of solar activity. Add to these other geophysical influences, such as volcanism, forest fires, and dust storms, which control the concentration of nuclei in the air, and we discover why weather forecasting has been so largely dependent on empirical methods. At least, empirical considerations have played an important role in the past, although some of the major contributory factors are beginning to appear.

Great as our desire may be to simplify the problem, we find it difficult to rule out many theories or hypotheses at the present stage. Indeed, the rising and falling of continents, the formation and disappearance of land bridges, the changing courses of ocean currents and similar factors usually embraced in the term "continentality," introduce such complications that we cannot clearly separate the purely astronomical effects from the geophysical. Our comments, therefore, may overlap those of other contributors.

One of our major problems concerns possible variations in the heat of the sun itself. Ionospheric records clearly show the influence of the

* The research reported in this paper has been sponsored in part by the Geophysics Research Directorate of Air Force Cambridge Research Center, Air Research and Development Command, under Contract No. AF19(604)–146.

11-year sunspot cycle. Hence we infer that the sun does vary appreciably in its output of energy, especially in the far ultraviolet, where the ionosphere is most absorptive. The percentage of solar energy located in this region is probably small compared with the total. However, if conditions in the upper atmosphere do have an appreciable effect on the lower levels, the mere fact that ultraviolet energy is completely absorbed before it reaches the ground, whereas the more abundant energy in the visible range passes through essentially unhindered, suggests that solar variability may be one factor that influences climate.

By the same argument, even though corpuscular energy from the sun probably represents only a small fraction of the total solar energy, the fact that all of this corpuscular radiation is absorbed somewhere in the atmosphere may also have some significance from the standpoint of day-to-day weather. This corpuscular radiation, of course, is responsible for the aurora borealis.

I recently carried through an analysis of the way that an ionized stream, consisting essentially of electrons and protons, can break through the earth's magnetic field, which ordinarily acts as a sort of protective "umbrella." Chapman and Ferraro [1] have outlined the initial stages of such an interaction, but they were more concerned with magnetic effects than with the aurora borealis. D. F. Martyn,[2] employing magnetohydrodynamic arguments, carried the study somewhat further, and showed that the quantity and energy of these particles in the solar ion stream were reasonably consistent with the location of the observed auroral zone, which extends some 23° from the geomagnetic pole.

A further extension of these principles indicates that irregularities, which undoubtedly exist in the ion clouds coming from sun to earth, can cause the magnetic lines of force to bend under the strain and, under some circumstances, even to "give way." When a convex surface (system of magnetic lines) becomes concave, the normal action of the field is reversed. Instead of being a magnetic "umbrella," it acts like a "funnel," collecting quantities of matter from a large volume of space and concentrating it near the base of the funnel in a long, thin sheet roughly along a parallel of magnetic latitude.

An astrophysical analysis of the observed intensity of the hydrogen emission in this region, according to the measures of Gartlein [3] and Meinel,[4] indicates that the incoming stream may at times carry with it an energy density — over only this limited area, to be sure — roughly equivalent to that of solar radiation itself. Although the estimate is uncertain, because of some unknown factors, the analysis suggests that a large amount of energy must be absorbed in the portions of the terrestrial atmosphere responsible for the luminous aurora. And, in turn, we should expect that the surrounding regions of the atmosphere might well be intensely heated, might expand, and might even undergo a minor chemical change, especially in the ozonosphere.

Dr. Richard Craig,[5] in an analysis of weather patterns, has found a correlation between pressure patterns and time elapsed after intense magnetic storms, which, presumably, may have been accompanied by an aurora visible somewhere. The above analysis suggests a possible physical mechanism for the interaction, though much work needs to be done in order to prove a connection between aurorae and weather. The study should, for example, include a special investigation of pressure patterns in the geographical areas where intense auroral activity has occurred. In another paper in this volume, Dr. Bell discusses the phenomenon from the standpoint of the ice ages.

The observations suggest that either the onset or the disappearance of an ice age may result from a rare large departure from average conditions. For example, if a winter of exceptionally heavy snowfall were to be followed by an unduly cold summer, so cold that the winter snow might not entirely melt, the increased cloudiness and the increased reflectivity from the snow itself would lower temperatures still more and might initiate an ice age. I have always believed that an ice age is not, of necessity, a cold age. In other words, a sudden diminution of the solar constant may not bring on an ice age, even though it would undoubtedly lower the temperature of the earth as a whole. In fact, as others have noted, an increase of solar radiation rather than a decrease may very well bring about the ice age, because of the greater evaporation from the oceans produced by the stronger solar radiation.

As I see it, we need both greater precipitation and greater cloudiness — two primary agencies necessary to ice formation. But, as recent experiments by Schaefer [6] have shown, an increase in the moisture content of the atmosphere does not of itself guarantee either the formation of clouds or the precipitation of rain or of snow. We need, in addition, innumerable minute condensation or sublimation nuclei in the atmosphere. Without these nuclei to act as centers, the condensations so necessary for the formation of rain or snow simply will not occur.

Almost any minute particle can act as a condensation nucleus. When atmospheric air carrying a certain amount of water vapor is cooled below the dew point, the excess moisture will separate out to form small droplets of water, that is, cloud or fog, as long as there are condensation nuclei present around which the droplets can form. Without the nuclei, the air simply remains supersaturated and retains its moisture until nuclei become available or until the temperature drops to a point where instability sets in and condensation becomes automatic. Among the natural sources of condensation nuclei are particles of salt from the evaporated spray of ocean waves, smoke from forest fires, and — especially in the vicinity of large industrial centers — the heavy smoke from imperfectly burned coal. This last source gives rise to the familiar "smog" associated with such areas.

If, now, we lower the temperature of either the vapor-laden air or even air containing a certain amount of fog below the freezing point of water, 0°C, the cloud droplets will not of themselves automatically crystallize or form solids until, as Schaefer has shown, the temperature reaches $-38°5C$, at which temperature ice crystals automatically separate.

Between the ranges of $-38°5$ and 0°C the droplets will remain in a supercooled state unless additional nuclei of a special nature can be provided. Any nucleus that can cause the supercooled droplets of fog to form into ice crystals is called a sublimation nucleus. Experiment has indicated that silver iodide is the most effective sublimation nucleus found to date, which accounts for its extensive use in the new profession of rainmaking. However certain types of rock soil or even volcanic ash have been reasonably effective in this role.

It seems not at all unreasonable, therefore, to suggest that one of the important trigger mechanisms necessary to the production of clouds and precipitation is the presence of large amounts of finely divided sublimation nuclei in the atmosphere. A simple calculation shows that cosmic dust or micrometeorites could not possibly provide any significant amount of such nuclei. A world-wide forest fire, following a period of drought, might produce them. But a far more reasonable source of such nuclei may very well be extensive volcanism, which we know must have existed at certain phases of the earth's history. I am indebted to Dr. Schaefer for information about the properties of sublimation nuclei, as well as for permission to refer to his work, since he himself has been speculating that volcanically produced sublimation nuclei may prove to be the missing clue to the ice ages.

A rough calculation establishes the order of magnitude of the effect. For purposes of condensation let us say that we require roughly one particle per 10 cm.[3] Since the volume of the earth's atmosphere (at standard temperature and pressure) is of the order of 5×10^{24} cm[3], we need 5×10^{23} particles to produce the effect. The sublimation nuclei are about 10^{-12} grams per particle, so that some 5×10^{11} grams are necessary or 5×10^{5} tons. With volcanic material of density 3, the total volume of rock, *in situ*, necessary to produce the powder of the most effective dimensions would comprise a cube roughly 70 meters on a side. This amount of material is at least 1000 times less than that put into the earth's atmosphere by the famous Krakatoa eruption of 1883. Hence there seems to be nothing wrong quantitatively with the idea of associating volcanism and the ice ages. Incidentally, Schaefer has detected very minute particles $(10^{-4}$ cm$)$ of SiO_2 in an Alaskan glacier.

REFERENCES

1. S. Chapman and V. C. A. Ferraro, *Terr. Mag. and Atm. Elec.* 45, 245 (1940).
2. D. F. Martyn, *Nature 167*, 92 (1951).
3. C. W. Gartlein, *Mém. de la Société des Sciences de Liège 12*, 195 (1952).
4. A. B. Meinel, *Astrophys. Jour. 113*, 50 (1950).
5. R. Craig, *Proc. Amer. Acad. Arts Sci.* 79, 280 (1951).
6. V. J. Schaefer, "Snow and its relationship to experimental meteorology," *General Electric Research Laboratory Reprint No. 1852* (no date); "Experimental meteorology," *Jour. Applied Math. and Phys. 1*, 153 (1950); "The occurrence of ice crystal nuclei in the free atmosphere," *General Electric Research Laboratory Reprint No. 308* (Jan. 15, 1950); "The detection of ice nuclei in the free atmosphere," *General Electric Research Laboratory Reprint No. 138* (Feb. 1, 1949); "Project Cirrus," *General Electric Research Laboratory Reprint No. 655* (Mar. 1, 1952).

8

SOLAR VARIATION AS AN EXPLANATION
OF CLIMATE CHANGE *

Barbara Bell

For Hot, Cold, Moist, and Dry, four champions fierce,
Strive here for mastery, and to the battle bring
Their embryon atoms.
Paradise Lost, II.

DURING MOST OF EARTH'S HISTORY the forces of Moist and Hot have prevailed. The normal climate of geological time is nonglacial, characterized by low-lying lands, extensive seas, and warm ice-free polar regions. At irregular intervals these conditions have been interrupted: geologically, by folding of the earth's crust into mountain ranges and associated plateaus at high elevations; climatologically, by low polar temperatures and the formation of large continental ice sheets. Major glaciations, recurring at intervals of about a quarter billion years during the last billion years, have never developed except during periods of high land elevation. Periods of mountain building have occurred more frequently, and marked land elevation has often existed without appreciable glaciation.

In the normal nonglacial periods the difference between the temperature at the equator and the temperature at the pole is very small as compared with the present temperature difference, and smaller yet in comparison with the glacial-period temperature difference. Figure 1, from C. E. P. Brooks,[1] compares the glacial and nonglacial temperature variation with latitude. This change in temperature gradient may be considered the outstanding difference between glacial and nonglacial climates.

Brooks has especially emphasized the problem of the warm polar climates. Coral reefs grew in the vicinity of England in the Jurassic, and as far north as 80° in the Silurian. In general, temperate-type flora and fauna grew well within the Arctic circle during these warm periods. As Brooks has pointed out, the warm poles of the nonglacial climate offer a difficult problem to any theory of climate change. One can easily suggest

* The research reported in this paper has been sponsored in part by the Geophysics Research Directorate of Air Force Cambridge Research Center, Air Research and Development Command, under Contract No. AF19(604)–146.

a cause that will raise or lower the temperature of the whole earth by a given amount, or even change the temperature of the equator more than that of the poles, as, for instance, simply a change in the amount of the solar radiation reaching the earth surface. A satisfactory theory, however, must account for a change of more than 50°F at the poles, with only a small change at the equator.

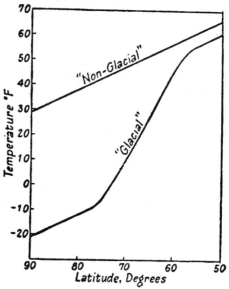

Fig. 1. Temperature difference between "glacial" and "nonglacial" climate. (Reproduced from *Climate through the ages*, by permission of Ernest Benn Ltd.)

Brooks has shown that actually the problem is not as difficult as these conditions might suggest. A much smaller drop in the polar temperature will suffice for the formation of a permanent ice cap. Once this ice is formed, it will have a strong cooling power on its surroundings and so will tend to increase in size and, by modifying the climate of high latitudes, create in turn more favorable conditions for the growth of a major ice sheet. Thus in fact we have only to explain a polar temperature change of 5 to 10° rather than 50°F. This consideration greatly simplifies but does not remove the problem. Brooks further points out that ice-free polar conditions are stable; and the presence of a large ice cap is also stable. Each condition tends to produce wind and ocean circulation patterns favorable to its own continued existence. Therefore, an appreciable external cause seems to be required in order to produce a change from one situation to the other.

In addition to the change from glacial to nonglacial climate, there exist also subcycles to be explained. The glacial epochs for which we have the best evidence are composed of several advances and retreats of the ice sheets. The Permian had three to five advances of glaciation, separated by more or less complete interglacials; the Pleistocene has so far had four advances of ice sheets in both Europe and North America, with interglacials free of Arctic sea ice and generally approaching the conditions of nonglacial periods. The advance of a single ice sheet also has its fluctuations. The Riss glaciation had two or three distinct maxima and the Würm had three maxima, while the most recent or Würm glaciation also retreated irregularly. Radiocarbon dating indicates that the pattern of retreat of the last ice sheet was closely parallel in Europe and North America. Following the recession of the last ice sheet about 8000 B.C. the climate became considerably warmer than at present, resembling, during the Climatic Optimum (5000–1000 B.C.), the climate of an interglacial period. Then in the Sub-Atlantic or Peat-bog period the climate became again more glacial, with increased storminess and precipitation, and the re-formation of many glaciers that had disappeared at the time of the Optimum. Subsequent oscillations have occurred, with decreasing amplitude and duration. Available evidence indicates that these climatic changes are world-wide.

Willett [2] has emphasized the similarity of the long-period and the short-period changes with respect to the pattern of atmospheric circulation. He has pointed out that glacial climate corresponds to an expanded polar vortex and a generally vigorous atmospheric circulation, with the westerlies weakened and all zonal weather belts displaced toward the equator. Conversely, in interglacial periods the westerly winds strengthen at the expense of the polar vortex, and the weather belts are displaced toward the poles from their present intermediate position, with a general relaxation in the atmospheric circulation. Willett has pointed out that this similarity in the change of the circulation pattern, whether the change in climate be of the order of hundreds or thousands or tens of thousands of years, constitutes a powerful argument in favor of a single variable factor underlying all of the changes.

Most geologists and meteorologists will agree that slowly changing geographical factors can play only a minor role in the short-period world-wide variations in climate, and that these variations most likely have a solar origin. Thus, as Willett pointed out,[2] if we look for a single principal cause for all the world-wide changes in climate, whatever their length, solar variation appears to offer the only hope for a satisfactory explanation.

In advancing solar variation as a hypothesis to explain the major climate changes in geological history, I by no means wish to deny the importance of topography. There can be little doubt that favorable topographic conditions, as well as solar conditions, are necessary to the development of large-scale glaciation. However, the proponents of a purely geological hypothesis have provided no adequate explanation of the time lag, sometimes of millions of years' duration, that occurs between outbursts of mountain building and the glaciation. While glaciation never develops in the absence of extensive land elevation, a considerable degree of land elevation can occur without producing glaciation. This situation suggests that ice ages have more than one necessary cause and no single sufficient cause. As a necessary but not sufficient cause, high mountain ranges and elevated plateaus provide positions wherein ice sheets can flourish when solar conditions are also favorable.

The sun can conceivably vary in two respects. First, it can vary in the intensity of its electromagnetic radiation, that is, in the solar "constant." The solar constant is defined as the quantity of radiant energy received normally just outside the earth's atmosphere, and is currently equal to about 2 cal/cm^2 min. Second, the sun can vary in the intensity of its corpuscular radiation.

In the 50 years covered by the observations of Abbot, there is some, but by no means conclusive, evidence for fluctuations of the order of 1 percent in the visible solar radiation. Conditions in the upper atmosphere indicate, however, that the solar ultraviolet radiation varies widely over the 11-year sunspot cycle. No observations exist, of course, other than indirect climatic data, either to prove or to disprove the postulated occurrence of larger solar variations over long periods of time. The size of the variation in the solar constant that I assume for this discussion is of the order of 10 to 15 percent about the present mean value. Fossil evidence for the continuous existence of life on the earth for over a billion years conclusively demonstrates that much larger changes in the solar radiation cannot have occurred.

If this postulated change in the solar constant results from a change in the effective solar temperature — and it is difficult to see how else it might arise — then, application of Stefan's law ($E = \sigma T^4$) reveals that a $\pm$ 10-percent change in the solar constant should result from a change of about $\pm$ 140°K in the solar temperature from the present value of 5700°K. By Wien's law ($\lambda_{max} T$ = constant), the 140° change in solar temperature would shift the wavelength of maximum intensity about 120 A to the violet for an increase in the solar temperature and solar constant, and to the red for a decrease. Further, Planck's law for the distribution of energy with wavelength indicates that much the largest

part of the change in radiation, resulting from a small change in temperature around 5700°K, would occur in the violet and ultraviolet. Thus from
the radiation laws we may conclude that a large variation should occur
in the blue and ultraviolet for only a small change in the red and infrared.
In most of the earlier discussions, however, the variation is assumed to be
independent of wavelength.

Let us now consider what solar variations need to be postulated to
explain best the observed periods of extensive glaciation. The more obvious
hypothesis states that the ice ages result from a decrease in the solar
radiation, with a consequent lowering of the earth's temperature. But Sir
George Simpson[3] has severely criticized this hypothesis. He points out
that the principal consequence of such cooling would be a great decline
in the moisture content of the atmosphere, in precipitation, and in general
vigor of atmospheric circulation. With such a decline in precipitation,
the Arctic seas would doubtless freeze, but it would be virtually impossible to build up any appreciable ice sheet on the land. This criticism
has received no satisfactory answer from the proponents of the "ice age
with low solar constant" point of view.

As a result of this consideration, Simpson proposed that ice ages
result from an increase in the solar radiation. Figure 2 illustrates Simp-

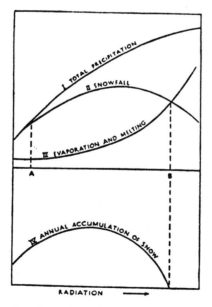

Fig. 2. Influence of changing solar
radiation on snow accumulation. (From
Simpson.[3])

son's argument. He considers that the principal consequence of an increase in solar radiation would be an increase in evaporation, cloudiness, and precipitation, with intensification of the atmospheric circulation, and only a slight increase in the earth's average temperature. The increased storminess and precipitation are favorable for the formation of an ice sheet, so long as the winter snowfall exceeds the summer melting. But if the solar radiation increased greatly, the summer melting would predominate and the ice sheet would melt.

Simpson has applied these ideas in an attempt to explain the succession of glacial and interglacial periods within the Pleistocene Ice Age, as illustrated in Fig. 3. He postulates two maxima of solar radiation to

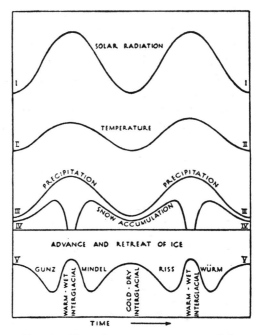

Fig. 3. The solar variation suggested by Simpson to explain the Pleistocene Ice Ages. (From Simpson.[3])

account for the four glacial periods. As the solar radiation rises from the minimum the precipitation gradually increases and the ice sheet begins to grow; it continues to grow so long as the winter snowfall exceeds the summer melting. As the solar radiation continues to increase the melting becomes dominant and we enter the first interglacial period. As the solar intensity, declining again, reaches the point where the snowfall exceeds the melting, the glaciers re-form, making the second glacial period. The glaciers then recede finally as the solar intensity falls too low to permit adequate precipitation.

Several criticisms have been brought against the details of this theory, although the basic idea appears sound. According to this theory, the Gunz-Mindel and Riss-Würm interglacial periods should be warm and wet, while the Mindel-Riss should be cool and dry. These predicted differences do not appear, however, in the vegetation patterns in temperate latitudes. The available evidence indicates [4] rather that the general succession of vegetation in the Riss-Würm and in the Mindel-Riss followed very nearly the same pattern. In each case the recession of the ice sheet was followed by a rise in temperature to a level somewhat above the present temperature, and then by a gradual decline to the onset of another glaciation. Further, Simpson's theory predicts that in the tropics one pluvial period represents two glaciations, while the available evidence rather suggests that each glacial period was a pluvial period in the tropics, and each interglacial was an interpluvial. The rises and falls in the levels of the large central African lakes appear to correspond to the advances and retreats of the equatorial mountain glaciers. Apparently, therefore, each interglacial had about the same maximum temperature, reached fairly early in the period; and further, a substantial part of each interglacial period was rather arid, as indicated by the low level of the African lakes.

These lines of evidence have led Willett to suggest [2] a modification of Simpson's theory, with the postulate of four solar maxima instead of two to account for the four glacial periods.

The introduction of four solar maxima, besides providing better agreement with geological evidence, has other advantages not, I believe, previously pointed out. Each ice sheet, I postulate, would develop on a rise to maximum of solar radiation, following a period of cold, dry climate. The preceding low solar constant would be favorable for a cooling of the oceans, reducing the heating effect in high latitudes of warm currents such as the Gulf Stream, and, more important, permitting the formation of permanent ice in the polar seas. Brooks has shown that once a permanent polar ice cap is formed, it will have a strong cooling power on its surroundings, and, by thus modifying the climate of high latitudes, produce conditions most favorable for the growth of an ice sheet when the solar radiation, and consequently the precipitation, increases. As the young ice sheets grow, the ice fields will reflect to space an increasingly large percentage of the radiation incident on the earth, and may thereby for a time counteract the effect of increasing solar radiation and prevent any significant rise in the earth's temperature. As the solar radiation increases further, however, summer melting will eventually predominate, the ice sheet will recede as in Simpson's theory, and the Arctic ice will melt, ushering in an interglacial period. As the solar radiation then again decreases, the climate grows cooler, but by the time the polar seas, warmed by a recent solar maximum, are permanently frozen the precipitation has fallen to too low a level for large-scale glaciation. Without the aid of the ice cap the glacial sheets do not succeed in developing. Furthermore, each ice sheet would by this theory recede at a maximum of solar radiation, which fits with the observation that ice sheets disappear by melting from the edge inward. Disappearance of an ice sheet by starvation, from the center outward, would seem more suggestive of inadequate precipitation due to a solar minimum.

Application of this theory to the principal stages of Pleistocene glaciation is illustrated schematically in Fig. 4. To explain the fluctuations in

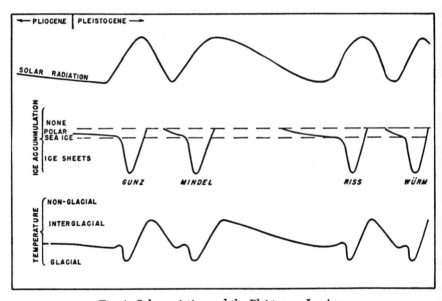

Fig. 4. Solar variation and the Pleistocene Ice Age.

the development of a single ice sheet, one postulates solar fluctuations of smaller amplitude and duration superposed on the major fluctuations shown in Fig. 4.

Reference to Fig. 1 emphasizes the difficulty of forming glacial sheets in the absence of a polar ice cap. As we have noted, the large change in the polar temperature from a nonglacial to a glacial period would be very difficult to bring about, were it not that a drop of a few degrees in the polar temperature would suffice for the formation of a polar ice cap. The ice cap and later the ice sheet tend to have an anticyclonic pressure pattern, and the outwardly directed winds spread Arctic conditions in a broad zone around its margin and provide conditions favorable for glaciation. These considerations and modifications in Simpson's theory may lessen the understandable difficulty many geologists feel in accepting a "hot-sun, cold-earth" theory of the ice ages.

In further support of this hypothesis, I should like to point out that the climate of the Tertiary began warm and mild, with temperate-type life far within the Arctic circle. By slow degrees and with fluctuations the climate grew colder through the Oligocene, the Miocene, and the Pliocene. At the Symposium on Climatic Changes, R. Revelle presented evidence that the ocean temperature of North Pacific coastal waters gradually declined through the Tertiary, while E. S. Barghoorn and E. H. Colbert agree, from plant and vertebrate fossil data respectively, that high-latitude life became increasingly restricted, with equatorward migration of various groups from the time of the Mid-Tertiary onward. The climate of the Pliocene, immediately preceding the Pleistocene glaciation, was not only cold but also markedly arid. According to W. B. Scott,[5] the principal other Post-Cambrian period of widespread aridity centered about the Permian, extending somewhat into the Carboniferous and more into the Triassic. Brooks notes that evidence for the withdrawal of coral boundaries toward the equator, and for changes in some and extinction of other species of fauna and flora, indicates a general decrease in temperature during the Upper Carboniferous. Sir T. W. Edgeworth David estimates a decrease of about 10°F in the temperature of the tropical oceans, and a sufficient cooling in high latitudes to permit freezing of the polar seas. The dating of changes occurring in the Carboniferous and Permian periods is not yet sufficiently precise for reliable comparison of conditions in various parts of the world at a given time. Lacking evidence to the contrary, however, and by analogy with the Cenozoic period, one may infer that a substantial part of this cooling preceded the Permian glaciation.

Thus the evidence seems compatible with the hypothesis that, given a favorable topography, *extensive glaciation results from a rise in the solar radiation, this rise occurring within a period of general depression of the solar radiation.* The earth, especially the oceans in high latitudes, must be precooled, as it were, in preparation for the growth of an ice sheet.

The fluctuations in solar radiation were perhaps substantially less in the Permo-Carboniferous than in the late Tertiary-Pleistocene depression, so that in the former period precipitation was adequate for extensive glaciation in tropical regions only, while widespread aridity prevailed in temperate latitudes.

In developing this hypothesis to explain glaciation I have not considered the problem of whether or not the sun could vary as seems necessary. Öpik's theory of changes in energy generation in the interior of the sun, in spite of its being an "ice age with low solar constant" approach, predicts variations of solar radiation in the order required by this paper. Öpik's theory, discussed further in this volume by P. L. Bhatnagar, predicts first a decline in solar radiation, followed by a recovery. This process may repeat several times before the sun recovers to complete stability.

Let us consider next the problem of the warm polar climate of nonglacial periods, when temperate life forms flourished well within the Arctic circle, and coal-forming vegetation flourished on the continent of Antarctica. These presumably were times of solar radiation somewhat more intense than at present. The oceans were warmer — probably, as Urey suggested at the Symposium, not merely near the surface but throughout their entire depth — and warm currents had free access to the polar seas. Even with favorable topography, however, other factors may be required to explain the nearly uniform climate that prevailed during much of Paleozoic times. It is by no means clear that solar radiation sufficiently intense to keep the poles as warm as they appear to have been at times would not heat the tropics more than observations indicate.

Here I should like to call attention to the possible variation in the solar corpuscular radiation. The intensity of the corpuscular radiation is known to vary in an 11-year period, with the auroral maxima lagging 1 to 2 years behind the sunspot maxima, and may well vary in longer periods. The solar corpuscular radiation strikes the earth primarily in the auroral zones, that is, in the high-latitude regions. Menzel, in his theory of the aurora,[6] has calculated that the corpuscular radiation incident on the upper atmosphere during an auroral storm of moderate intensity is about equal in energy content to ordinary solar radiation. Moreover, the kinetic energy of the particles will be entirely absorbed in the upper atmosphere, and they will not penetrate to the earth like much of ordinary radiation. In addition to the kinetic energy, the recombination of ionized protons with their electrons should produce Lyman radiation equal to about 1 percent of the total solar radiation (which covers all wavelengths, of course), and should thus provide a substantial increase in the ultraviolet for heating the ozone layer. Some ionized-helium radiation at 1640 A may also be expected, because of the great abundance of helium in the sun. The corpuscular radiation associated with an auroral storm acts, of course, only for a short time, of the order of minutes or hours, over a few thousand square kilometers. This solar corpuscular radiation, however, is the only known source of energy that acts exclusively in high latitudes. Therefore, I suggest that a solar corpuscular radiation considerably stronger and more continuous than at present should be favorable for the occurrence of a warm polar climate, whereas a weak corpuscular radiation should favor cold polar climates.

Until we understand better the way in which conditions in the stratosphere influence the circulation patterns in the troposphere, this hypothesis can be only a perhaps plausible speculation.

In support of the hypothesis, however, I should like to cite the results of Craig on pressure changes following magnetically disturbed days. The magnetic disturbance is caused by solar corpuscular radiation. Craig[7] found, with a high statistical significance, that the average change of pressure following disturbed days was in the opposite direction from that following quiet days at the same location. The sign of the effect varies with latitude. Increased solar corpuscular radiation tends to cause a rise in pressure in high latitudes, 60° to 70°N, and a decline in pressure around 40°N. The distribution of pressure changes after disturbed days is markedly in the direction of a higher zonal index, as compared with conditions after quiet days. A high zonal index, with its contracted and weakened polar vortex, is characteristic of an interglacial climate, as Willett has pointed out.[2]

Let me carry this speculation somewhat further. In the troposphere the temperature decreases upward at the average rate of about 12°F/km, as far as the tropopause. Above this, in the stratosphere, the temperature remains constant or even rises a little. This change in the nature of the temperature gradient defines the height of the tropopause. The height of the tropopause is not constant, but varies systematically with latitude. According to Brooks, over the equator its average height is about 18 kilometers, over the British Isles about 11 kilometers, and near the north pole only about 7.5 kilometers. The warm stratosphere thus extends to lower altitudes near the pole than at the equator, and the air 10 miles above the pole is warmer than the air 10 miles above the equator. Since air tends to flow from cold, high-pressure regions to warm, low-pressure regions, we have two opposing tendencies. The temperature distribution with latitude above 8 kilometers tends to produce westerly winds at all levels from the surface up to nearly 20 kilometers, while the temperature distribution below 8 kilometers tends to produce easterly winds at the surface. As Brooks points out, the resultant surface wind in high latitudes depends upon whether the weight of the cold air in the lowest 8 kilometers is sufficient to predominate over the contrary effect. Thus very cold poles tend to produce a pole cap of east winds, which hinder the approach to the poles of warm winds and warm ocean currents; warm poles, on the other hand, tend to produce westerly winds. These tendencies contribute importantly to the stability of glacial and of nonglacial conditions, respectively.

The isothermal stratosphere may perhaps extend lower over the poles and contain a greater proportion of the polar air when the solar corpuscular radiation is strong and fairly constant. By bringing extra energy to high latitudes and tending to warm the polar upper atmosphere, intense solar corpuscular radiation may significantly aid the stratospheric tendency to westerly winds. By promoting the tendency to westerly winds at the surface in high latitudes, corpuscular radiation may contribute importantly to establishing or maintaining a warm polar interglacial or nonglacial climate. The corpuscular radiation would not have the seasonal variation of ordinary solar radiation, and should be especially important during the long polar winter nights.

Much further research is of course needed to establish the degree of truth in the above hypothesis. Observational study of the relation between ozone temperature and geomagnetic and auroral conditions should be valuable in this connection. We have noted that Lyman radiation from recombination of the ionized corpuscles may be expected to heat the ozone layer of the atmosphere. The intensity pattern of the ozone bands is very sensitive to temperature, and the details of this relation between temperature and intensity pattern are currently being investigated in the laboratory by French scientists of the Institut d'Astrophysique.

A substantial increase in the corpuscular energy incident upon the earth may result either from an increase in the solar output of corpuscles, or, as Menzel's theory indicates, from an increase in the strength of the earth's magnetic field. Intensification of the earth's magnetic field would permit the capture of corpuscles from a wider region of space, and would also act to decrease the present 23° angle between the magnetic axis and the circle of maximum frequency of aurorae, thus bringing in corpuscles at a higher geomagnetic latitude. On the other hand, if the earth's field remains constant, and any large variation seems very unlikely, then an increase in the energy content of solar corpuscular radiation would act to increase the angle. This prediction is in accord with the observation that the most intense auroral storms tend to occur somewhat equatorward of the normal auroral zone.

According to L. A. Bauer,[8] the earth's magnetic field has for the past 80 years shown a secular decrease of 1/1500 per year. Bauer regards this not as a unidirectional change, but as most probably part of a long-period oscillation in the total magnetic moment of the earth. Wolbach, in a paper in this volume, discusses evidence from the work of Graham and others of a periodic variation in the direction of the earth's magnetic axis with respect to the axis of rotation. The presently available evidence suggests a semiperiodic variation in the direction of the magnetic axis, from east to west of the axis of rotation, with a period of 1500 to 4000 years and an amplitude of 20° to 30° on either side of the pole. The amplitude appears to differ from one cycle to another. The best observations cover the period around 15,000 to 20,000 years ago, but older desposits suggest that some such variations occurred in Tertiary times as well. The cause of such variations is not understood.

It is not possible at present to say what, if any, the climatic consequences of these changes in the direction of the earth's magnetic axis might be. Since major climate changes are world-wide in scope, it appears unlikely that these changes can depend to any primary degree on the position of the magnetic axis of the earth. On the other hand, the direction of the magnetic axis certainly determines the position of the auroral zone, and thereby the region of incidence of the greatest part of the energy of the solar corpuscular radiation. Thus some effect, significant even if small compared to the changes in the solar radiation, may not unreasonably be expected.

The results, presented in this volume by R. F. Flint, on the substages of the Wisconsin (Würm) glaciation are interesting in this connection. The close correlation in time and relative intensity of the substages in Europe and in North America suggests that they were controlled primarily by variations in the solar radiation. Flint further points out, however, that while the development of successive substages in North America kept the same general form, the positions of some of the lobes were shifted slightly to east or west from one stage to another; and also that in some regions the ice sheet came from the northwest in one substage, and from the northeast in the next. These minor variations in position and direction of the substages suggest to me a corpuscular influence on the circulation pattern of the atmosphere, the glacial variations arising from the changed direction of the earth's magnetic axis.

At present, of course, this hypothesis is very speculative. But when sufficient data are available, a detailed comparison between the history of the Wisconsin ice sheet and the changes in the direction of the geomagnetic axis could be extremely significant for increasing our understanding of the influence of corpuscular radiation on the circulation patterns of our atmosphere.

REFERENCES

1. C. E. P. Brooks, *Climate through the ages* (Ernest Benn, Ltd., London; McGraw-Hill, New York, 1949).

2. H. C. Willett, "Long period fluctuations of the general circulation of the atmosphere," *Jour. Meteorol. 6*, 34–50 (1949).

3. Sir George Simpson, "Ice Ages," *Proc. Roy. Inst. 30*, 125–42 (1937).

4. C. E. P. Brooks, "Geological and historical aspects of climate change," *Compendium of meteorology* (American Meteorological Society, Boston, 1951).

5. W. B. Scott, *An introduction to geology* (Macmillan, New York, 1932), vol. 2, *Historical geology*.

6. D. H. Menzel, "On the causes of the ice ages," *this volume*.

7. R. A. Craig, "Solar variability and meteorological anomalies," *Proc. Amer. Acad. Arts and Sci. 79*, 280–90 (1951).

8. J. A. Fleming, ed., *Terrestrial magnetism and electricity* (McGraw-Hill, New York, 1939), p. 325.

ADDITIONAL REFERENCES

R. A. Craig and H. C. Willett, "Solar energy variations as a possible cause of anomalous weather changes," *Compendium of Meteorology* (American Meteorological Society, Boston, 1951), pp. 379–90.

A. Holmes, *Principles of physical geology* (Ronald Press, New York, 1945), chap. 12.

9

INTERNAL CONSTITUTION OF THE SUN
AND CLIMATIC CHANGES

P. L. Bhatnagar

As our knowledge of the physical processes which occur inside stars increases, our picture of stellar evolution is becoming clearer. At present, however, it is possible to deal only with certain general features of this problem, and even on this basis our conclusions are open to some doubt. The evolution of a star involves, of course, *slow, secular* changes in such parameters as radius and luminosity; but at this stage we cannot answer with any degree of certainty the question whether "temporary" changes in the luminosity of a star may occur, lasting only for periods of the order of a hundred thousand or a few million years.

The Öpik Model. E. J. Öpik [1] was the first to make an attempt to explain the temporary variations in the luminosity of a star on the basis of sudden changes (sudden as compared with a time scale of the order of 10^9 years) in the structure of the star. He bases his discussion on the stellar model consisting of (i) a central convective core with polytropic index 1.5, in which the energy transport is partly by convection and partly by radiation; (ii) an intermediate radiative shell in which radiation alone transfers the energy from point to point; and (iii) a peripheral convective region with polytropic index 1.2, which is a broad average for dwarf stars according to Biermann.[2] Öpik takes the chemical composition to be uniform in the core at all stages on account of mixing by convection, and assumes that the hydrogen content increases outward from the surface of the core, in the radiative shell. According to present views, some thermonuclear process, such as the proton-proton reaction or the carbon-nitrogen cycle, is responsible for the energy generation. These reactions convert hydrogen into helium, leaving the abundance of heavier elements practically unchanged, so that, as time advances, the hydrogen content of a star decreases and the helium content increases at each point. The generation of energy depends, among other factors, on the temperature, which decreases outward from the center; consequently the rate of consumption of hydrogen decreases outward from the center. The convectional mixing does not, however, allow any gradient of hydrogen content to be set up in the core, but in the intermediate radiative shell we expect the gradient to become steeper with time.

Self-Regulation of Energy. The effective temperature is extremely sensitive to the extent of the peripheral convective region, but it cannot vary much from the equilibrium value because a slight increase in the extent of the peripheral convective region leads to a considerable decrease in the effective temperature and hence in the radiation to space. This means that a considerable fraction of the heat generated inside cannot be radiated to space; the extra heat is stored up inside in the form of gravitational potential energy and causes expansion. On account of expansion, the central temperature decreases and consequently the nuclear energy sources are slowed down until the equality between energy generation and radiation to space is again approached. This self-regulation of energy balance is favored by the situation that a decrease in the internal energy flux produces automatically a shrinking of the peripheral convective region as an inherent property of the solution of the equations of radiative equilibrium. Hence, we conclude that if the energy balance is disturbed by any cause whatsoever, automatic adjustments will take place in the structure of the model, and these adjustments will be such as to restore the energy balance.

Metastable Layer in Radiative Shell. Let p, ρ, T, μ be the pressure, density, temperature, and mean molecular weight at a point distant r from the center of the model. If we neglect radiation pressure,

$$p = \frac{k}{\mu H} \rho T, \tag{1}$$

where k is the Boltzmann constant and H the mass of a hydrogen atom. For a high degree of ionization,

$$\mu = \frac{1}{2x + \tfrac{3}{4}y + \tfrac{1}{2}(1 - x - y)} = \frac{2}{1 + 3x + \tfrac{1}{2}y}, \tag{2}$$

where x, y are the abundances of hydrogen and helium by weight. The quantity x increases outward; hence μ decreases outward in the intermediate shell; since p also decreases outward,

$$\frac{d \log \mu}{d \log p} > 0. \tag{3}$$

The stability of the radiative temperature gradient at any point depends on the magnitude of the effective polytropic index, n,

$$n = \frac{d \log \rho}{d \log T} = \frac{d \log \rho / d \log p}{1 - (d \log \rho / d \log p) + (d \log \mu / d \log p)}, \quad (4)$$

with the help of (1).

For the gas in convective equilibrium,

$$p \propto \rho^{5/3}, \quad (5)$$

so that

$$\frac{d \log \rho}{d \log p} = \frac{3}{5}. \quad (6)$$

Substituting for $d \log \rho / d \log p$ from (6) in (4), we define the critical value n_c of the effective polytropic index,

$$n_c = \frac{1.5}{1 + 2.5 \, d \log \mu / d \log p}. \quad (7)$$

If μ does not vary with distance from the center, we have, as a particular case of (7)

$$n_{c0} = 1.5. \quad (8)$$

In view of (3)

$$n_c < n_{c0} = 1.5. \quad (9)$$

The radiative equilibrium will prevail in a layer if

$$n > n_c, \quad \text{when } \mu \text{ varies} \quad (10)$$

and

$$n > n_{c0}, \quad \text{when } \mu \text{ is constant.} \quad (11)$$

We shall call a layer metastable if

$$n_c < n < n_{c0} = 1.5. \quad (12)$$

Öpik [3] has constructed models which actually possess a metastable layer in the radiative shell. As an example we may take his c-models in which the hydrogen content is assumed to increase smoothly but steeply outward from the boundary of the core according to the formula

$$\log \frac{x}{x_0} = \frac{\epsilon_1}{\epsilon_i} \frac{\rho \, T^s}{\rho_1 T_1{}^s} \log \frac{x_c}{x_0}, \quad (13)$$

where x_c, x_0 are central and photospheric values of x, $\epsilon_1/\bar{\epsilon}_1$ is the ratio of rate of energy generated at the surface of the core to the average rate of energy generated inside the core, and the rate of energy generation, ϵ, per gram per second is

$$\epsilon = E \, x \, \rho \, T^s, \tag{14}$$

E being a constant.

This distribution of x is similar to the distribution that would result from nuclear transmutations, with the given law of energy generation, when the production of helium is not considered. Thus, strictly speaking, this distribution cannot be regarded as the result of such transmutations, but rather as something given a priori.

Convective Disturbance. Let us for a moment suppose that mixing takes place in a *small* limited portion of the metastable layer. Suddenly started turbulence is quite sufficient to start this type of mixing. The mixing destroys the gradient of mean molecular weight and equalizes the hydrogen content in this portion. Since in the disturbed portion $n < 1.5$ originally, the radiative temperature gradient becomes unstable and convective equilibrium replaces the radiative equilibrium. This is a structural change. The mixing introduces a discontinuity in the hydrogen content at the two surfaces of the disturbed portion of the layer. In the disturbed portion convection is present, whereas in the undisturbed portions on its two sides radiative equilibrium prevails and convection is absent. Partly by the "surf" effect of convection currents and partly by thermal diffusion we expect interchange of hydrogen through an interface. Thus the next adjacent layer gets its hydrogen content equalized with the newly created convective portion and this allows convection to stretch out to this adjacent part, and so on. Thus from a disturbed shell, however narrow, convection spreads in two directions, inward and outward, until mixing becomes complete throughout the metastable layer.

As a result of mixing, the distribution of hydrogen is changed, and consequently the distribution of energy sources in the model is altered. This alteration in turn affects the luminosity directly as well as indirectly through changes of structure. In fact, the mixing transfers hydrogen to regions nearer to the center, which are poorer in hydrogen content, from the regions farther from the center which are comparatively richer in hydrogen content. This process speeds up the nuclear reactions and increases the energy output, and results in expansion and consequent decrease in luminosity of the model. The replacement of the radiative equilibrium by convective equilibrium in the metastable layer also affects the luminosity, and we can show that the combined effect of the expansion and this structural change is to decrease the luminosity in the initial stages. The disturbed energy balance will gradually be restored by the property of self-regulation of the energy balance.

Time of Relaxation. The extent to which the luminosity varies depends on the size of the metastable layer, which ultimately depends on the initial stratification of hydrogen in the radiative shell. The steeper the stratification gradient outward, the greater will be the change. The question of the time intervals needed for the propagation of the convective disturbance is mathematically involved, but with certain simplifying assumptions we can make a rough estimate of the time of relaxation of the convective disturbance.

If we neglect the small effect of structural change on luminosity, and assume that the star expands through homologous configurations, and that the expansion and variation in luminosity respond instantaneously to a disturbance in energy generation, we find according to the calculations by Öpik [4] that the relative change in luminosity is given by

$$\frac{L - L_0}{L_0} = - \lambda e^{-t/t_0}, \tag{15}$$

where λ is the relative change in energy generation and t_0 is the time of relaxation

$$t_0 = \frac{\Omega_0}{4L_0 (s + 3)}. \tag{16}$$

In (16), Ω_0 and L_0 are the gravitational potential energy and the undisturbed luminosity, and s is the temperature exponent in the law of energy generation (14). For the sun,

$$\Omega_0 = 4 \times 10^{48} \text{ ergs} \quad \text{and} \quad L_0 = 3.8 \times 10^{33} \text{ ergs/sec.}$$

From (16) we then have

$$t_0 = 3.8 \times 10^5 \text{ years, taking } s = 18 \text{ for carbon-nitrogen cycle}$$
$$= 1.1 \times 10^6 \text{ years, taking } s = 4 \text{ for proton-proton reaction.}$$

These periods may be compared with the duration of the Pleistocene glaciation.

From (15) we find that to produce a 1-percent decrease in the solar constant we need an equal but opposite change in the energy generation, and we find also that the luminosity decreases suddenly. The sudden decrease in luminosity is the outcome of our assumption that the variation in luminosity responds instantaneously to the change in the energy generation. In any real case the decrease in luminosity will be continuous.

Öpik[4] has considered the problem of the time interval needed for the spread of the convective disturbance more thoroughly than we have done here, but we have avoided the discussion of his laborious calculations as they essentially confirm the fundamental conclusions discussed above. It has not yet been determined conclusively whether a decrease or an increase in the solar constant would result in climatic changes responsible for an ice age. Discussions by Dr. Barbara Bell in the preceding paper (see her Fig. 4) suggest that the most favorable situation for producing the required type of climatic conditions is an initially cool sun which gradually gets warmer, and that it is at some stage between the cool and the hot sun that the formation of ice exceeds melting. It is interesting to note that the theory discussed above provides such a situation.

Recurrence of Convective Disturbance. The nuclear reactions taking place with different rates in different portions of the radiative layers may again produce in course of time a stratification of hydrogen which may result in the formation of a metastable layer. This suggests the possibility of recurrence of convective disturbance a number of times in the life history of the sun.

REFERENCES

1. E. J. Öpik, *Tartu Observatory Publications 30*, No. 3 (1938).
2. L. Biermann, *Zs. f. Astrophysik 21*, 320 (1942).
3. E. J. Öpik, *Contributions from Armagh Observatory*, No. 3 (1951).
4. E. J. Öpik, *Monthly Notices, Roy. Astr. Soc. 110*, 49 (1950).

10

INTERSTELLAR MATTER
AND THE SOLAR CONSTANT*

Max Krook

ACCORDING TO PRESENT-DAY THEORIES, rather more than half the total mass of matter in our Galaxy is spread out thinly and rather unevenly in the space between the stars. This view is supported — is even demanded — by a considerable amount of observational evidence. In fact, as new data accumulate, there seems to be a trend toward assigning still higher values to the fraction of galactic matter that is interstellar.

By far the larger part of this interstellar medium has the form of a very rarefied gas. The rest is made up of fine grains or dust particles. In our region of the Galaxy the gas has an average density of about 10^{-23} gm/cm^3, which amounts roughly to one hydrogen atom per cubic centimeter. The interstellar matter shows a marked tendency to aggregate into clouds. This is evidenced, *inter alia*, by the patchiness in the obscuration of starlight. The linear dimensions of such clouds vary within wide limits, but 10^{14} km may be taken as a reasonable order of magnitude. The density within a particular cloud will vary from place to place; the average density may be of the order of 100 times the general space average. It should be pointed out that our knowledge of the interstellar medium is still, in many respects, rather scanty. Figures quoted, and conclusions derived from them, are to be regarded only as order-of-magnitude estimates.

The various units comprising the Galaxy possess, in the first instance, *ordered* velocities due to the galactic rotation. Superposed on these they have also *random* velocities which vary all the way from zero to 50 km/sec and even higher. If we possessed detailed knowledge of the necessary distribution functions, we should be able to compute the average time interval between passages through interstellar clouds by a particular

* The research reported in this paper has been sponsored in part by the Geophysics Research Directorate of Air Force Cambridge Research Center, Air Research and Development Command, under Contract No. AF19(604)–146.

star, say the sun. Values between 10^8 and 10^9 years result from fairly reasonable assumptions consistent with both present knowledge and present lack of knowledge. The actual times between encounters would of course exhibit a dispersion about such a mean time. It appears likely that, during the life history of the earth, the solar system will have made a number of passages through clouds. Each passage may have lasted for a period of the order of a million years.

We now turn to the central problem. What physical effects will occur when the sun passes through a cloud, and how large will these effects be? In particular, can significant variations in the value of the solar constant be produced in this way? The problem is an extremely difficult and complex one and we are still far from having a satisfactory solution of it. Attempts to settle the question have thus far been based on rough approximations and disputed assumptions, and have led to widely divergent conclusions.

There seems, however, to be one conclusion that can be drawn with safety. It is that any obscuring or blanketing effect by interstellar matter on the sunlight reaching the earth can be neglected. At the densities required to make this effect significant it would be completely overshadowed by other effects, in particular by accretion.

In considering the accretion problem, we shall for the moment neglect the dust and consider only the gaseous constituent of the cloud. The mean free path of a molecule in such a tenuous gas is large, of the order of 10^{10} cm. On this account the cloud has properties that are intermediate between those of a gas and those of a system of independent particles. In certain contexts the gas properties will predominate; in other contexts the independent-particle properties will predominate. This ambiguity is responsible for a large part of the difficulty associated with any precise treatment of the accretion problem.

If the sun were at rest in a cloud, matter would fall upon it almost radially. As a result of the gravitational attraction, the matter incident on the sun's surface would have very high kinetic energy (the velocity of escape from the surface of the sun is about 600 km/sec). This energy would then ultimately be converted into other forms and augment the normal luminosity of the sun. With these conditions, very appreciable changes in the solar constant would result; in addition, the internal constitution and the whole evolutionary pattern of the star could undergo considerable modification.

In general, however, the sun would have a nonzero velocity, say v km/sec, relative to the cloud. Material from the cloud would still fall into the sun, but at a lower average rate than in the case of zero velocity. The point at issue is the magnitude of this rate.

If one adopts an extreme independent-particle point of view, that is, if one consistently ignores any gas properties of the material, the problem is easily solved. The particles describe hyperbolic orbits about the center of the sun. All particles whose perihelion distances do not exceed the solar radius would be captured. The energy that becomes available in this way turns out to be far too small to produce any appreciable effect on the sun's luminosity, except for very small values of the velocity v.

The extreme independent-particle model is, however, certainly not correct. It provides only a lower limit to the accretion rate. The gas properties of the medium must be taken into account and would lead to a higher value for this rate. The opinion of some authors is that even this enhanced value would still be inappreciable. Others, notably Hoyle and Lyttleton,[1] claim that the modification may be considerable.

Hoyle and Lyttleton have suggested a model in which the gas properties are taken into account in a rough sort of way. In their picture, collisions occurring downstream from the sun and between streams that have flowed in opposite directions round the sun lead to an approximate cancellation of the angular momentum of the material in the two streams. If the residual radial velocity of this material is less than the velocity of escape at that distance, it will eventually fall into the sun or describe highly elliptic orbits about the sun. In the steady state there would be an increase of density in the region where this collision mechanism operates; this would improve the efficiency of the mechanism.

With this model, material crossing a much larger area than in the extreme free-particle model would be accreted. Hoyle and Lyttleton estimate that with a cloud density of ρ gm/cm^3 and a relative velocity of v km/sec, the energy available by accretion is $5 \times 10^{53} \rho/v^3$ ergs/sec. With $\rho = 10^{-21}$ gm/cm^3 and $v = 5$ km/sec, this energy accretion gives an increase of about 0.5 percent in the solar constant. In their original estimates Hoyle and Lyttleton used a cloud density of 10^{-18} gm/cm^3, which is now regarded as rather too high. They also use the large-scale variations of density within a particular cloud to explain variations in the modified value of the solar constant as the sun passes through the cloud.

There is another aspect of the problem that has been neglected in all treatments hitherto. This is the role played by shock waves. The velocity of sound in a cloud is of the order of 0.5 km/sec. The velocity of the star relative to the cloud is probably several times as large. The motion is thus supersonic with a Mach number that may be much greater than 1. Under such circumstances we should expect shock phenomena to be of considerable importance. It is not yet clear how large an effect this would have on the rate of accretion. We hope to attack this shock-wave problem in the near future.

I should like to emphasize again that there is considerable divergence of opinion on the question of the order of magnitude and the importance of accretion. In my view, neither the arguments for nor the arguments against the accretion hypothesis are completely conclusive and it is worth while to keep an open mind on the subject. The problem will be resolved finally only by means of a proper mathematical treatment of the very complicated gas-dynamical problems involved.

REFERENCE

1. Hoyle and Lyttleton, *Proc. Camb. Phil. Soc.* 35, 405 (1939).

11

THE ASTRONOMICAL THEORY
OF CLIMATE CHANGES

A. J. J. van Woerkom

THE FIRST ATTEMPT AT AN ASTRO-
nomical explanation of the ice ages was that by Adhémar in
Les Révolutions de la mer, déluges périodiques (Paris, 1842). His judgment of the effects that would be produced by changes in the earth's orbit
was entirely erroneous. In 1875 James Croll gave in his famous *Climate
and time* (London, 1875) a more appropriate discussion of the influence
of orbital changes. His argument is that at the times when the earth
passes the perihelion of its orbit at the summer solstice, the Northern
Hemisphere will have short hot summers and long cold winters. At perihelion the velocity of the earth in its orbit is greatest and the distance to
the sun is least. At such times of coincidence of perihelion passage with
the summer solstice the earth moves in a considerably shorter time from
the vernal equinox to the autumnal equinox than from the autumnal
equinox back to the vernal equinox. The larger the eccentricity the more
pronounced the effect will be. Conditions will be reversed when the earth
is at the aphelion of its orbit at the summer solstice.

Croll reasoned that during the long cold winters the ice caps (permafrost) will increase to such an extent that the increased summer heat is
not sufficient to reduce it again to normal. By the extension of the ice caps
the summer heat will be reduced by reflection, cloud formations, and
changes in the system of sea currents. As early as 1876 Simon Newcomb [1]
criticized Croll's hypothesis on the basis of quantitative insufficiency. A
more profound criticism is that during the long cold winters the precipitation will decrease and for that reason also the ice output of the glacial
regions will decrease. Low summer temperatures are of greater importance than low winter temperatures for the advance of an ice sheet. In all
this earlier work the changes in the obliquity of the ecliptic are discussed
in a qualitative way only.

In 1924 Köppen and Wegener, in *Die Klimate der geologischen Vorzeit*,
supported a theory according to which shifts in the continents are the
explanation of glaciations, while the details of the repeated advances and

regressions during a period of glaciation are ascribed to astronomical causes. The latter feature is a revival of Croll's theory by M. Milankovitch, *Théorie mathématique des phénomènes termiques produits par la radiation solaire* (Belgrade, 1920), who introduces some important changes in Croll's conceptions. In the light of the then existing evidence of the causes for the advance of an ice sheet, Milankovitch divides the year into two equal halves in such a way that the heat received during any day of the summer half is greater than that of any day of the winter half. His calculations of the insolation are made for the two equal halves of the year so divided. A second improvement is his quantitative discussion of the influence of the obliquity.

Milankovitch's earlier computations are based upon the calculations of the variations of the elements of the earth's orbit by Ludwig Pilgrim,[2] based on J. N. Stockwell's solution.[3] The computations used in Milankovitch's more recent publication [4] are based on Leverrier's expressions, corrected by V. V. Michkovitch for changes in the planetary masses. No further details are given concerning the basic data on which the numerical results furnished by Milankovitch depend. Even if these had been available, an independent calculation based on the more recent solution for planetary masses by Dr. Brouwer and myself would have been worth while.[5]

Numerical Results. Table 1 gives the reciprocals of the planetary masses as used by Stockwell and in our recent solution. According to

Table .1. Reciprocals of planetary masses.

Planet	Stockwell	New Solution
Mercury	4,866,000	6,000,000
Venus	390,000	408,000
Earth-Moon	370,000	329,390
Mars	2,680,000	3,093,500
Jupiter	1,047.88	1,047.35
Saturn	3,501.6	3,501.6
Uranus	24,905	22,869
Neptune	18,780	19,314

Milankovitch the modification of Leverrier's solution by Michkovitch is based on the masses given in the *Connaissance des temps*, which are practically identical with the masses used in our new solution.

The data given in Table 2 refer to the expressions:

$$e \frac{\cos}{\sin} \pi = \sum_{1}^{10} M_j \frac{\cos}{\sin} (s_j t + \delta_j).$$

The periods listed are proportional to the reciprocals of the mean motions s_j of the various arguments. The terms $j = 9, 10$ in Table 2 are the effects of the second-order terms caused by the great inequality in the motions of Jupiter and Saturn ($s_9 = s_6 - 2s_5$; $s_{10} = 2s_6 - s_5$). The principal effects on the earth's orbit due to this improvement of the solution are the changes in the terms $j = 5, 6$.

Table 2. Coefficients and periods of terms in the expressions for the eccentricity and perihelion of the earth's orbit.

j	Stockwell		New Solution	
	M_j	Period (y)	M_j	Period (y)
1	0.00548	237,200	0.00392	237,200
2	.01536	178,800	.01634	176,500
3	.01131	76,200	.01043	74,800
4	.01626	72,900	.01483	72,000
5	.01634	348,700	.01834	301,700
6	.00238	57,700	.00283	46,700
7	.00058	475,000	.00044	476,600
8	.00001	2,101,600	.00001	2,046,400
9	––	––	.00012	67,600
10	––	––	.00015	25,300

Table 3 gives the corresponding data concerning the expressions:

$$\sin I \begin{matrix} \cos \\ \sin \end{matrix} \theta = \begin{matrix} \text{const.} \\ \text{const.} \end{matrix} + \sum_{1}^{7} N_j \begin{matrix} \cos \\ \sin \end{matrix} (s_j't + \epsilon_j).$$

Table 3. Coefficients and periods of terms in the expressions for the inclination and longitude of the ascending node of the earth's orbit referred to the ecliptic of 1950.0.

j	Stockwell		New Solution	
	M_j	Period (y)	M_j	Period (y)
1	0.01065	252,800	0.00849	249,200
2	.00632	196,600	.00810	197,200
3	.02448	70,400	.02448	69,100
4	.00695	74,500	.00453	73,500
5	.00273	50,000	.00281	50,400
6	.00162	444,400	.00173	446,500
7	.00133	1,963,100	.00130	1,912,900

The values for the eccentricity and the longitude of the perihelion of the earth's orbit that correspond to the new solution of Table 2 are represented in Fig. 1. The abscissa gives the time before 1950 in units of 1000 years. The longitude of the perihelion is counted from the fixed equinox of 1950.0. The eccentricity is seen to vary between 0.053 and zero. This indicates that the line of apsides does not have a real mean motion. The period covering a revolution changes from 226,000 years around 1950 to 49,000 years around −600,000. The average period for the past million years is 96,600 years. At the year −525,000, when the eccentricity goes to zero, the longitude of the perihelion changes by 180°. Very much the same behavior is found for the inclination and the

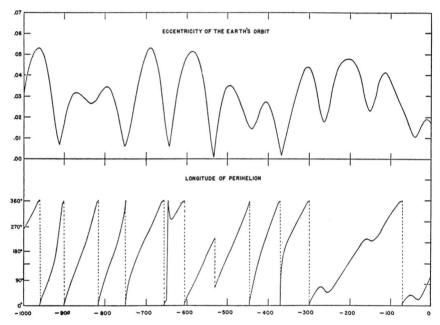

Fig. 1. Computed values of the eccentricity and the longitude of the perihelion of the earth's orbit. Abscissa, time before 1950; unit, 1,000 years.

longitude of the node of the earth's orbital plane. However, in this latter case, the one outstanding term will make the average period 69,000 years. The inclination varies between 4°53 and 0°. The variation is smaller if we choose as plane of reference the plane represented by the total angular momentum of the planetary system, the so-called invariable plane. The variation with respect to that plane is only 2°95.

Another important quantity relevant to climatic changes is the orientation of the pole of the earth's rotation with respect to the moving ecliptic. If the ecliptic were fixed in space this pole would describe with a uniform motion a circle around the pole of the ecliptic in about 26,000 years, a motion caused by the torque exerted on the equatorial bulge of the earth by the sun and the moon. In that case the obliquity would be constant. However, the ecliptic is not fixed in space and its motion will cause slight variations in the motion of the pole of the earth's rotation. A numerical integration has been carried out for the motion of the pole, based on the previously mentioned results for the motion of the ecliptic. The variations in the eccentricity and the longitude of perihelion give rise only to variations in the precession, but not in the obliquity. From the integration the position of the pole with respect to the fixed ecliptic of 1950.0 was obtained and the result was then transformed to the moving mean ecliptic of date. Figure 2(a) shows the motion of the pole for the interval − 437,000 to − 491,000 with respect to the fixed ecliptic, and Fig. 2(b) the motion of the pole for this same interval with respect to the moving ecliptic. The inclination of the earth's equator to the fixed ecliptic of 1950 varies from 28°.1 to 18°.5. The inclination of the earth's equator to the moving mean ecliptic, that is, the obliquity, has varied in the past one million years only from 24°.4 to 21°.8. This variation can be seen from Fig. 3, which gives the obliquity for the entire interval of the past million years. The period of the variation of the obliquity is mainly determined by the large term in the motion of the ecliptic, with a period of 69,000 years, combined with the precessional motion. The result is a period of nearly 41,000 years. The variation of the equinox from its mean position, which has a period of revolution of 25,700 years, is never more than 4°. For all problems connected with the astronomical climate it will be sufficient to use the mean value for the position of the equinox.

In Table 4 are listed the times of coincidence of the perihelion of the earth's orbit with the summer and winter solstice. This table shows that the period of revolution of the line of apsides with respect to the moving equinox varies from 13,500 years to 29,000 years with an average of 21,000 years.

The Astronomical Climate. The astronomical climate, to the extent that it is affected by orbital considerations, is determined by the following three quantities:

(a) The eccentricity of the earth's orbit;

(b) The longitude of perihelion with respect to the mean equinox of date;

(c) The obliquity.

The first two determine the difference between the summer and winter half-years. The effects are opposite in the Northern and Southern Hemi-

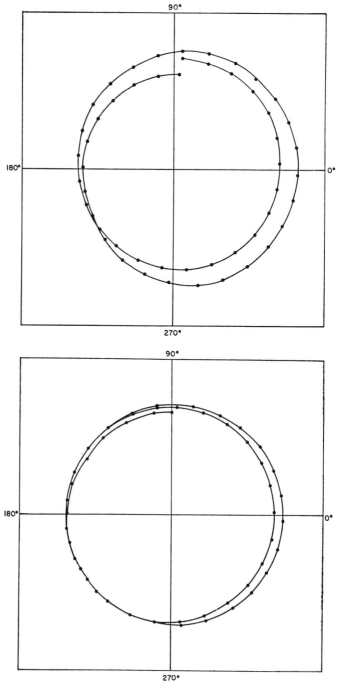

Fig. 2. Motion of the north celestial pole with respect to (*a, upper*) the north pole of the ecliptic of 1950; (*b, lower*) the moving north pole of the ecliptic. The interval represented is that between −437,000 and −491,000.

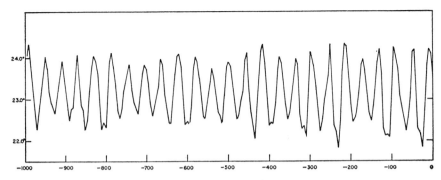

Fig. 3. Computed values of the obliquity of the ecliptic. Abscissa, time before 1950; unit, 1,000 years.

Table 4. Time of coincidence of perihelion with summer and winter solstices and values of eccentricity; time is in units of 1,000 years before 1950.

Summer Solstice				Winter Solstice			
Time	e	Time	e	Time	e	Time	e
11.2	0.0192	525.9	0.0128	00.0	0.0167	516.0	0.0250
33.2	.0121	535.9	.0024	22.1	.0169	546.8	.0199
60.1	.0193	556.9	.0364	47.5	.0126	567.3	.0445
82.4	.0288	577.9	.0502	71.2	.0244	588.8	.0513
105.9	.0396	599.4	.0489	94.1	.0342	610.0	.0436
126.9	.0380	621.1	.0339	116.1	.0412	632.1	.0202
151.0	.0230	649.6	.0124	138.8	.0297	661.2	.0307
175.7	.0389	672.3	.0447	163.6	.0288	682.4	.0516
197.7	.0475	692.6	.0526	186.9	.0452	703.1	.0481
220.3	.0465	713.8	.0399	208.8	:0477	724.3	.0299
242.0	.0353	734.4	.0197	231.1	.0429	743.9	.0101
268.1	.0190	751.3	.0062	253.9	.0235	758.6	.0110
291.0	.0399	767.8	.0201	280.2	.0305	777.4	.0281
313.2	.0422	787.6	.0332	302.2	.0440	797.9	.0342
334.4	.0296	807.0	.0323	323.4	.0371	816.4	.0292
355.6	.0125	826.1	.0268	345.2	.0214	835.4	.0264
369.5	.0027	845.0	.0278	364.7	.0039	854.7	.0297
388.2	.0201	864.8	.0313	377.9	.0109	875.7	.0312
407.7	.0271	885.3	.0282	397.8	.0256	895.1	.0218
427.4	.0194	904.6	.0126	417.8	.0244	911.8	.0076
444.4	.0149	919.0	.0131	436.2	.0153	928.3	.0259
464.2	.0241	937.9	.0382	453.7	.0183	948.2	.0478
484.3	.0334	958.9	.0525	474.0	.0292	969.2	.0523
505.4	.0328	979.6	.0484	494.7	.0353	990.6	.0414

spheres. Mathematically we can express the difference in summer heat with the present condition by the equation

$$\Delta Q_s = - m \Delta (e \sin \pi'), \tag{1}$$

in which ΔQ_s is the difference in summer heat, m is a factor depending upon the latitude, and π' is the longitude of the perihelion reckoned from the moving mean equinox.

Changes in the obliquity cause changes in the amounts of summer and winter heat. Milankovitch showed that the insolation during the summer half-year increases for almost all latitudes for increasing obliquity, and the winter insolation decreases for all latitudes. The *total* yearly insolation decreases for latitudes below 43° and increases for latitudes above 43°. The effect on both hemispheres is the same. Table 5 is a copy of Milankovitch's Table 13. It gives for different latitudes the change in winter and summer insolation corresponding to a change of 1° in obliquity, expressed in percentages of the total radiation. This table shows that the amount of radiation received during the summer half-year changes more than the total for the entire year. A detailed study for the summer half-year only is therefore called for.

The complete expression of the change in insolation during the summer half of the year becomes:

$$\Delta Q_s = p\Delta\epsilon - m \Delta(e \sin \pi') \tag{2}$$

where p is given by Table 5. With the aid of expression (2) and the new results for the secular changes in the earth's orbit and in its axis of rotation, Milankovitch's results for 65° latitude, for both the Northern and Southern Hemispheres, were recomputed. They are shown in Fig. 4 after having been converted to equivalent latitude. The insolation curve for the Northern Hemisphere is almost identical with the one given by Milankovitch.[6] Because the curves give the changes relative to the insolation at the present epoch, the amplitudes of the variations in the Southern Hemisphere are greater than in the Northern.

As is seen from Table 5, the influence of the obliquity on the insolation is insignificant at the equator and increases slowly with the latitude. For this reason, changes in the eccentricity and the longitude of perihelion are predominant at lower latitudes, while at higher latitudes changes in the obliquity become more and more significant.

At higher latitudes an extreme decrease in summer heat is caused by an extreme decrease in the obliquity occurring simultaneously with an extreme lengthening of the summer. Because the period in the obliquity is 41,000 years, and a long summer in the Northern Hemisphere changes to a long summer in the Southern Hemisphere in about 10,000 years, an extreme minimum in summer insolation in one hemisphere will as a rule be followed by one in the other hemisphere within about 10,000 years. This may be seen from Fig. 4. The mean period of the zigzag line of the insolation curve is practically determined by the period in the obliquity.

Milankovitch, and with him several other authors, correlate the insolation curve with the climatic changes in the Pleistocene.[7] There is no doubt that there are similarities between the curve and the geological record. Milankovitch called particular attention to the fact that large departures in the insolation curve occurred in groups of two or more and also that

Table 5. Changes in insolation for a change of 1° in the obliquity.

Latitude	p_s	p_w	p_t
0°	−0.35	−0.35	−0.35
5	− .20	− .52	− .35
10	− .04	− .69	− .34
15	+ .11	− .87	− .33
20	+ .26	−1.07	− .30
25	+ .42	−1.29	− .27
30	+ .59	−1.54	− .22
35	+ .76	−1.83	− .16
40	+ .96	−2.17	− .08
45	+1.17	−2.60	+ .03
50	+1.41	−3.14	+ .19
55	+1.69	−3.84	+ .42
60	+2.04	−4.78	+ .78
65	+2.51	−5.77	+1.39
70	+3.18	−4.62	+2.49
75	+3.57	−4.31	+3.17
90	+4.02	+0.00	+4.02

the long interval from the year −400,000 to −220,000 was free of large departures. The latter is not true any more in the recomputed curve, where a large departure occurs around the year − 320,000. On the whole the large departures show a little more regularity in the recomputed curve than in Milankovitch's original. A change in this direction was indicated by the difference between Milankovitch's curve that was based on the Stockwell solution and that based on Leverrier's solution as revised by Michkovitch.

The maximum around −10,000 is very suggestive in connection with the thermal maximum (climatic optimum). Modern determinations of geological chronology by means of the carbon 14 isotope indicate that the last regression of the ice sheet occurred at about 10,000 B.C. and the

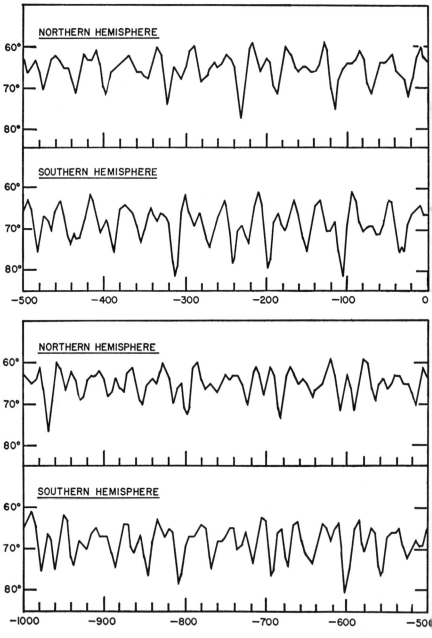

Fig. 4. Insolation for the summer half-year for latitude 65°, converted to equivalent latitude. Abscissa, time before 1950; unit, 1,000 years.

thermal maximum about 5,000 B.C. Those data certainly do not fit the insolation curve too well.

Criticism of another nature has been given by G. C. Simpson.[8] He points out that the temperature changes caused by the changes in radiation are largely overestimated by Milankovitch. Changes in insolation as given by the insolation curve will cause changes of only 1° to 2° in temperature, which is insignificant with respect to glaciations. Our conclusion must be that *the changes in insolation, caused by the changes in the earth's orbit and in its axis of rotation, are insufficient to explain the periods of glaciation.* Nevertheless, they must have had their consequences.

Evidence of the consequences is indicated by periodicities found for varves in various geological formations. For instance, Wilmot H. Bradley of the U. S. Geological Survey finds, besides periodicities of 11 and 50 years, a period of about 21,000 years in the varves of the Green River Epoch.[9] Since this formation is located around 40° latitude, the period could be identified as the mean period of revolution of the line of apsides with reference to the moving equinox. In this respect it would be interesting to see whether at higher latitudes, where the change in the obliquity must be predominant, anything like a period of 41,000 years could be detected.

REFERENCES

1. Simon Newcomb, *Amer. Jour. Sci. and Arts 11* (1876).
2. Ludwig Pilgrim, *Jahreshefte für vaterländische Naturkunde in Württemberg* (1904).
3. J. N. Stockwell, *Smiths. Contr. to Knowledge,* No. 232 (1873).
4. M. Milankovitch, *Canon der Erdbestrahlung* (Belgrade, 1941).
5. D. Brouwer and A. J. J. van Woerkom, *Astr. Papers Amer. Ephemeris,* vol. 13, part 2 (Washington, 1950).
6. Reference 4, p. 544.
7. M. Milankovitch, "Die Chronologie des Pleistocäns," *Bull. Acad. Sci. Math. et Nat. Belgrade 4,* 49 (1938).
8. G. C. Simpson, "Possible causes of change of climate and their limitations," *Proc. Linnean Soc. 152,* 190–219 (1940).
9. W. H. Bradley, "The varves and climate of the Green River Epoch," in *Shorter contributions to general geology* (U. S. Geological Survey, Washington, 1929), pp. 87–119.

12

THE POLAR MOTION AND CHANGES
IN THE EARTH'S ORBIT

Dirk Brouwer

THE ASTRONOMICAL EVIDENCE PRE-
sented in this communication consists of (1) the polar motion
of the earth, and (2) changes in the elements of the earth's orbit.

THE POLAR MOTION

We are concerned with changes in the direction of the axis of rotation
in a coördinate system fixed in the earth. Accurate systematic observations
began in the last decade of the nineteenth century. Küstner in 1888 had
demonstrated the reality of changes in the latitudes of three European
observatories amounting to a few tenths of a second of arc within about
a year. The problem of a motion of the earth's axis that would cause
changes in latitude had been considered theoretically by Euler. On the
assumption of perfect rigidity and rotational symmetry, the path of the
instantaneous pole about the axis of figure is a circle described in $A/(C-A)$
sidereal days, if A, B, and C are the moments of inertia about the principal
axes and $A = B$ on account of the rotational symmetry. The period,
computed from the known value of the rate of precession of the equinoxes,
is 305 days. Chandler's analysis of the observational material showed that
the movement of the pole is a complicated one in which two periods are
present, a period of a year and a period of 14 months. The fact that others,
before Chandler, had looked in vain for a displacement with a period of 10
months caused the delay in the discovery.

It was shown by Newcomb that the lengthening of the free period
from 10 months to 14 months may be ascribed to non-rigidity of the body
of the earth and the presence of the oceans.

The explanation may be presented graphically as follows.[1] Let R
(Fig. 1) be the instantaneous pole of rotation, and P the pole of figure. In
consequence of the rotation about R the pole of figure will be displaced to a point P' on the arc joining R and P. The movement of the pole
of rotation is now an Eulerian movement about P', so that after an
interval dt the pole of rotation moves to R_1. But at that instant P' has

shifted to P_1'. As a consequence of the yielding of the earth, the effective motion of the pole of rotation is still a circular one about P but at a rate reduced in the ratio $P'R/PR = 0.7$.

The annual component of the observed polar motion may be ascribed either to periodic changes in the position of the pole of figure P, caused by displacements of masses in the body of the earth, or to the presence of a periodically varying torque. Of particular interest is the question of a possible progressive motion of the pole. Various determinations have been made. W. D. Lambert found for the years 1900 to 1917 a motion of the North Pole southward along the meridian 87° west at the rate of 0″0062 per annum.[2] For the years 1900 to 1925, B. Wanach finds 0″0047 per

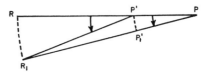

Fig. 1. Motion of the instantaneous pole of rotation R relative to the pole of figure P.

annum along the meridian 42° west.[3] Such displacements, if continued, amount to about 1 second of arc in 200 years. However, later data do not confirm this rate; they indicate that over longer intervals a progressive motion of the mean pole, always in the same direction, does not correspond to the observed facts.

At various times it has been suggested that a relation may exist between the irregular changes in the earth's rate of rotation and the polar motion.

A discussion of the observed changes in the length of the day shows that its principal features are compatible with the assumption that the angular velocity of rotation Ω is affected by cumulative random changes having a standard deviation in $\Delta\,\Omega/\Omega$ amounting to 6×10^{-9} per annum. This value was obtained recently by van Woerkom from a statistical analysis of modern data;[4] a less accurate earlier evaluation by me from the cumulative effect in time over the past 25 centuries gave only one-half this amount.[5]

If the earth rotates as a solid body, the conservation of angular momentum would require that the moment of inertia C be affected by cumulative random changes such that $\Delta\,C/C = -\Delta\,\Omega/\Omega$. The standard deviations in the changes from year to year in the two quantities must then necessarily be the same. It was remarked by W. D. Lambert that there should be corresponding changes in the other moments of inertia and products of inertia, which would affect the motion of the pole. An estimate of the order of magnitude to be expected is easily made by assuming that the changes in C are due to radial movements of masses randomly distributed over the earth's crust. The standard deviation of the annual random displacement of the pole of figure then amounts to $\frac{1}{2}C(C-A)^{-1} \times 6 \times 10^{-9}$ radians $= 10^{-6}$ radians $= 0''.2$. Other hypotheses instead of radial movements may change the factor $\frac{1}{2}$ introduced in this evaluation, but the order of magnitude remains unaltered. If the displacements of the pole accumulate as in a random-walk problem, the mean deviation is proportional to the square root of the time; hence: $2''$ in 100 years, $2000''$ in 10^8 years. In this manner a progressive motion of the pole of the order of $2°$ in 10^9 years could be obtained. This is a maximum estimate. The observed progressive motion of the pole appears to be much smaller, of the order of one-tenth the amount obtained by this computation. If fully substantiated, this result may turn out to be a strong argument against the mechanism used in this evaluation.

Variable motion within the fluid core of the earth has recently been advanced as a possible cause for the variations in the length of the day. The seat of the variations is in the boundary between the fluid core and the mantle. Viscous coupling is negligible, but electromagnetic coupling appears to provide the necessary mechanism. Independently, W. H. Munk and R. R. Revelle at the Institute of Geophysics and the Scripps Institution of Oceanography, University of California,[6] E. H. Vestine of the Department of Terrestrial Magnetism, Carnegie Institution of Washington,[7] and S. K. Runcorn of the Department of Geodesy and Geophysics, Cambridge University,[8] arrived at this conclusion. An important feature of this explanation is that it brings about a connection between the observed changes in the earth's magnetic field and the observed changes in the length of the day. It was shown by Vestine that the varying rate of the westward drift of the earth's magnetic field between 1890 and 1950 is in satisfactory agreement with the changes in the length of the day over the same period.

This attractive theory may account for the remarkable smallness of the observed progressive motion of the pole. It does not compel any upward revision of the conclusion arrived at above that the astronomical evidence is strongly against displacements of the axis of rotation relative to the earth's crust by more than a few degrees at most during the past 10^9 years.

CHANGES IN THE ELEMENTS OF THE EARTH'S ORBIT

In ordinary astronomical practice, expansions in powers of the time suffice. They are adequate for intervals of, say, five or ten centuries. If information over longer intervals of time is desired, a trigonometric expansion is used. The form is

$$e \begin{matrix} \cos \\ \sin \end{matrix} \pi = \sum_{1}^{8} M_j \begin{matrix} \cos \\ \sin \end{matrix} (s_j t + \delta_j),$$

$$\sin I \begin{matrix} \cos \\ \sin \end{matrix} \theta = \begin{matrix} \text{const.} \\ \text{const.} \end{matrix} + \sum_{1}^{7} N_j \begin{matrix} \cos \\ \sin \end{matrix} (s_j' t + \epsilon_j),$$

where e is the eccentricity, π the longitude of the perihelion, I the inclination, θ the longitude of the ascending node of the instantaneous ecliptic; I and θ are referred to a fixed plane; M_j, N_j, s_j, s_j', δ_j, ϵ_j are numerical constants obtained in the solution of the differential equations.

The foregoing results are obtained by the very drastic process of disregarding the periodic terms in the development of the disturbing function and limiting the disturbing function to the quadratic terms in the eccentricities and inclinations.

The system of differential equations for the elements of the principal planets then breaks up into two separate systems, one for $e \cos \pi$, $e \sin \pi$, and one for $\sin I \cos \theta$, $\sin I \sin \theta$. The expressions are linear, homogeneous differential equations of the first order with constant coefficients. A determinant equation furnishes the periods of the individual terms.

A solution for the eight principal planets was made by Stockwell 80 years ago.[9] A new solution was recently made by Dr. van Woerkom and myself.[10] The improvement over Stockwell's results is attained through (1) the use of improved planetary masses, and (2) the evaluation of a second-order effect produced by the great inequality in the motions of Jupiter and Saturn.

Concerning the effect of the great inequality of Jupiter and Saturn, G. W. Hill had shown that the inclusion of this second-order effect causes an appreciable change in one of the periods in the eccentricity-perihelion solution.[11] Stockwell's period is 57,700 years; the revised period is 46,700 years. The term with this period in the eccentricity of the earth has a small coefficient (about 0.003) and the change is therefore not significant. Of more importance is the change in another term also due to the same refinement:

	Period	*Coefficient*
Stockwell	348,700 years	0.01634
New solution	301,700	0.01834

The new representation of the elements of the earth's orbit over long intervals of time, when compared with Stockwell, shows differences up to 30 percent in various terms. Nevertheless, the character of the variations remains the same.

We had hoped to include the effect of Pluto. The difficulty with Pluto is that if the perihelia and nodes of the orbits of Neptune and Pluto are permitted to vary without restriction, the two orbits may intersect. This makes it impossible to obtain a convergent solution by the ordinary procedures. We have made several attempts to avoid the difficulty, but have not yet succeeded. Hence Pluto was left out of the present solution. I am fairly confident that further study of the problem will yield a pleasing and perhaps elegant solution of the difficulty. The effects due to Uranus and Neptune on the earth's orbit are small. The modification due to Pluto will be even smaller.

The procedure used for obtaining long-range changes in the elements of planetary orbits involves a drastic simplification of the mathematical problem of planetary motions. The results obtained are admittedly of a very limited accuracy. What evidence is available to show that the results mean anything at all, and what quantitative or qualitative indication of its reliability can be furnished?

First: The same method has been used with good success in the treatment of satellite systems in which the periods may be shorter by factors of about 10^4. Thus 100 years in such a satellite system may correspond to a million years in the planetary system.

Second: The solution has been applied to the motion of minor planets in which the periods present in the system of the principal planets appear as forced oscillations. The Japanese astronomer Hirayama, using the Stockwell solution, so discovered certain families of minor planets having nearly common secular elements. By means of our new solution it was found that some of these families, especially in the inner part of the ring of minor planets, became more determinate.[12] This application indicates a general reliability to about the third decimal place, but does not indicate anything concerning the interval of time for which the developments may be trusted.

Important modifications of these developments may arise from commensurabilities among the periods of the principal planets. The effect of the principal near commensurability in the system, that between Jupiter and Saturn, was included. The near resonance among Uranus, Neptune, and Pluto may produce some changes in coefficients and periods, but will not seriously affect the solution for the earth.

Next we may consider the effects of near commensurabilities among the periods arising in the expressions for the secular variations. These commensurabilities are troublesome only if a linear combination of two periods with small integers as coefficients is very close to zero. The resulting beat period is then long compared with either of the two periods, perhaps of the order of 100 times one of the shorter periods or about 7×10^6 years. Over an interval of about a million years such commensurabilities will not seriously affect the solution.

The most serious limitation of a practical nature arises from the uncertainties of the periods themselves. These are obtained as functions of the masses and the orbital elements of the planets. They would be modified by the inclusion in the solution of terms of higher powers than the second in the eccentricities and inclinations. If any one of the principal periods should need a correction of 1 percent, it is clear that the contribution due to this particular term would be a full period out of phase after 100 periods. The representation by these series thus becomes less and less reliable as to detail as the interval of time from the epoch increases. If an uncertainty of 1 percent in a period of 70,000 years is a reasonable estimate, as I believe it may well be, then the representation by these series has lost all its meaning as to detail in 7×10^6 years. To sum up, the representation of the elements of the earth's orbit in the simple trigonometric form may be considered to be reliable in detail to two significant figures for approximately a million years in the past or in the future. On account of the uncertainty of the periods involved, the details of the representation become more and more uncertain, the farther the epoch to be considered is removed from the present. Nevertheless, the general character of the representation remains the same even for very distant epochs.

We expect that our current work on the orbits of the principal planets will eventually lead to a more precise solution. For the present, the data used in Dr. van Woerkom's paper are the best we can offer.

REFERENCES

1. W. D. Lambert, "Variation of Latitude," *Bull. Nat. Res. Coun.* No. 78 (1931), pp. 245–277.
2. W. D. Lambert, *Astr. Jour.* 34, 103 (1922).
3. B. Wanach, *Zs. f. Geophysik*, 3, 102 (1927).
4. A. J. J. van Woerkom, *Astr. Jour.* 58, 10–21 (1953).
5. D. Brouwer, *Proc. Nat. Acad. Sci.* 38, 1–12 (1952).
6. W. H. Munk and R. R. Revelle, *Monthly Notices Roy. Astr. Soc. Geoph. Supp.* 6, 331–343 (1952).
7. E. H. Vestine, *Proc. Nat. Acad. Sci.* 38, 1030–1038 (1952).
8. Personal communication.
9. J. N. Stockwell, *Smiths. Contr. to Knowledge*, No. 232 (1873).
10. D. Brouwer and A. J. J. van Woerkom, *Astr. Papers Amer. Ephemeris* 13, pt. 2 (1950).
11. G. W. Hill, *Astr. Jour.* 17, 81–87 (1897); *Coll. Math. Works* (Carnegie Institution, Washington, 1907), vol. 4, pp. 123–135.
12. D. Brouwer, *Astr. Jour.* 56, 9–32 (1951).

13

EVIDENCE FROM GLACIAL GEOLOGY
AS TO CLIMATIC VARIATIONS

Richard Foster Flint

T HE AIM OF MY DISCUSSION IS TO SUM-
marize recent evidence from research in glacial geology that
carries with it climatic implications.

The investigation of glacial phenomena in relation to their climatic
implications falls naturally into two categories: measurements on existing
glaciers, and study of the geologic record of glaciers that have disappeared.

Measurements on existing glaciers extend back only about 100 years.
I summarized the data very briefly in a contribution to the *Compendium
of meteorology*.[1] From the data two inferences emerged. The first is the
existence of a close relation between changes in glaciers and changes in
climate, particularly in temperature, since glacier shrinkage is correlated
with temperature increase. The second inference is the apparent similarity
in the character of glacier variations throughout the world.

FLUCTUATION OF GLACIERS AND SUNSPOT NUMBER

I have little to add to my earlier summary beyond mention of the
recent interesting study by Lawrence,[2] which establishes an apparent
correlation between the fluctuations of outlet glaciers of the Juneau Ice
Field in Alaska and sunspot number. Successive end moraines were approximately dated by means of the growth rings of the oldest trees growing on each, and the dates were found to agree with sunspot minima, as
shown in Stetson's tables, through the measured period, a span of nearly
200 years. Lawrence inferred that at each sunspot minimum each glacier
expanded and built an end moraine.

These results essentially parallel those obtained by Thorarinsson,[3] who
found agreement between sunspot minima and recent minor glacial
expansion. Both sets of data carry the strong implication that there is a
direct connection between one type of solar activity and the fluctuations
of glaciers.

COMPARATIVE EXTENTS OF THE FOUR MAJOR DRIFT SHEETS

Recent additions to knowledge of the stratigraphy of the Pleistocene series support with increasing strength the established view of the glacial sequence in North America. This view is that the sequence is sevenfold, consisting of four principal sheets of glacial drift, separated from each other by weathering profiles, soil zones, and sediments containing organisms, recording thereby nonglacial conditions of probably much longer duration than the glacial times. This sequence is shown in Table 1.

Table 1. Sequence of stages of the Pleistocene series, and of subdivisions of the Wisconsin stage, in North America, in order of superposition.

Stages	Subdivisions
Wisconsin glacial	Mankato Cary Tazewell Iowan (and Farmdale?)
Sangamon interglacial	
Illinoian glacial	
Yarmouth interglacial	
Kansan glacial	
Aftonian interglacial	
Nebraskan glacial	

Through the southern sector of the glaciated region the limits of the four major drift sheets are broadly parallel (Fig. 1) and lie in the vicinity of the 40th parallel of latitude. These relations suggest (1) that the general conditions of origin and growth of the glaciers were much the same during each of the four glacial ages, and (2) that in the southern sector the regimens of the successive ice sheets reached in about the same latitude the equilibrium that ended the phase of expansion and began the phase of shrinkage. It seems that (2) was more likely the result of some threshold meteorologic condition than of periodicity in time.

In this connection at least two factors are discernible in the control of the position of the outer margin of the ice sheet: (1) intensity and duration of climatic influences, such as winter precipitation totals and mean summer temperatures, and (2) topography. The near congruence of the borders of at least two of the drift sheets, around the north and east sides of the Driftless Area in central Wisconsin, is the result of a topographic barrier that opposed glacial encroachment. The reëntrant in all drift borders in western Pennsylvania probably is attributable to the presence of the high Allegheny Plateau, the highest country traversed by the drift border east of the Mississippi River.

Although the drift borders in the southern sector are broadly parallel, they differ in detail. The Kansan drift extends notably beyond the others in Nebraska, Iowa, and Missouri. The Illinoian drift extends beyond the

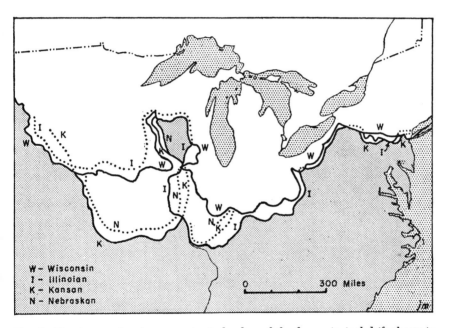

Fig. 1. Sketch map showing approximate borders of the four principal drift sheets in central and eastern United States.

others in Illinois and Indiana. The Wisconsin drift extends beyond the others in the Dakotas. Yet the measurements on glacial striations are consistent with the view that all the successive ice sheets had much the same general directions of flow.

The greatest discrepancy in drift-border position is little more than 200 miles — a small fraction of the radius of the ice sheet — and is possibly related to differences in snow accumulation incidental to the atmospheric circulation pattern. The cause, however, can be considered more effectively by the climatologist than by the geologist.

COMPARATIVE EXTENTS OF THE WISCONSIN SUBSTAGES

The Wisconsin stage, as shown in Table 1, consists of a bundle of glacial-drift sheets deposited by successive advances of the ice sheet. Within the members of the bundle, the names of which are given in Table 1, there are noteworthy differences of extent.

West of the Mississippi River, at least as far west as North Dakota, the Iowan drift is the outermost member, whereas east of the Mississippi, as far as Ohio and probably also in New York and Pennsylvania, the Taze-

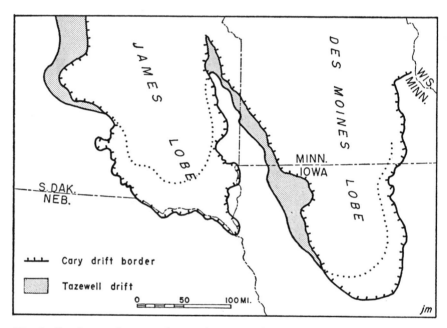

Fig. 2. Sketch map showing relation of Tazewell drift to Cary drift in the James and Des Moines lobes.

well member is the outermost, although there is reason to believe that the Iowan border is not far back underneath it. Differences in meteorologic conditions between the eastern and western regions are implied.

In the two adjacent lobes of Wisconsin drift west of the Mississippi — the Des Moines lobe in Iowa and the James lobe in South Dakota — the Tazewell drift extends beyond the succeeding Cary drift on the west sides, but on the east sides it lies buried beneath the Cary drift (Fig. 2). In this respect the two lobes are virtually duplicates; the repetition of the pattern lends credence to the view that a common cause, presumably meteorologic, is involved.

There is a general relation between the form and the date of a lobe of Wisconsin drift. The older (Iowan and Tazewell) lobes are relatively wide and short, whereas the successively younger Cary and Mankato lobes are longer and progressively narrower. As the lobes occupy broad valleylike depressions, these differences must imply increased control by topography with the passage of time. Presumably such control further implies progressive thinning of at least those parts of the ice sheet that constituted the lobes.

This relation is confirmed by measurements on the flanks of the James lobe in South Dakota, where a lateral moraine marking the lateral margin of the Mankato glacier is traceable for 200 miles along the steep eastern side of the valley that contained the ice. The moraine descends from an altitude of 1850 feet at the northern end to 1400 feet at the southern terminus. On the same highland the Cary drift border lies 50 to 100 feet higher than the Mankato, and the Iowan drift is higher still, but as it covers the highland entirely, it possesses no lateral margin there, and consequently no comparable measurements can be made.

THICKNESS OF THE GLACIER ICE

From the foregoing figures crude data on the thickness of the ice in the James glacial lobe can be inferred. From the base of the Mankato drift beneath the floor of the valley along the axis of the lobe to the lateral moraine along the margin, the vertical distance is of the order of 700 feet near the northern end of the lobe, and much less than 700 feet at the southern end. These values represent a minimum thickness of the ice, but not the true thickness, because the upper surface of the ice was certainly convex-up in cross profile, and the amount of convexity is unknown. Comparison with existing glaciers, however, suggests that the thickness of the Mankato ice along the lobe axis probably was not more than 1000 feet at most.

If we turn to the Lake Michigan glacial lobe, we find that the floor of the lake (presumably consisting of Mankato drift and overlying later sediments) has a minimum altitude of −432 feet. In nearly the same latitude the western border of the Lake Michigan lobe of Mankato drift in eastern Wisconsin is at about 1000 feet. The thickness of the ice was therefore 1432 feet plus the thickness of Mankato deposits beneath the lake floor and plus the difference in altitude between the lateral margin and the axis of the lobe. The actual thickness therefore may have been as much as 2000 feet. In Mankato time, therefore, the Lake Michigan glacial lobe was certainly 1.5 times and very likely twice as thick as the James lobe. Presumably the difference is a function of the same climatic factors that operate today to give the Lake Michigan region a moister climate than the region of the Dakotas.

The accumulating results of the study of glacial striations, and of the transport of rock fragments of known areas of origin in the bedrock, have made it clear that the process of deglaciation, from the Wisconsin glacial maximum to the present, was far more complicated than was formerly believed. The older view visualized the vast Laurentide Ice Sheet as shrinking inward, more or less as a unit, toward northern Quebec and the Hudson Bay region. The newer evidence points to the persistence — or renewal — of local glaciers on highlands in eastern North America after those highlands were uncovered by the main ice sheet.[4]

The highlands on which such local glaciers are inferred to have existed include the Catskill, Adirondack, and White Mountains, Mount Katahdin, the central highlands of New Brunswick, the Shickshock Mountains, highlands in extreme northern New Hampshire and Vermont, the upland of southwestern Nova Scotia, the Cobequid Mountains, highlands north of Quebec City and northwest of Montreal, and mountains in Newfoundland and coastal Labrador.

The inferred conditions on these highlands vary from one mass to another. On some the local glaciers were small and seem to have been quite separate from the main ice sheet. On others the local ice was confluent with the main ice for a time, separating later. On at least one the main ice sheet was succeeded first by an ice cap and later, under warmer conditions, by small cirque glaciers.

Furthermore, as will be mentioned hereafter, the general process of deglaciation was not steady, nor even continuous. In the Great Lakes region there is plain evidence of readvances of the ice-sheet margin. Apparently two of these readvances were of the order of hundreds of miles, measured radially. Farther east, the same readvances can be expected to have been reflected in the local glaciers beyond the main ice sheet, where fluctuations, locally amounting to reincorporations into the main ice sheet, and elsewhere to the renewal of vanished local glaciers, can be deduced with confidence.

The persistence of glacier ice on local highlands during general deglaciation implies that glaciers must have formed on the same highlands during the earlier phases of general glaciation.

In addition to these highland centers in eastern North America, lowland centers can be inferred from striations, from the orientation of hills molded by the flowing ice, and from the transport of rocks of identifiable origin. By lowland centers I mean areas from which glacier ice flowed outward, but which, unlike the eastern centers, are not topographic highs. Evidently the nourishment of glaciers on a highland center was the result of orographic snowfall. Over a lowland center, on the other hand, outward flow would seem to have been accomplished by ice flowing away from a domed area of the ice sheet itself — the dome localized by extra snow accumulation on that area.

Fragmentary evidence of lowland centers is known from various districts from Maine to Saskatchewan, but the data lack sufficient detail, as yet, to permit the reconstruction of a sequence of events. Perhaps the clearest evidence comes from Minnesota, where mutual overlap of glacial drift sheets can be discerned owing to striking differences between the bedrocks of the northeastern and northwestern parts of the state.

From these overlaps it is evident that in Cary time the ice first entered Minnesota from the Rainy Lake district on the north, later from the northwest, and still later from the northeast via the Lake Superior basin. In Mankato time the ice reëntered Minnesota first from the northeast again, via Lake Superior, and later from the northwest.[5] It is evident that the effective center of outflow of ice into Minnesota shifted repeatedly. The shifts may have resulted from changes in the distribution of snow accumulation through periods probably of the order of a very few thousand years.

The available evidence suggests a late center of outflow located on or near the Quebec-Labrador divide. All the centers mentioned are relatively late, dating from the later part of the Wisconsin age. Evidence of earlier centers, of which there were probably many, has been erased by the glacier flow of later times.

STRATIGRAPHY OF THE ILLINOIAN DRIFT

The recent recognition of buried soils in the Loveland (Illinoian) loess in eastern Nebraska records multiple bursts of deposition of wind-blown silt, and therefore probably fluctuations in the Illinoian ice sheet, which is now believed to have touched eastern Nebraska. This recognition parallels the reclassification, by German geologists, of the Warthe drift sheet in Germany. Formerly placed at the base of the Fourth glacial, that drift is now considered to form the highest member of the Third glacial. It parallels also the recognition of two cold phases in the Third glacial (Drenthian) sequence in the Netherlands. Hence there appears to be direct evidence, on both sides of the Atlantic, of the fluctuation of the ice sheets of Third-glacial time. Thus the process of subdivision continues as knowledge becomes more refined, and the implied climatic record becomes correspondingly more complex. It seems likely that the simplicity of the Kansan and Nebraskan stratigraphy is apparent only, and is the result merely of lack of knowledge.

The last few years have witnessed substantial advances, some of them still unpublished, in the subdivision of the Wisconsin stage. My present picture of the sequence is shown in Table 2.

The outstanding dividing line in this sequence is the Brady horizon, because it represents a more conspicuous break than any other within the Wisconsin stage. It consists of a weathering profile, marked by oxidation and leaching, that is substantially better developed than the profiles on

Table 2. Suggested subdivisions of the Wisconsin stage, and suggested dates (before A.D. 1950) calculated from radiocarbon determinations.

Subdivisions	Dates (approximate only)
Present-day conditions	0
"Postglacial" Thermal Maximum	4,000+
Mankato substage	10,000
Two Creeks horizon	11,500
Cary substage	
Brady horizon	>17,000
Tazewell substage	
Iowan substage	

the Cary and Mankato drifts where those drifts lie at the surface. The Brady horizon therefore can be thought of as dividing the Wisconsin substages into two groups.

The lower group consists of the Iowan and Tazewell substages and, if evidence from the loess that fringes the Wisconsin drift border in Illinois is accepted, possibly of a pre-Iowan glacial advance as well. The Iowan and possible pre-Iowan advances were short-lived, and were followed by the Tazewell advance and by later, lesser advances recorded by successive end moraines constituting part of the Tazewell drift sheet. The "Peorian interval," once believed to constitute a conspicuous separation between the Iowan and Tazewell drifts, has been reduced by accumulated evidence to a very short interval marked by the deposition of thin loess and probably by only moderate shrinkage of the ice sheet.

The upper, post-Brady group consists of the Cary and Mankato substages. These glacial members alternate with two nonglacial ones, the Two Creeks and Thermal Maximum horizons, respectively.

Probably the Cary drift represents a radial enlargement of the ice sheet of the order of hundreds of miles, but no direct evidence on the amount of enlargement is known. However, we have some information on the radial enlargement that occurred in Mankato time. In the Lake Michigan basin the Mankato substage represents a glacial readvance of at least 275 miles, and there is reason to believe that in the eastern United States the radial expansion was comparable.

Between the Cary and Mankato substages lies the Two Creeks horizon. This is represented by subarctic-forest peat in Wisconsin, by a low-water phase in the Lake Michigan basin, and possibly by marine deposits, since covered by till, in the Saint Lawrence valley. At this ime the ice margin stood at least as far north as the Strait of Mackinac.

The features here correlated with the Thermal Maximum include (1) marine sediments in the Saint Lawrence valley with fossil organisms implying a climate as warm as or slightly warmer than the present climate in the area, and (2) a low-water phase in the upper Great Lakes.

INFERRED CLIMATIC VARIATIONS DURING THE WISCONSIN AGE

The Wisconsin glacial age is therefore seen to be a time of repeated climatic variation of amplitude sufficient to cause radial lengthening and shortening of the ice sheet of the order of hundreds of miles. An attempt to graph the variations, as far as they have been inferred from the data available, is represented by Fig. 3. The graph is not quantitative, and cannot be, because we lack even approximate time values for all but the latest part of the Wisconsin age, and also because we lack direct evidence of the amplitudes of most of the climatic variations.

The known time values are based on radiocarbon determinations, and are plotted for post-Cary time only. The time values for Cary and pre-Cary events are largely conjectural, controlled only by such crude factors as relative amounts of chemical alteration of deposits, thicknesses of loess between layers of till, and the existence of end moraines. That the successive end moraines associated with any drift sheet record glacial readvances is now almost beyond doubt, but they have not yet been mapped with sufficient accuracy to justify general correlations. Accordingly the graph shows, conventionally, three readvances following the Tazewell, Cary, and Mankato glacial maxima, as an indication that each of those drift sheets is marked by several end moraines. Whatever their number, time must be allowed for these readvances.

The amplitudes of the fluctuations, also necessarily mainly conjectural, are largely relative. In Fig. 3 the horizontal line represents present-day conditions. During the Wisconsin age only two temperature maxima are known probably to have exceeded present-day conditions: the Thermal Maximum and the warm period around the end of the first millenium A.D. The Brady interval may possibly have had maxima exceeding present temperatures, but evidence from the Brady weathering profile is not decisive. The temperature minima (equivalent to the glacial maxima of stratigraphic terminology) are based on the relative radial extents of the various drift sheets in central North America, where major topographic barriers, as a disturbing influence, are at a minimum. As already stated, the fluctuations following the major glacial advances in the Wisconsin age are shown conventionally as series of three. Their relative amplitudes are based on the offlapping positions of the successive end moraines.

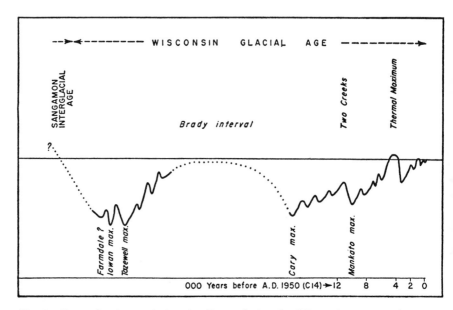

Fig. 3. Curve showing variations in climate during the Wisconsin age, mainly as inferred from glacial-geologic data. Not quantitative; conjectural segments indicated by dotted line.

COMPARISON OF NORTH AMERICAN AND EUROPEAN SEQUENCES

Except for very recent variations (which have been taken from various published sources, derived mostly from European data) the graph of Fig. 3 is based on evidence from North America. It is therefore desirable to see to what extent the American and European stratigraphic sequences and areal extents of drift sheets are comparable.

A somewhat generalized stratigraphic correlation chart for western and northern Europe, with the American sequence for comparison, is shown in Table 3. This chart is a much-simplified version of a chart I elaborated in 1951, as a result of observations and conferences with many European geologists, mainly in the field. Although the knowledge, judgment, and cordial coöperation of many persons have contributed to it, responsibility for the correlations it shows rests with me.

Table 3. Comparison of the subdivisions of the Wisconsin glacial stage in North America with those of the Fourth glacial stage in Europe (generalized), with suggested correlations.

North America	Ireland (S = South; N = North)	Scotland	England	Northern Europe
Thermal Maximum	Thermal Maximum	Thermal Maximum	Thermal Maximum	Thermal Maximum
Mankato	Cirques	Highland Readvance	Windermere Readvance; cirques	Fennoscandian moraines
Two Creeks	Alleröd	Alleröd	Alleröd	Alleröd
Cary	Antrim Coast Readvance (N) Athdown Mountain glaciation	Scottish Readvance	Scottish (Solway) Readvance; Welsh Readvance	Pomeranian
Brady horizon (weathering)	Lough Derg– Carlingford drift border of W. B. Wright (S); Donegal glacial maximum (N)	Peats at Burn of Benholm & Airdrie?	St. Bees peat?	Aurignacian zone (weathering)
Tazewell		General Scottish glaciation	Lake District– Pennine glacial maximum; Hessle till; main Irish-Sea drift	Brandenburg
Iowan Farmdale?	South Irish end moraine of Charlesworth (S); Early Scottish drift (N)		Early Scottish drift; Upper Purple till; main Irish-Sea drift	Pre-Brandenburg

(left margin, rotated) Wisconsin glacial age

(right margin, rotated) Fourth glacial age

Comparison of the American column with the European columns reveals that the two sequences are similar to a remarkable degree. The points of similarity are actually greater than can be shown on a chart, because the intensities of the Brady and Aurignacian weathering zones, the topographic expressions of the several drift sheets (in part a function of time), and the radial extents of the same drifts, are comparable on both continents.

The most satisfactory, because the most exact, evidence of correlation lies in the radiocarbon dates of material collected from the Two Creeks and Alleröd horizons. Five samples from the Two Creeks horizon gave a mean value of 11,400 ± 350 years. Four samples from the pollen-determined Alleröd horizon (from localities in Ireland, England, and Germany) gave a mean value of 10,800 ± 580 years.[6] These values agree very satisfactorily and lend high probability to the identity of Two Creeks with Alleröd. Therefore the Two Creeks – Alleröd horizon can be considered a firmly established key horizon. Its position beneath the Fennoscandian drift rests on such strong indirect evidence that this position is not doubted, despite the fact that no section exposing the two in sequence has yet been discovered. The evidence from pollen profiles and from fossil marine invertebrates records the warming from the time of the Fennoscandian moraines to the Thermal Maximum, with which the Littorina Sea coexisted.

In summary, the evidence presently accumulated strongly implies that the large-amplitude climatic variations during the Fourth glacial age on both sides of the Atlantic Ocean were contemporaneous. If so, the graph (Fig. 3) inferred mainly from North American data applies in general to Europe as well.

With the extension of the time range of radiocarbon dating, and the collection of suitable samples, it should be possible to establish, in addition to the Two Creeks – Alleröd correlation, a second firm transatlantic correlation at the position of the Brady horizon. Such correlation would strengthen the probability that the two sequences are contemporaneous from beginning to end.

SUMMARY OF CLIMATIC IMPLICATIONS

The climatic implications emerging from the foregoing review of recent developments in glacial geology can be summarized in nine statements:

1. There may be a direct relation between variations of glaciers and sunspot number.

2. The broad parallelism and near congruence of the margins of the

glacial drift sheets in central North America suggest that the climatic controls of the origin and growth of the first ice sheet were repeated during subsequent glaciations.

3. Local departures of drift-sheet borders from general parallelism imply local variations in snow supply and possibly therefore in the atmospheric circulation pattern.

4. During the Wisconsin age the ice sheet was much thicker in the Great Lakes region than in the Dakotas. Progressive thinning of the ice sheet during Wisconsin time is likewise indicated.

5. During glaciation, local glaciers formed on many mountains and other highlands in eastern North America coalesced with the general ice sheet, and persisted through varying lengths of time after the shrinking ice sheet had uncovered the highlands.

6. Within the ice sheet itself lowland centers of glacial outflow formed and shifted from place to place, implying changes in the distribution of snowfall on the ice sheet.

7. Apparently the Illinoian glaciation consisted of at least two major pulses in both Europe and North America.

8. The Wisconsin glaciation consisted of at least five or six main glacial advances (plus many minor advances) separated by recessions of which one was outstanding.

9. Close similarity of North American and European events during the Wisconsin (Fourth) glacial age, reinforced by radiocarbon correlation of one horizon, strongly suggests that variations in climate during that age have been contemporaneous on both sides of the Atlantic Ocean.

REFERENCES

(References have been purposely kept to a minimum; those included are cited principally to obviate long explanations in the text. References supporting the new material are cited in other papers in course of publication.)

1. R. F. Flint, "Climatic implications of glacier research," Compendium of Meteorology (American Meteorological Society, Boston, 1951), pp. 1019–1023.

2. D. B. Lawrence, "Glacier fluctuation for six centuries in southeastern Alaska and its relation to solar activity," *Geog. Rev.* 40, 191–223 (1950).

3. Sigurdur Thorarinsson, "Present glacier shrinkage, and eustatic changes of sea-level," *Geograf. Ann.* 22, 131–159 (1940).

4. R. F. Flint, "Highland centers of former glacial outflow in northeastern North America," *Geol. Soc. Amer. Bull.* 62, 21–38 (1951).

5. H. E. Wright, unpublished.

6. R. F. Flint and E. S. Deevey, Jr., "Radiocarbon dating of late-Pleistocene events," *Amer. Jour. Sci.* 249, 261–267 (1951).

7. Matti Sauramo, "The mode of the land upheaval in Fennoscandia during

Late-Quaternary time," *Soc. Géol. de Finlande Comptes Rendus*, no. 13, Fig. 1, p. 4; *Comm. Geol. de Finlande Bull.* no. 125, p. 39–63.

8. Gordon Manley, "The snowline in Britain," *Geograf. Ann.*, 1949, p. 190.

ADDITIONAL

Frank Leverett, *Quaternary geology of Minnesota and parts of adjacent States* (U. S. Geological Survey, Professional Paper 161, 1932). Reviewed by W. A. Johnston in *Geogr. Rev.* 23, 346–347.

14

GEOLOGIC EVIDENCE OF
LATE PLEISTOCENE CLIMATES*

John T. Hack

Geomorphologists are becoming increasingly interested in the climatic controls of deposition and erosion. In the early part of this century, especially in America, the land forms of nonglaciated regions were studied primarily as indicators and measures of changes of level and diastrophism. Today the viewpoint has changed and the relation of climate to land forms is a major concern of geomorphology. We now agree that climate is a controlling factor in erosion and deposition. We are experimenting with new ideas and new applications of this concept, but the stage of evaluation and synthesis has hardly been reached. In Europe, on the other hand, the hypothesis of climatic control is accepted by many workers and the body of data on climatically controlled land forms is large enough to enable European geologists to make a significant contribution to the paleoclimatology of the Pleistocene epoch.

The rapidly growing literature in this field, far too voluminous to be reviewed here, indicates not only a growing interest but the large amount of data available. This subject has been reviewed by Smith.[1] Some of the work subsequent to 1949 is summarized by Taillefer,[2] and Büdel[3] discusses recent work in Germany. A series of papers on "periglacial morphology" by Taillefer,[4] Alimen,[5] Baeckeroot,[6] Guillien,[7] Enjalbert,[8] and Cavaillé[9] appears in one issue of the *Revue Géographique des Pyrénées et du Sud-Ouest*. In America, current work on Pleistocene and Recent frost action includes papers by Washburn,[10] Denny,[11] and Peltier.[12, 13] A study of the climatic significance of ventifacts in an area in Wyoming has been published by Sharp.[14]

The geologic evidence of Pleistocene climates is a field of study in which the stratigraphic method, by which geologic features are commonly related in time, is difficult to use because of the scarcity of fossils and

* Review of a paper by Büdel on the climate of Europe during the Würm stage. Publication authorized by the Director, United States Geological Survey.

because much of the evidence occurs on or near the surface of the ground. We cannot wait for a solution of all the basic problems of geomorphology before we attempt to interpret any of the evidence. One of the best methods of progressing is to attempt a synthesis of the available data to determine whether it will stand the scrutiny of specialists in our own as well as related fields, particularly meteorology and paleoecology.

This review offers a summary of a recent paper by Büdel [15] which contains many useful ideas, possibly new to American geologists, and is well deserving of careful reading. Büdel summarizes the European data and presents a map of Europe for the Würm maximum showing five climatic, geomorphic provinces north of the temperate forest border.

SUMMARY OF BÜDEL'S CONCEPT

Büdel believes that climatic fluctuations during the cold periods of the Pleistocene resulted in a shifting of climatic zones equatorward, but that their boundaries remained essentially parallel to those of today. The Pleistocene ice sheets were entirely a result of climatic change and not a cause, either primary or secondary. He pictures the Würm beginning with a cold moist climate, followed by a cold dry climate during the stand of the ice at its maximum. The cold dry climate was followed by a rather sudden change to a warm climate that preceded and persisted during the retreat of the ice mass. The argument begins with maps showing the altitudes of the snow line (isochionen or "isonives") of both the present and the Würm glaciation. By comparison of these maps Büdel is able to locate the July isotherms of the Würm. The 10°5C isotherm (Würm), reduced to sea level, corresponds to the northern limit of the forest (tree line) and extends across Europe from the mouth of the Gironde River along the northern margin of the Alps, as shown in Fig. 1. This line is not parallel to the margin of the continental ice sheet but is 1000 km south of it in France and gradually approaches it to the east, joining the ice sheet in Russia. Obviously the climatic zones of the Würm were not centered around the ice masses. The colder climate of the Würm glaciation displaced the climatic zones equatorward in belts generally parallel to those of today.

By reconstructing the 10°5C July isotherm of the Würm stage, with irregularities due to orographic control, Büdel outlines the southern limit of the tundra regions. He further subdivides Europe into smaller regions based in part on a synthesis of paleobotanical data and in part on the distribution of loess, as shown in Fig. 2. Contrary to the views of many Pleistocene geologists, he argues that the loess is itself an indicator of the distribution of certain climatic elements. Although source areas for wind-blown silt were widespread in Europe, the silt could not form a continuous ground cover except in areas of dense grassy and herbaceous vegetation, where the closely spaced vertical stems fixed the silt and protected it from deflation and erosion. Such grassy areas existed in two regions, (1) the tundra region of western Europe poleward from the 10°5 July isotherm and (2) the steppe areas of eastern Europe south

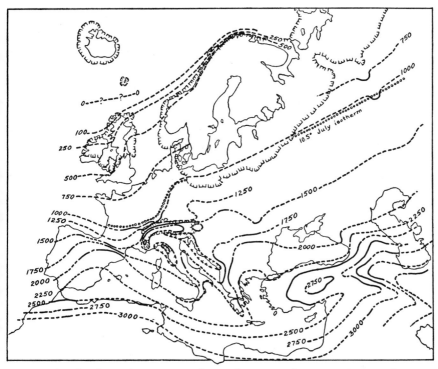

Fig. 1. Altitude of snow line in meters during the Würm glaciation in Europe, the Near East, and North Africa, after M. Brusch and J. Büdel. Interval between isonives is 250 meters. Circles indicate position of Würm 10°5C July isotherm (reduced to present sea level). Broken, hatched line indicates position of ice border at Würm maximum. Redrawn, with some information omitted, from *Die Naturwissenschaften 36*, 107 (1949).

of the 10°5 isotherm, where the border of the continuous forest was far south of the tree line because of insufficient moisture. Thus the loess areas form an enormous wedge-shaped area widening eastward from western France to the Carpathian Basin and the plains of Russia. It crosses the Würm 10°5 July isotherm (or tree line) in central Europe. The loess area north of the tree line Büdel calls the loess tundra. The loess area of eastern Europe south of the tree line he calls the loess steppe. Some moister areas south of the tree line contained scattered areas of

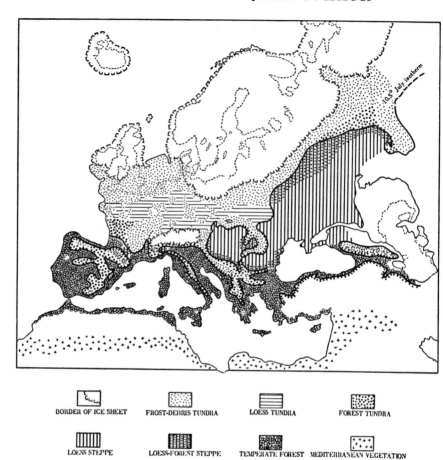

Fig. 2. Map of climatic zones in Europe during the Würm glaciation, after J. Büdel.

Frost-debris tundra: Zone of intense frost action and solifluction bordering the ice sheet. Deflation prevents eolian deposition.

Loess tundra: Loess-covered region on the poleward side of the tree line (10°.5C July isotherm). Loess deposition exceeds frost action and deflation. Dense, grassy, and herbaceous vegetation. No analogous regions in the present arctic.

Forest tundra: The tundra region nearest the tree line. Primarily in moist areas. Dense tundra vegetation with numerous groves of trees. Strong frost action and solifluction and no eolian deposition.

Loess steppe: Region of complete loess cover south of the tree line. Because of dryness, trees are scant. Dense herbaceous and grassy vegetation with vertical stems. Tree pollen makes up 15 percent of total pollen present.

Loess-forest steppe: Region of incomplete loess cover south of the tree line. Trees more abundant than in the loess steppe; they make up 50 percent of the pollen present. This is a moist marginal area of the loess steppe, occurring especially in areas bordering the mountains or the poleward limit of trees.

Temperate forest: Principally pine, birch, and willow, with larch and mountain pine in cooler areas, and "delicate" broad-leaved trees in warmer areas.

Mediterranean vegetation: The area of mediterranean vegetation is not closely defined.

Redrawn with some information omitted from *Die Naturwissenschaften 36,* 109 (1949).

forest, especially in northern Russia, marginal to the steppe, where loess was deposited in a discontinuous blanket. These areas form a third loess zone, the loess-forest steppe.

On the poleward side of the loess tundra, the climate was intensely cold; vegetation was scant, and intense frost action, solifluction, and deflation prevented the deposition and the retention of loess. This area forms a zone called the frost-debris tundra (Frostschutt-tundra). Another climatic zone existed in some areas north of and marginal to the tree line (10°5 July isotherm) where the climate was sufficiently warm and moist for trees to grow in scattered areas in which loess deposition was inhibited. This zone Büdel calls the forest tundra. Thus five climatic-morphologic zones, each with characteristic geologic as well as biologic features, are distinguished between the ice sheets and the temperate forest, which was displaced far southward to the Mediterranean region.

The boundaries between these climatic zones were closely related to altitude, as are the climatic boundaries of today, and Büdel describes the loess area of mountainous central Germany in support of this thesis. Below an altitude of 300 meters in the Weser country, for example, the loess is thick on the slopes. Above this altitude it is absent, but there is abundant evidence of frost action. The dividing line is marked by interbedding and mixing of solifluction debris and loess.

The dune systems in northern Germany, Poland, and Hungary, which are assumed to be contemporaneous with the Würm maximum, according to Büdel, offer additional evidence of the nature of the Würm climate. The dune sands were moved presumably only during the strong winds produced by a pattern of frontal storms similar to that of today. In this conclusion Büdel differs from Poser,[16] who believes that the wind directions shown by these ancient dune systems indicate a strong anticyclonic area over the melting Alpine ice cap.

In the second part of his paper, Büdel discusses the chronology of the Würm deposits in relation to climate. Two important generalizations are the following. (1) The Würm loess of western Europe as well as the Würm glacial drift are underlaid by abundant evidence of intense frost action, but on top of them evidence of such action is mostly lacking. (2) The Würm drift completely lacks a cover of loess and the loess is confined to an area considerably south of the terminal moraine. This indicates that during the advance of the ice the climate was cold and wet; during the maximum stand it was cold and dry, permitting the deposition of extensive areas of loess. Before the withdrawal of the ice the climate ameliorated to a warm moist phase, so that neither loess deposition nor intense frost action occurred on the surface of the terminal and retreatal moraines.

CRITIQUE OF BÜDEL'S CONCEPT

Büdel's synthesis, which is rich in many ideas not reviewed here, harmonizes diverse pieces of evidence in an ingenious manner and emphasizes many relations between the phenomena to be explained. That such a synthesis can be attempted so successfully is indicative to us of the great progress being made in Europe in this field. Nevertheless, many geologists will disagree heartily with some of the concepts presented. The major difficulty, it seems to me, is that we do not yet have sufficient understanding of the processes of erosion, weathering, and deposition to be able to interpret clearly their relation to climate. One of the most controversial of Büdel's ideas is perhaps that the deposition of loess in western Europe was favored by a certain climatic environment and was related to certain vegetation zones. At least this idea serves as an example of the complexity of the problem.

It is agreed by many who believe in the eolian origin of loess that the loess areas require only a suitable source of loess, free of vegetation, so that silt can be picked up by the wind and transported to leeward; the vegetation growing on the place of deposition does not affect the distribution appreciably. Work done by Benninghoff, Hopkins, and Péwé, of the United States Geological Survey in Alaska, indicates that wind-blown silt derived from floodplains is carried to high altitudes and is deposited as thick deposits in heavily forested areas (oral communication). Wind-blown silt in Alaska is discussed also in papers by Péwé [17] and Black.[18]

Unfortunately the term loess, although originally a descriptive term, has come to have a genetic significance and is now used by many geologists as synonymous with eolian silt. This evolution of the term has been accompanied by considerable controversy, generated in part probably by misunderstanding. The loess of the Eurasian steppes and the loess of the upper Mississippi Valley and the Great Plains are considered by most geologists to be wind-deposited silt. There has been more controversy over the loess in the more humid regions, high-lighted recently in North America by R. J. Russell's critical discussion and loessification theory for the lower Mississippi Valley loess.[19-21] There is certainly no question that silty deposits closely resembling eolian silt are deposited by streams, in lakes, and even in marine environments as primary sediments. Furthermore, eolian silt may be eroded and redeposited a long distance away and still preserve many of its primary eolian characteristics. Aqueous deposits, though originally stratified, may lose all traces of bedding. Jahns [22] shows in a valuable paper on the Connecticut Valley in Massachusetts that the loess of that valley consists only in part of wind-blown material. Stratified floodplain silts of the terraces pass upward into material of the same composition and texture that is devoid of stratification and has been modified by secondary processes.

The difficulty of interpreting the origin of silt from its texture alone is illustrated by Fig. 3, which presents a comparison of mechanical analyses of loess and loesslike sediments of the lower Mississippi Valley with water-laid silts, including a flood silt from the Potomac River floodplain and an estuarine silt from the fishweir site at Boylston Street in

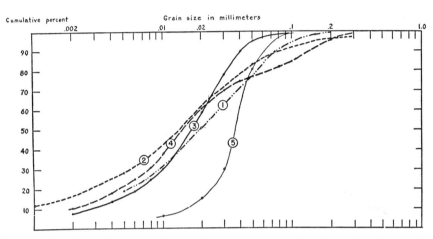

Fig. 3. Cumulative frequency diagram showing mechanical analyses of various sediments with high silt content. (1) Flood deposit of Potomac River.[23] (2) Estuarine silt from the Boylston Street fishweir site, Boston, Mass.[24] (3) Loess from Sicily Island, Louisiana.[25] (4) Loesslike material from terrace in northeastern Louisiana.[26] (5) Peorian loess believed to be eolian from Menard County, Illinois, NW¼ sec. 17, T. 19 N., R. 7 W.[27]

Boston, Massachusetts. An analysis of eolian loess (number 5) from Illinois is included for comparison. This is the only one of the five analyses that is distinct from the others.

My own work in Maryland, on which a report is in preparation, shows that an area of more than 1000 square miles west of Chesapeake Bay is mantled with massive deposits of loamy silts, in some places more than 10 feet thick, that are almost identical in composition with the flood deposits of the present Potomac River. The silts are confined to areas on top of gravel deposits, although in some places below the uplands they are intermixed with gravels. There is abundant evidence that the silt for the most part is of fluviatile origin but on the lowest terraces is of estuarine origin. Eolian activity may have deposited minor amounts. These deposits have been described as loesslike, though they do not resemble the upper

Mississippi Valley loess mechanically and are characteristically poorly sorted except in the A horizon of the soil.

Examination of the geologic map of the Leine River Valley in central Germany (Göttingen sheet, Geologische Uebersichtskarte von Deutschland, 1921, scale 1:200,000) shows that the loess occurs only on the flatter slopes of this narrow valley, and has a boundary which over large areas is remarkably close to the 200-meter contour. The boundary appears too close to the contour to be a climatic boundary. Furthermore, the boundary rises to the same altitude on both sides of the valley and suggests that the loess is water-laid.

Büdel does not discuss critically the origin of the loess in western Europe, but he implies that most or all of it is generally accepted as of eolian origin. I wonder if the loess of his "loess tundra" may not have a far more complex origin and if it is not quite a different sort of deposit from the loess of his "loess-steppe." Nevertheless it is evident that, whatever its origin, this material has a significant pattern of distribution in Europe. In North America east of the Mississippi Valley, loess has not been described except for isolated occurrences of thin eolian deposits. However, a zone of intense frost action borders the Wisconsin ice sheet in Pennsylvania and New Jersey, analogous to Büdel's frost-debris tundra. (The frost phenomena in Pennsylvania have been described by Denny [11] and by Peltier.[12, 13] Involutions, ventifacts, and other evidence of cold climate were observed in central New Jersey at a conference of the "Friends of Pleistocene Geology" conducted by Dr. Paul MacClintock in 1949.) Perhaps we have overlooked a zone of loess or loesslike deposits that have significant geographic limits farther south. Perhaps the weathering processes associated with intense cold may be a primary source of large quantities of silty material.

Another of Büdel's concepts that is controversial is the postulate of a sudden change in climate from cold-dry to warm-moist, which brought about the retreat of the ice and the cessation of loess deposition. We know that the Scandinavian ice sheet as well as the North American ice sheets had several periods of readvance during their retreat and that these were separated by relatively warm periods. This history does not suggest sudden change to a climatic regimen entirely different from that which prevailed during the maximum ice stand. In central North America and in Russia, where climates are drier than in northern Germany, there is evidence of loess deposition during the retreat from the Wisconsin maximum.[28] Does this fact also suggest a somewhat different mechanism for the deposition of the loess in the humid regions?

My discussion of Büdel's ideas concerning the loess is not intended as an unfavorable criticism. The extent of our knowledge of geologic processes is still so limited and so qualitative that any far-reaching conclusions concerning the importance or nature of climatic factors are necessarily controversial. The making of the synthesis is in itself a great step forward, as it serves to point out the areas in which more study is needed, and its discussion becomes a meeting place for the many specialists concerned with this field.

REFERENCES

1. H. T. U. Smith, "Physical effects of Pleistocene changes in nonglaciated areas; eolian phenomena, frost action, and stream terracing," *Geol. Soc. Amer. Bull. 60*, 1485–1516 (1949).

2. F. Taillefer, "Travaux de synthèse récents sur la période glaciaire," *Rev. Géog. des Pyrénées et du Sud-Ouest 22*, 218–222 (1951).

3. J. Büdel, "Neue Wege der Eiszeitforschung," *Erdkunde 3*, 82–96 (1949).

4. F. Taillefer, "Le modèle periglaciaire dans le Sud du Bassin d'Aquitaine," *Rev. Géog. des Pyrénées et du Sud-Ouest 22*, 113–123 (1951).

5. H. Alimen, "Actions périglaciaires et sols sur le versant nord-pyrénéen en Bigorre," *Rev. Géog. des Pyrénées et du Sud-Ouest 22*, 124–136 (1951).

6. G. Baeckeroot, "Formes de cryergie quaternaire en Montagne Noire occidentale," *Rev. Géog. des Pyrénées et du Sud-Ouest 22*, 137–153 (1951).

7. Yves Guillien, "Les grèzes Litées de Charente," *Rev. Géog. des Pyrénées et du Sud-Ouest 22*, 154–162 (1951).

8. H. Enjalbert, "Les vallées sèches et les vallées tourbeuses du Bassin aquitain septentrional," *Rev. Géog. des Pyrénées et du Sud-Ouest 22*, 163–198 (1951).

9. A. Cavaillé, "Les sols de boulbène de l'Aquitaine et les climats quaternaires," *Rev. Géog. des Pyrénées et du Sud-Ouest 22*, 199–206 (1951).

10. A. L. Washburn, "Patterned ground," *Rev. Can. de Geog. 4*, 5–54 (1950).

11. C. S. Denny, "Pleistocene frost action near the border of the Wisconsin drift in Pennsylvania," *Ohio Jour. Sci. 51*, 116–125 (1951).

12. L. C. Peltier, "Pleistocene terraces of the Susquehanna River, Pennsylvania," *Penn. Topog. and Geol. Serv. Bull. G-23* (1949).

13. L. C. Peltier, "The geographic cycle in periglacial regions as it is related to climatic geomorphology," *Annals Assoc. Amer. Geographers 50*, 214–236 (1950).

14. R. P. Sharp, "Pleistocene ventifacts east of the Big Horn Mountains, Wyoming," *Jour. Geol. 57*, 175–194 (1949).

15. J. Büdel, "Die räumliche und zeitliche Gliederung des Eiszeitklimas," *Naturwiss. 36*, 105–112, 133–139 (1949).

16. H. Poser, "Aolische Ablagerungen und Klima des Spätglazials in Mittel- und Westeuropa," *Naturwiss. 35*, 269–276 (1948).

17. T. L. Péwé, "An observation on wind-blown silt," *Jour. Geol. 59*, 399–401 (1951).

18. R. F. Black, "Eolian deposits of Alaska," *Jour. Arctic Inst. No. Amer. 4*, 89–111 (1951).

19. R. J. Russell, "Lower Mississippi Valley loess," *Geol. Soc. Amer. Bull. 55*, 1–40 (1944).

20. M. M. Leighton and H. B. Willman, "Loess formations of the Mississippi Valley," *Jour. Geol. 58*, 599–623 (1950).

21. H. N. Fisk, "Loess and Quaternary geology of the lower Mississippi Valley," *Jour. Geol. 59*, 333–356 (1951).

22. R. H. Jahns, "Geologic features of the Connecticut Valley, Massachusetts, as related to recent floods," *U. S. Geological Survey Water-Supply Paper* 996 (1947).

23. G. R. Mansfield, "Flood deposits of the Ohio River, January-February, 1937, a study of sedimentation," *U. S. Geological Survey Water-Supply Paper* 838 (1939), p. 728, sample P-1.

24. S. Judson, "The Pleistocene stratigraphy of Boston, Massachusetts, and its relation to the Boylston Street fishweir," *Papers of the Peabody Foundation for Archaeology 4*, 7–48 (1949), p. 30, sample 9.

25. Reference 19, p. 4, sample 3.

26. Reference 19, p. 4, sample 5.

27. G. D. Smith, "Illinois loess – variations in its properties and distribution," *University of Illinois Agricultural Experiment Station Bulletin* 490 (1942).

28. R. F. Flint, *Glacial geology and the Pleistocene epoch* (Wiley, New York, 1947), pp. 249–250, 330.

15

PEDOGENIC CRITERIA OF
CLIMATIC CHANGES

C. C. Nikiforoff

I{N SOIL SCIENCE THERE ARE TWO}
principal schools — agronomic, to which the majority of soil
students belong, and geochemical, which is represented by a rather small
minority of the whole body. The basic concepts and definitions of soil by
these two schools are naturally different. The soil of agropedologists is
first of all the natural medium for the growth of plants. The main concern
of this school is soil-and-plant relations. "Productivity" stands high among
essential features which collectively define the soil. The soil of the second
school is just an excited integument of the outermost thermodynamic
geochemical shell, which consists largely of four elements — oxygen,
silicon, aluminum, and iron.

This last definition of soil is not particularly informative. A few other
statements about soil may help to crystallize the basic concept. The first
and foremost of these statements is that soil is not static. It is a dynamic
system. By soil dynamics is understood the totality of movements that are
continuously taking place in this body as long as it exists. Some movements are fast, others are geologically slow. They range from the movements of individual ions in the lattice of clay minerals to the movements
that result in transportation from the continents into the ocean of billions
of metric tons of dissolved matter per year. Hence, some movements
cover the distance of a few angstroms, whereas others cover many miles.

Every movement is a change of place or position and represents a
certain quantity of work which consumes energy. The soil system operates
and uses energy continuously throughout geologic time, but it is not a
"perpetuum mobile." It steadily consumes energy and must be recharged.
Without such a recharging it would cease to operate and would either
deteriorate or become a mummy.

Soil is charged with energy from the surface by the incoming solar
radiation and from below by outgoing terrestrial energy generated by
atomic decay of radioactive elements in the earth's crust. This continuous

recharging of the earth's skin with energy is the cause of the permanently excited state of such a skin; and such a state, in turn, is the foremost characteristic that defines the geochemical nature of the soil.

The second statement about soil is that operation of the soil or its dynamics is a function of the environment, the latter being a certain combination of physiographic conditions, including the kind of initial material, the land form, the climate, and the biologic pressure. Usually, although somewhat incorrectly, it is postulated that soil itself is a function of the environment. Emphasis in this definition is made on the word function. Soil is a function of the environment rather than a product of it. The term product has some connotation of finality. After being finished, the product no longer depends upon the technological process by which it has been brought into being. It may exist and, perhaps, operate irrespective of whether or not the process by which it has been created continues to work. Function, on the other hand, is an entity only as long as its determinants are operative. It changes with every change in the factors on which it depends and vanishes when these factors cease to exist. Hence, dynamic soil is inseparable from its environment. Taken away from its natural place, it ceases to be a dynamic system. A soil sample brought into the laboratory does not represent the soil any better than a piece of dry wood represents a living tree.

A logical conclusion from the discovery of functional relations between soils and the environmental factors was that soils are not fixed formations but are capable of readjustment to the changing conditions under which they exist. It has been postulated by Kossovich that soils which exist now could have been different in the past and might change again in the future, although the changeability of soils was clearly conceived earlier by Dokuchaev. Thus, it has been established that soils are capable of evolutional changes or evolutional development.

There is an ever-present danger when one discipline borrows concepts or only terms from other sciences. From the biological sciences the soil scientists first borrowed the term "evolution" and soon afterward adopted the underlying concept. Now, if evolution implies the development of new and more highly organized forms and species, then it may or may not apply to soils. Soils are capable of changes, but whether these changes lead to the development of new and higher soil species is still an open question. Space does not permit me to go into a detailed analysis of the theory of autogenic evolution or changes in soils independent of changes in the environment and due only to the time factor. I must mention, however, that many soil geneticists share such ideas, which put particularly strong emphasis on time as the fifth essential component of the environment of soil evolution.

The other view is that soil evolution consists merely of endless readjustments of the soil systems to changes in climate, relief, conditions of its parent material, and vegetation. Changes in climate do not imply development of some peculiar new climates that did not exist before. In all geological times, there were cold and warm, humid and dry climates, and their extremes presumably did not change much throughout geological history. Hence, changes in climate refer essentially to changes in geographical pattern of climates and relocations of climatic boundaries, with individual climatic types remaining fairly constant.

The same holds true as regards the "evolution" of land forms. Mountains and valleys, plateaus and lowlands existed throughout most of geological history with the exception of the little known childhood of the globe. Again, there are no traces of gradual perfection of land forms from one period to another.

If we turn our attention to the soil's parent material, we meet the same situation. The same minerals, in the same paragenetic systems, are attacked by the same physical and chemical agencies and are altered in the same general ways to yield the same secondary atomic structures. Clays and sands that form now do not differ from those that were formed in Mesozoic or Paleozoic times. Hence, there is now no specific type of weathering that would not have operated in the past.

Only in the biosphere does one see marked qualitative changes with time. I emphasize the term "qualitative changes," because the amount of life on our planet, in all likelihood, has been fairly constant throughout a very considerable part of geologic history. Probably this quantity is a geochemical and geophysical constant. Again, I exclude the earliest stages of the existence of the earth. Thus, of all major factors of so-called soil evolution, only life could affect significant qualitative changes in the general character of soils. That is to say, for example, that the present forest soils might be unlike the forest soils of the Carboniferous or any of the Mesozoic periods. This problem, however, is entirely academic. Modern forms of plant life, particularly the generic composition of forests and prairies, deserts and tundras, were already in existence in the earlier part of the Cenozoic era and it is improbable that any recognizable paleopedogenic record of greater antiquity would survive. In fact, it is doubtful that any pedogenic fossil older than early Pleistocene could be sufficiently preserved to be of value for tracing the ways of soil evolution.

It follows that as far back as evolution of soils might be traced all principal lithologic, geomorphic, climatic, and biotic factors of soil formation were essentially the same as they are now. Therefore, the general character of soils could not be much different during any particular part of this period. Then, what is the meaning of soil evolution?

Obviously, the term soil evolution may refer merely to the never-ending changes in the pattern of geographic distribution of various soils in respect to one another. Thus the postulate of Kossovich should be reworded to read that any area which is occupied now by certain soils could have been occupied by different soils in the past and might be occupied by still other soils in the future. This does not imply that the old soils which have occupied this area, say in middle Pleistocene, are now wholly extinct and that similar soils do not exist in some other regions. In other words, neither in the past stages of evolution, throughout at least the later part of the Cenozoic, were there peculiar soils which do not exist now, nor are there now some ultramodern soils which did not exist — let us be conservative — during any stage of the Pleistocene. Soils, as we know them now, belong to all geologic times, although the pattern of their distribution throughout the land is subject to continuous slow change.

Now, one may inquire into the nature of these changes which affect the soil of some particular area. Being merely the function of its environment, the soil of any given area acquires a distinct individuality. This individuality is expressed by the soil profile, which is determined by a set of physical and chemical characteristics. The latter are imparted to the soil in the process of alteration of the initial material by the agencies of the environment. Therefore, there is a fairly close correlation between these characteristics, or their summation in the soil profile, and the elements of the environment in which this profile is being acquired.

In the process of evolutional changes of the soil various characteristics that could have been imparted to this soil during earlier stages of its evolution gradually fade away, being replaced by some other characteristics. At least one case of such a reworking of the soils is believed to be fairly well established. It is the degradation of the grassland soil under forest vegetation, a process accompanying the encroachment of forest upon the prairie. In this process, practically all external characteristics of the original soil are lost and its profile is thoroughly reshaped.

The next question asks how drastic such evolutional changes of the soil might be. Is it possible that various characteristics which have been imparted to the soil in earlier stages of its development could be entirely obliterated so that no traces of these earlier stages would be carried over to the later stages? In order to answer this question one should inquire into the nature of these various soil characteristics as well as into how and why they have been acquired by the soil.

The first thing to be remembered is that not all peculiarities of the soil profile are due to pedogenic alterations of the parent materials. A great many of these features are due to the stratification of geological bodies which have subsequently acquired a pedogenic skin. In all such cases, the pedogenic profile is superimposed upon the original geologic profile. Various layers of finely stratified sediments may differ from one another in essentially the same characteristics as the genetic soil horizons, as, for example, in mineralogical and mechanical composition, in texture, color, or consistence. Rightly or wrongly, the building up of the deposits is not considered a part of the pedogenic process. The latter consists of the alteration of the deposits by atmospheric and biotic agencies. Such an alteration may or may not be interfered with by the mechanical processes of either up-building of the deposits or normal, geologic sheet erosion.

The principal difference between genetic soil horizons and mechanical layers of the stratified deposits is that pedogenic horizons in every natural soil represent a definite system of paragenetic units, while various layers of stratified materials may or may not relate to one another. Each layer might be formed at a different time, probably from different source material, and usually by different agencies. One layer might be spread by running water, another by wind, and still another by creeping ice.

Strictly pedogenic characteristics of soil may be divided into three general groups according to their being inherited, acquired, or introduced. Inherited characteristics of the soil are those properties of the initial material which could not be obliterated or altered by the pedogenic process in the course of remodeling of such material into the soil. Acquired soil characteristics are those which were not possessed by the initial material, but were imparted to it through the pedogenic process. And finally, introduced characteristics are those which were neither present in the initial material nor acquired by the soil in the natural process of its development, but were imparted to the soil somewhat artificially, especially by the agricultural practices of men. Of course, no sharp lines of demarcation between these three groups exist. Some characteristics are partly inherited and partly acquired; others were originally introduced and later became acquired. Still others were acquired during the earlier stages of evolution of the soil and became inherited by the soil in subsequent stages of development. In other words, inherited soil characteristics derive not only from the initial source material, but also from the earlier stages of evolution.

Presently we are interested especially in the last group or subgroup of soil characteristics, that is, characteristics which could have been acquired by the soil during the earlier stages of its evolution and passed on to the later stages. The mere existence of such characteristics indicates that the possibility of evolutional changes of soils is limited and, hence, that the general assumption that soils are not fixed formations is not absolute. At least some acquired characteristics are inheritable, Naturally, these characteristics should be ones that are sufficiently resistant to alterations; some of them, perhaps, are wholly irreversible. Irreversibility of acquired characteristics, whether total or partial, indicates a certain degree of fixation of these characteristics. Collectively, these peculiar characteristics represent what may be conceived as a sort of soil memory, or ability of the soil to remember what has happened to it in the past.

Now, how can these peculiar characteristics be recognized? How can these pedogenic records be deciphered? All such identifications and interpretations are based essentially on the assumption that certain features are not in harmony with their present environment. Lack of harmony between the would-be causes (environment) and would-be consequences (some out-of-place features) naturally leads to the conclusion that the present "causes" are working on "consequences" of other causes which no longer exist, and that some of these inherited consequences prove to be quite indigestible. It is essentially the same principle that was employed in the reconstruction of Pleistocene events on the basis of inherited morainic records.

That certain observable characteristics of the soil are not in harmony with their present environment is just an assumption which may or may not be correct. In some instances, what appears now as lack of harmony might be just our own failure to see the facts in their proper perspective and comprehend their proper coördination. Therefore, the principle, which is basically sound, should be employed with great care. Unfortunately, this is not always the case.

Conclusions about the misfit of certain integral parts in the soil systems are based on comparative studies of contemporary soils developed in different environments. In these studies every attempt is made to examine the functional significance and the mode of development of individual properties in which soils of various regions differ, and to find the relation between each property and some specific aspect of the environment that could cause and condition its development. In this way, it is hoped that eventually we might learn enough about soils to be able to use their characteristics as indicators of certain conditions under which these characteristics are being or could have been imparted to the soil.

Postulating that soil is a function of the environment, we postulate that everything essential to the make-up of the soil is a function of the environment. In other words, every dynamic characteristic of the active soil is individually a function of the environment; and — as such — it is a definite entity only in its particular environment, outside of which it either changes or vanishes altogether. Exceptions to this rule are possible only because of the inherent irreversibility of certain characteristics or subsequent fixation of others.

Formation of hardpans due to cementation of certain parts of the soil body by various substances, such as colloidal silica, iron hydroxides, gypsum, or lime, is, probably, the commonest form of fixation. Silica-cemented hardpans probably represent a partial petrification or fossilization of the soil, similar to the petrification of wood. Hardpans are not a rarity. Some hardpans are of very considerable thickness. We do not know, however, of a single case of fossilization of the whole soil body.

Another form of fixation of soil characteristics is due to a thorough sterilization of the soil. Obviously, this form of fixation refers to the fixation of certain properties which are imparted to the soil by biochemical activity — for example, humification and ultimate mineralization of organic residue.

Inherently irreversible soil characteristics are "fixed" by their very nature. Characteristics of this group are largely lithologic, being due to differential changes in mineralogic composition of the initial material in various soil horizons. The bulk of igneous rocks consists of juvenile aluminosilicates which crystallize under hydrothermal conditions. Alteration of these minerals in the thermodynamic field of pedogenesis is wholly irreversible, although this process itself is only one short stage of a much broader geochemical and cosmochemical cycle. This stage is called weathering, the general trend of which is toward an ionic dispersion of the solid mineral matter with a strong tendency for an ultimate cosmic dissemination of it. Such an "end," however, is reached only by a very minor part of the matter acted upon by weathering. By far the greater mass of the finely comminuted rock waste is intercepted by erosion, in the course of which it is usually somewhat assorted, then redeposited in enormous beds of sediments to be reconsolidated and, perhaps, recrystallized with or without preliminary fusion. All of this directs the course of the geochemical process into other channels, saving the material from the disgrace of an immediate ionic dispersion.

Nevertheless, the essential part of weathering, particularly of the pedogenic division of it, consists of exergonic reconstruction of juvenile mineralo-chemical systems with a negative free-energy change, which renders the new systems more stable under the conditions on the land surface and, hence, they fit better into the framework of this environment. In this process various juvenile aluminosilicates are thoroughly decomposed, perhaps into the chaos of disunited ions. Some products of such decomposition might be lost to leaching, while the others are immediately reassembled in place to form entirely new vadose minerals such as various clay minerals, free hydroxides, carbonates, and other salts.

Destruction of alterable juvenile minerals, say feldspars and ferro-magnesian minerals, naturally, is accompanied by a relative increase in content of chemically stable minerals, such as quartz, zircon, or rutile, as well as an accumulation of vadose minerals. Any one of these effects may serve as an inbred marker or pedogenic activity and, once engraved upon the soil profile, is likely to stay indefinitely. These effects might be destroyed mechanically together with the whole body, for example, by the same erosion, but cannot be erased otherwise, except for such drastic treatments as fusion and recrystallization.

Lithologic markers of past stages of soil evolution are reliable only if their origin is definitely known. Accumulation of clay in certain horizons is a good marker, provided it can be ascertained that this clay is residual. A conspicuous increase in the content of some chemically stable mineral, say zircon or rutile, is another good marker, provided, again, that such an increase is due to the destruction in place of a large quantity of less stable minerals of the original matrix. Morphologically similar features can develop in more than one way. Pedogenic development is only one of these ways. Stratification of sediments and sorting of materials in transportation is the other. In many cases, it is difficult, if at all possible, to ascertain the real nature of what may appear to be a fine record of past time; and this uncertainty virtually nullifies its diagnostic value.

These are the most common examples of peculiar formations which may be spoken of as paleopedologic bones. Their variety is not too rich, indeed, and the diagnostic value of many of them is rather questionable. Generally, these records of earlier stages of soil evolution are preserved in two different ways. In some places profiles of modern soils are superimposed upon the skeletons of old soils or whatever has been left of them. A new term, "polygenetic soils," has been suggested for these soils. A polygenetic soil is a soil some characteristics of which, presumably, could not have been acquired under existing conditions, and explanations of which require postulating some recent changes in the environment.

In other places, old soils are buried under younger deposits, the outermost layer of which is reworked into a modern soil. Reports about buried soils are numerous; it is not certain, however, that all formations which are referred to as buried soils, or certain horizons thereof, are actually what they are believed to be. There is an almost irresistible temptation to find a buried soil at every contact plane throughout the Quaternary. Some of these discoveries, undoubtedly, are genuine; many others, however, are just imaginary.

Comparison of the buried soil (or whatever might be left of it) with the new soil, whether formed above the former or in similar topographic conditions elsewhere, may or may not yield sufficient criteria for judging whether the old and new soils were formed under different or similar conditions. To begin with, burial, even under the most favorable conditions, is not a guarantee of a good preservation of the old soil. The new soil is an active system in operation, whereas an old one, at best, is nothing more than a mummy — more commonly just a faint trace of what could have been an active soil before its burial. In what respect and how fast a buried soil changes after being cut off from the sources of its energy we still do not know. So, again, the paleopedologist is left with only a few reasonably well-preserved bones, but no complete skeletons.

At the present time, we are dealing largely with what is believed to be the fossils of the subarctic (probably periglacial), subtropic, and perhaps steppe climates, which are found in various places well outside of the regions that are characterized by these respective climates now.

Fossils of subtropical climate consist of what is believed to be the traces of laterization of soils or their underlying materials in the regions in which laterization does not take place now. Such traces are found, for example, in various parts of Pennsylvania, New Jersey, and Maryland, as well as in other places in our country and on other continents, particularly throughout Australia.

Some marks of this kind consist of conspicuous and in places rather brilliant red mottling or general reddening of the deeper soil horizons. Such mottling and coloring are typical of lateritic soils that develop in the humid tropical and subtropical climates, but are unknown in soils of any other climatic region, unless these soils are formed from the materials which could have been laterized previously. Other relics of ancient laterization are represented by the lateritic ferruginous hardpans and concretionary materials.

Traces of subarctic climate are preserved in certain peculiar characteristics similar to those of various present soils of the tundra. Particularly striking among these characteristics are the so-called involutions or "Brodelboden," the solifluction deposits, the casts of ground-ice wedges, stone rings, and certain forms of microrelief. It is believed that all such characteristics should have been imparted to the soils by frost action, especially under conditions of perennial freezing of the ground. Various features of this kind are described in detail by Smith,[1] and an interested reader is referred to his report.

Soils with these characteristics are forming now throughout the regions that are affected by deep perennial ground frost in northern Canada, Alaska, and Eastern Siberia. Hence, one may study the mechanism of development of such soils in their specific environment. Presence of remarkably similar features in the regions that are not now affected by perennial frost, for example, in northern Germany, Belgium, France, and elsewhere, leads one to believe that, here, these features are out of harmony with present conditions and are inherited from the past.

Deep perennial freezing of the ground is not strictly a pedogenic phenomenon. Local changes in temperature throughout the frozen layer, however, clearly indicate marked changes in climate in respective regions and, since these facts are comparatively little known, it may be of interest to bring them to the attention of geophysicists.

The temperature of the uppermost layer of the perennially frozen ground is affected by seasonal changes in temperature of the air just above the ground. Ranges of such annual changes in the temperature gradually narrow with depth so that at a depth ranging from about 12 feet to about 15 feet they become negligible and the temperature of the ground is constant. Usually such a temperature is one or two degrees higher than the mean temperature of the air above the ground. From this level downward the temperature slowly increases with depth and at a certain level its gradient crosses the freezing point. The distance from the surface to this point is the thickness of the perennially frozen layer, which ranges from several feet to considerably more than a thousand feet.

Now, it has been reported that in some places the temperature decreases with depth and reaches a minimum at a considerable distance from the surface. Unfortunately, these reports are somewhat amateurish and not truly reliable. But there are other reports. For example, at the Chita station on the Trans-Siberian railroad (lat. 52°02′ N) a well has been dug. To the depth of 17.32 meters (about 56 feet) the ground was not frozen but its temperature decreased to the freezing point. Below this level the ground was frozen to the depth of 28.96 meters (about 95 feet). Thus, this frozen layer was 39 feet thick. Another similar case is at Petrovski Zavod (in Transbaikalia, lat. 51°17′ N). Here, the surface of the frozen layer was encountered at a depth of about 96 feet and the frozen layer itself was about 64 feet thick. Similar situations are reported from more than a dozen points between lat. 51° N and lat. 53° N in Transbaikalia.[2] These data, however, were obtained somewhat incidentally. A systematic geophysical survey, no doubt, would increase the number of points by hundreds.

It hardly can be disputed that these deep frozen layers represent residual freezing. Obviously, the ground at a depth of say 80 or 100 feet could not be frozen without the entire layer above it having been frozen and having the temperature progressively lower (upward) than that of the coldest part of the still undefrosted layer. The minimum temperature at the time of freezing should have been near the surface and the mean temperature of the air above the ground should have been a few degrees still lower than that. In other words, freezing of these deep layers of the ground should have been taking place during the time when climate was considerably colder than now. This is one example of the paleopedogenic bones.

Paleopedologic records of steppe climates are not as clear as those of the subarctic or subtropical climates. Perhaps it is due to the fact that soils of the steppe climate do not acquire any too strongly etched specific characteristics which would survive subsequent changes in the environment. The outstanding feature of the steppe type of soil formation is a relatively high degree of carbonation of the soil system. This carbonation occurs largely in two forms. First, rather slow biochemical mineralization of organic residues leads to the development of conspicuous humus horizons, rich in organic carbon. Some of the best soils in this group hold well over a hundred metric tons of organic carbon per acre. Second, there occurs the enrichment of the horizons below the humus layer in carbonates of alkaline earths. Somewhat less conspicuous is a relative general salinization of the soil due to the inefficiency of leaching and fairly strong evaporation of the soil moisture. Accumulation in the subsoil of sulfates, especially gypsum, comes next in prominence after that of carbonates.

All these are the principal acquired characteristics of the steppe soils; and none of them is particularly stable. The balance of organic carbon is maintained only by a steady renovation of the soil humus. A certain amount of humus is continuously oxidized to carbon dioxide and the loss is made good quantitatively by the simultaneous humification of fresh residues of organic matter built by photosynthesis. Some compounds of humus are oxidized fast, others slowly, but there is hardly a single molecule that would escape ultimate break-down and oxidation. Preservation of the humus horizons would require a thorough sterilization of these horizons. Indeed, such a treatment cannot be ruled out entirely under certain conditions, particularly in quickly and deeply buried soils; but under ordinary conditions sterilization of soils does not take place. Furthermore, the presence of organic carbon in some layers of stratified deposits is not necessarily a valid symptom of buried steppe soil.

Somewhat better, although not too good by any means, are chances for preservation of horizons enriched in carbonates, especially of the lime-cemented hardpans (caliche). Calcareous hardpans, however, are not an essential feature of steppe soils. They develop locally, and causes of their formation are not too well understood. Therefore, even if their fossil nature is ascertained, their diagnostic value is rather doubtful.

Typical of the steppe soils are not the lime hardpans but, rather, the more limited precipitation of carbonates in various forms, as nodules, veinlets, films, etc. The stratigraphic position of the calcareous horizon in the soil profile, the degree of carbonation, and the distribution of carbonates through this horizon are not fixed. Carbonates are not entirely immobile. All these values, therefore, are subject to readjustment to the changing environment. It is doubtful that any particular feature of those horizons would survive any significant environmental change. Therefore, it is impossible to assume that every layer peculiarly enriched in carbonates represents a fossil of the calcareous horizon of an old steppe soil. This is not to say that preservation of such horizons is impossible. Perhaps it is possible, and even more widespread than one may think. The whole problem, however, needs a great deal more study. The reader interested in further discussion of this subject is referred to a thought-provoking article by Bryan and Albritton.[3]

Paleopedologic data are not confined to the three cases which are mentioned above. Buried soils include soils which probably were formed in other than subtropic, subarctic, and steppe climates. Reports have been made on fairly well-preserved forest soils in regions which are now occupied by the prairie — soils that could have been formed under conditions more humid than those which prevail now in the region of their burial. Interesting as they are, these reports are still too few and somewhat too sketchy to warrant any broad generalization.

REFERENCES

1. T. U. Smith, "Physical effects of Pleistocene climatic changes in non-glaciated areas: eolian phenomena, frost action, and stream terracing," *Bull. Geol. Soc. Amer.* 60, 1485–1516 (1949).

2. M. I. Sumgin, *Perennial freezing of soils in the U.S.S.R.* (1927).

3. Kirk Bryan and C. C. Albritton, Jr., "Soil phenomena as evidence of climatic changes," *Amer. Jour. Sci.* 241, 469–490 (1943).

16

CLIMATIC CHANGES AND
RADIOISOTOPE DATING*

J. Laurence Kulp

INTRODUCTION

ANY EXAMINATION OF CLIMATIC change must be related to the time dimension. Indeed, throughout this series of communications it has become increasingly evident that whether we are concerned with short- or long-scale climatic changes, the origin of life, the early history of the planet, or the mechanism of climatic changes, it is imperative to know at what time events occurred. We must be able to follow the sequence in some quantitative fashion. Beyond written history, the significant quantitative methods involve radioactive isotopes of the chemical elements and their products. Even within historical time, we must turn to radioisotopes to find out certain important climatological facts, such as the rate of exchange of air masses between the hemispheres or the exchange of carbon between atmosphere and ocean.

Consider the hypotheses of volcanic action or mountain building as a cause of widespread continental glaciation. Evidence for or against such hypotheses from geologic sources is significant only when times are accurately known. Actually, at present, the accepted dates are so poorly established that the hypotheses cannot be proved or disproved. However, methods that can provide adequate numbers are now known and are being improved and applied in a number of laboratories. Further, new methods are in the stage of development. It appears possible that in the next decade much quantitative information on the times of world-wide climatic events will be amassed. For certain problems considerable information is already at hand. Let us review some of the radioisotope methods that are applicable to these climatic problems. Then we can discuss some recent results that bear on the problems raised in this series of papers.

* Lamont Geological Observatory Contribution No. 60 (1953).

METHODS

The methods by which the dates of significant climatic changes may be determined can be classified according to the time interval over which they are applicable.

1. *From 3,000,000,000 to 10,000,000 Years B.P.* For the interval from the beginning of planet history to the Pliocene, some 10,000,000 years ago, a number of methods are available which are applicable to different types of rocks. In this interval, for example, the exact dating of rocks from the proper location might make it possible to determine whether a correlation exists between volcanic activity or mountain building and continental glaciation of the Proterozoic or Permian. The uranium-lead method would be usable for metal veins or pegmatites containing uranium minerals, and possibly for other igneous rocks if isotope dilution techniques are employed. (While the present Geologic Timetable is based on uranium-lead ages, it is noteworthy that there are very few which can be considered highly accurate. But researches at the University of Toronto, the California Institute of Technology, the United States Geological Survey, and the Lamont Geological Observatory should change this unsatisfactory situation greatly in the near future.) The uranium-helium method is applicable to igneous rocks in general, particularly to lava flows. The rubidium-strontium and the relatively untried potassium-argon and potassium-calcium methods also could be used for granitic igneous rocks. The strontium-isotope ratio method may make it possible to date limestones and fossils directly. Recent work in our laboratory suggests that the ratio of Sr^{87} to Sr^{86} is a function of time yielding a difference of 1 percent between modern and Silurian limestones. The present precision of measurement is about 0.2 percent.

The interesting work of Thode,[1] in which the time of the origin of photosynthetic life is suggested from systematic variations in the sulfur-isotope ratios, requires accurate knowledge of the age of the sulfide and sulfate minerals measured.

2. *From 10,000,000 to 30,000 Years B.P.* For the period from 10,000,000 to 30,000 years ago there has been no age method available for continental rocks. It appears, however, that this period, so important from the point of view of climatology, may very well be spanned by the helium method through utilizing new high-sensitivity mass-spectrometric techniques to measure the helium. It is calculated that an increase in sensitivity of 10^3 over the conventional volumetric procedure should be realized. If this is accomplished, the helium method could be used up to 10,000 years ago and would make possible the dating of Pleistocene volcanism.

For the interval from the present to about 400,000 years ago a method has been proposed by Piggot and Urry[2] for deep-sea sediments. This is based on the assumption that deep-sea sediments remove ionium from sea water, preferentially to its parent uranium. Since ionium [a thorium isotope in the uranium 238 decay chain] has a half life of about 80,000 years and since about five half lives must elapse before it can no longer be accurately measured, a useful range of several hundred thousand years seems likely. Thus if one has a homogeneous, continuously deposited core, a graph of ionium content against depth should theoretically yield an ionium decay curve and thus permit the estimation of ages back to about 400,000 years ago. Further, since glacial marine deposits and other changes in sediment type accompany climatic changes, the use of this graph should make possible the recording of world-wide effects. Also, if the rate of sedimentation can be accurately determined by this method over 400,000 years of Pleistocene history, reasonable extrapolations could be made to at least 1,000,000 years ago.

3. *From 30,000 years B.P. to Present.* The most valuable method of age determination in this recent period of geologic history and probably the most important for climatic study is the carbon 14 method discovered by W. F. Libby[3] of the University of Chicago. The method depends on the constant concentration of carbon 14 dioxide in the CO_2-air-water photosynthetic cycle. With a constant rate of production of carbon 14 atoms in the upper atmosphere by neutron bombardment, a constant carbon reservoir, and a constant rate of decay, living animals and plants, as well as surface ocean water, contain a constant concentration of carbon 14. Once an object is removed from the cycle, for example, by death of the animal or submergence of some Arctic water, its supply of C^{14} is no longer replenished, but that which was present decays away at the rate required by the half life of 5568 years.

The technical problem of measuring the C^{14} is largely one of extremely efficient shielding. The system developed at the Lamont Geological Observatory has extended the range of the method back to about 30,000 years ago. The apparatus is placed inside a 12-ton iron shield to eliminate natural gamma radiation and soft cosmic-ray components; the C^{14} Geiger counter is surrounded by a ring of anticoincidence counters to eliminate hard cosmic components, and finally an inch of mercury is placed inside the anticoincidence ring to eliminate gamma rays from the iron shield itself.

It is generally believed that the maximum sensitivity of the Geiger-counter technique has been essentially achieved. Calculations based on the experimental work by Professor Yost at the California Institute of Technology suggest that the ion-chamber method will yield no improvement. In principle, proportional counting of CO_2 or CH_4 at high pressures would increase the sensitivity, and hence the range of the method. However, the technical difficulties probably would prevent practical application. The scintillation-counting technique is very promising in principle and may ultimately extend the method to 50,000 or 60,000 years B.P.

Natural-radiocarbon measurements have been made on plant and animal remains, on CO_2 from air, water, and carbonate sediments and shells. By such means the details of late Pleistocene chronology on land and in the ocean are amenable to study. Even air and ocean circulation may be examined. The only difficulty in this method is that very recent or very fast movements, that is, those which are completed in less than a century, are not susceptible to test with carbon 14 at the present stage of development.

Another radioisotope which may serve to fill this gap is tritium. Tritium may also be produced by cosmic radiation in the upper atmosphere $(_0n^1 + _7N^{14} \rightarrow _2He^4 + _1H^3)$. A recent paper by von Grosse and others [4] demonstrates the existence of natural tritium in concentrations of about 3×10^{-18} gram per gram of hydrogen. Since tritium has a half life of about 12.4 years it would be an excellent tracer for following rapid surface currents in the oceans and possibly in glacier ice, since it would decay away in about 60 years after having been brought to the surface in the form of rain water. It should be noted, however, that this very attractive tracer for following surface ocean currents has a practical difficulty — to obtain the tritium one needs as a first step a heavy-water plant to concentrate deuterium from large quantities of ordinary water.

RESULTS

Now let us turn to a few results of significance to the study of climate supplied by the carbon 14 method. The most significant numbers that have appeared refer to the end of the Wisconsin glaciation. Libby's excellent data on the Two Creeks wood and peat, to which Dr. Flint has referred in his communication, gives a date for the pre-Mankato warm interval. In order to examine this problem from the viewpoint of world-wide climatic changes, a series of samples were taken on the mid-ocean island of Bermuda. Table 1 shows the results obtained at the Lamont Geological Observatory. The stratigraphy originally worked out by Sayles [5] consists of an alternating series of (semiconsolidated) wind-blown limestones and soils. In addition, on Greater Bermuda — now under water — there was an extensive cedar forest which is overlaid by mud and water ranging upwards of 50 feet. On top of this wood are several patches of peat which are probably related to the various stands of the sea as the last dregs of the continental glaciers melted away. The cedar forest was wiped out about 11,000 years ago. This gives an excellent world-wide date near the end of the Wisconsin. Since one of the peat layers measured about 8,600 years, it is clear that the final retreat of the glaciation took several thousand years more. This result is in good agreement with the rate of retreat obtained by De Geer for the varves in Scandinavia. It should also be noted that the sea-level lowering during the Wisconsin was certainly several times greater than the level lowering represented by the Bermuda cedar forest. Thus the measures give only a point near the end of the glacial period. Detailed evidence from the Mississippi Delta area presented by Fisk[6] suggests that there were only two major world-wide phases of the

Table 1. Bermuda stratigraphy.

Major Period	North America	Bermuda	Relative length *	Carbon 14 (years)
Recent	Recent	Erosian + soil formation	1	
		Peat		8,600 ± 500
		Cedar forest drowned		11,500 ± 700
Wisconsin	Mankato Interstadial	Southampton eolianite		14,300 ± 400
		McGall's soil	⅔	
	Cary Interstadial	Somerset eolianite		older than 25,000
	Tazewell			
	Interstadial	Signal Hill soil	⅔	older than 25,000
	Iowan	Warwick eolianite		
Sangamon Interglacial		St. George's soil	5	
Illinoian Glacial		Pembroke eolianite		older than 25,000
Yarmouth		Belmont limestone		

* Based on relative thicknesses of soil derived from underlying eolianite.

Wisconsin. In this Delta area two deeply entrenched valley systems are eroded to about 400 feet below present sea level. Wood from the erosion surface of the last ice maximum gives a carbon 14 age of more than 25,000 years. Another specimen some 73 feet down in the valley fill below the present surface gives 8850 ± 150 years, while one at 25 feet gives 2900 ± 300 years. These results suggest that the last glacial maximum in the Wisconsin occurred around 30,000 years ago. The details will be forthcoming as numerous additional samples are measured. It appears that the classical fourfold subdivision of the Wisconsin, based on upper Mississippi Valley glacial stratigraphy, may not truly reflect the major world-wide climatic changes, and that the most satisfactory data on this problem will come from nonglaciated areas.

To return to Bermuda, it will be noted in Table 1 that a specimen of the Southampton or uppermost eolianite has an age of about 14,300 years, presumably lying within the last substage. A sample taken somewhere in the Somerset eolianite was older than 25,000 years. Now while it is clear that many more measurements in this area are required, several things of great importance stand out. First, the Wisconsin tapered off between 11,000 and 7,000 years ago. Second, the last substage may have been of the order of 5,000 years long. Third, at least part of the preceding substage appears older than 25,000 years. Fourth, and by no means least, the carbon from old semiconsolidated limestone does not seem to have been exchanged with a measurable concentration of carbon 14 from rain or ground water. The Signal Hill, St. George's, and Pembroke samples were taken quite near the surface.

Libby[7, 8] reported quite a number of dates on wood samples reported to be Tazewell or older. These all came out to be older than 17,000 years, which was his limit at that time. We have measured a considerable num-

Table 2. Carbon 14 measurements on core C–10–5.

Depth (cm)	Description	Average apparent age for the interval (year B.P.)
0– 10	Warm water — slow deposition	5,850 ± 250
149–160	Cold water — more rapid deposition	19,000 ± 2,200
		21,100 ± 1,800
	Average	19,600 ± 900

ber of Alaskan samples. Some of them consist of peat overlaid by the latest till. They range from 16,000 to 20,000 years in age, suggesting that this interval may have included an interglacial. The lack of correlation between warm intervals in the midwest and Alaska may only reëmphasize the local nature of such fluctuations.

Other specimens, including a Superbison specimen frozen in the permafrost, are older than 30,000 years. It would appear that the permafrost had started forming at the beginning of the second major ice period of the Wisconsin.

Another interesting application of carbon 14 for climatology is found in the deep-sea cores. While this work is only in the preliminary stages, Table 2 presents results from a typical North Atlantic core taken on one of the Ewing scientific cruises. The core shows a clear case of recent warmer-water slow deposition, below which is cold-water deposition. The sample taken in the cold water at a depth of 149–160 cm was about 19,600 years old. A sufficient number of cores with many points on each core should elucidate the late Pleistocene history of the ocean floor. A correlation of the carbon 14 with the ionium method in a single core could demonstrate the constancy of cosmic-ray flux over the last 30,000 years. This possibility is being examined.

Another application of the C^{14} method is the determination of the rate and direction of movement of deep ocean water. By taking 200-gallon samples of the water at the surface and at depth, extracting the carbon as carbon dioxide, and then processing it in the laboratory, it is possible to determine the natural radiocarbon content. Table 3 shows some of the

Table 3. Deep ocean water,

Location	Depth	Counts per minute	Age (years B.P.)
41°00′N, 54°35′W	Surface	(1) 6.82 ± 0.09 (2) 6.74 ± 0.07	Recent
		Ave. 6.77 ± 0.06	
	Average modern hells	6.72 ± 0.10	
58°19′N, 32°56.8′W		5.38 ± 0.07 5.60 ± 0.11	
		Ave. 5.45 ± 0.06	1600 ± 130
53°52.6′N, 21°06′W		5.31 ± 0.12 5.36 ± 0.12	
		Ave. 5.34 ± 0.10	1750 ± 150

Direct Comparison		
	Difference in counts per minute	
	From Averages	Direct Measurement
Surface sample vs. 58°19′N	1.32 ± 0.10	1.15 ± 0.12

preliminary results obtained from samples taken on cruises by the Woods Hole *Atlantis* and the U.S.N. *Hydro San Pablo* in the summer of 1951. It can be seen that the deep-water samples give apparent ages of about 1600 to 1700 years at approximate latitude 50°. If this sample water started near the surface in the Arctic, then the rate of turnover of the oceans must be on a scale of at least 10,000 years.

An exact knowledge of this important oceanographic parameter should certainly be of interest in the study of world-wide climatic changes. Pulses of particularly cold centuries might be reflected in the climate some thousands of years later as the water returns to the surface. It is possible, however, that the water would not all return to the surface in a sufficiently short time interval to give any significant effect. In any event, such information from many more samples will fill in an important blind spot in our understanding of ocean circulation. In certain problems the heat flow from under the oceans is important. If the actual rate of circulation is as slow as is indicated by these preliminary experiments, the heat evolution under the oceans is very small — a tenth or a hundredth of that on the continents.

Another possible application bearing on climatic change is the dating of glacial ice, either by the removal of the carbon dioxide from the ice itself, or by taking organic material from certain strata. The apparently stagnant ice of the Antarctic and Arctic regions may be susceptible to age analysis.

Finally, an exciting tracer experiment on a global scale would attend the explosion of a hydrogen bomb, since appreciable quantities of carbon 14 might be added to the atmosphere. One could follow by the radioisotopic measures the atmospheric and oceanic circulations, as well as the rate of exchange between atmosphere and ocean. But first the present uncontaminated concentrations should be measured.

REFERENCES

1. H. G. Thode, "Variation in the abundances of the sulfur isotopes in nature and their significance," abstract of paper, 120th Meeting, American Chemical Society, New York City (1951).

2. C. S. Piggot and W. D. Urry, "Time relations in ocean sediments," *Bull. Geol. Soc. Amer. 53*, 1187 (1941).

3. W. F. Libby, E. C. Anderson, and J. R. Arnold, "Age determination by radiocarbon content," *Science 109*, 227–228 (1949).

4. A. U. von Grosse, W. H. Johnston, R. L. Wolfgang, and W. F. Libby, "Tritium in nature," *Science 113*, 1–2 (1951).

5. R. W. Sayles, "Bermuda during the Ice Age," *Proc. Amer. Acad. Arts and Sci. 66*, 381 (1931).

6. H. N. Fisk, "Loess and Quaternary geology of the Lower Mississippi Valley," *Jour. Geol. 59*, 353 (1951).

7. J. R. Arnold and W. F. Libby, "Radiocarbon dates," *Science 113*, 111 (1951).

8. W. F. Libby, "Radiocarbon dates, II," *Science 114*, 291 (1951).

17

TREE-RING EVIDENCE FOR

CLIMATIC CHANGES

Edmund Schulman

To some students of climatic changes the centuries-long sequences of annual tree-ring widths have offered inviting data in the search for solar-terrestrial relations and climatic cycles.[1] Basically important in such analysis, of course, is the significance of the growth ring in terms of climate.

Of the hundreds of forest stands throughout much of the world which have now been sampled in dendroclimatic studies, those in regions where temperature or rainfall is a severely limiting factor in growth have yielded the most clearly interpretable climatic indices.[2] Indeed, the number of factors tending to destroy the recording by trees of any one meteorological element is in theory so great that it is, in a sense, quite unexpected to find that tree-ring indices from even the most critically limiting sites can be of significance as weather gages.[3]

Pioneer work in the development of rainfall chronologies in ponderosa pine of the semiarid southwestern United States by Douglass paved the way for later work discussed below. Extensive surveys by the forest ecologists of Scandinavia [2,4] have uncovered many growth series, from two to five centuries in length, that appear to record with fair fidelity the fluctuations in summer temperature, particularly that of July, near the arctic tree line. Similar conclusions were reached by Giddings in Alaska. In environments in which no one factor is notably limiting, however, the complex reactions of tree growth pose a severe restriction, at present, on the backward extension of gage records by growth indices.[5]

Since a short, general survey of the field of dendrochronology has recently appeared,[2] it is perhaps appropriate to limit this discussion to the indices now available for the western United States and southwestern Canada. Throughout that region the University of Arizona has supported a continuing search, since 1939, for the oldest and most sensitive trees — a fundamental phase of a research program the main objective of which is the derivation of centuries-long rainfall indices of quantitative value.

The results of this survey, in the light of evidence from other localities, have led to the conclusion that no other region in the world is apparently so naturally favored as a source of dendroclimatic history. An indeed remarkable combination of favoring factors has been found to exist there. Several long-lived coniferous species, with great geographic range and with ability to live on very arid sites, make possible wide and selective sampling. Growth indices, showing rather high fidelity to the rainfall of the entire year, are now known to be obtainable across twenty degrees of latitude. And perhaps most fortunate of all, on the most adverse sites on the lower forest border, stunted, inconspicuous, yet highly sensitive trees have been discovered which far exceed the usual maximum age for the species.

With the support of the Office of Naval Research * it has been possible during the past two years to derive a large number of new ring chronologies. Although the analysis of the statistical and other properties of these indices is still in progress, the series themselves are here presented, in addition to earlier data, as a basis for discussion.

No tree can possibly provide a perfect history of yearly river flow, but some show a rather extraordinary approach to this status, as may be noted in Fig. 1. Although correlation coefficients between ring growth and annual rainfall or river flow of the order of $+0.7$ have been found for such trees, it is of course necessary to average many individual records to derive a stable, long-term index.

Regional mean annual growth, as an index of yearly rainfall ending in June, and water-year runoff ending in September, are illustrated for four well-separated basins in Fig. 2. Superposed smooth curves accentuate the general maxima and minima. Correlation coefficients between the smoothed growth and gage records, of the order of $+0.8$, are probably near the greatest possible value. The great minimum in rainfall and river flow near 1900 in southern California and the Colorado River basin disappears farther north, and at Banff, in Alberta, rainfall near 1900 is at a major maximum; the growth records show the same reversal. A detailed study of such graphic comparisons provides a very live picture of the limitations of even the better regional tree-ring series as climatic indices.

By far the most intensive work on drought chronologies has been done in the Colorado River basin. Summarized in Fig. 3 are well over 100,000 measured rings representing about 75 sample plots. To show best the general fluctuations in the indices, only smoothed series are presented here; in this and the following illustrations three-year means of the annual data were plotted and graphically smoothed by the formula $b' = (a + 2b + c)/4$. The index for 1951 was derived by a different

* Under Contract Nonr–02000 with the University of Arizona.

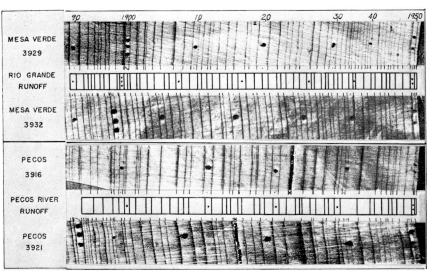

Fig. 1. *Upper panel*: Two ring sequences in Douglas fir (*Pseudotsuga taxifolia*) of high sensitivity from southwestern Colorado parallel the water-year runoff of the Rio Grande at Del Norte. *Lower panel*: Growth of the same species near Santa Fe, New Mexico, is compared with the runoff of the Pecos River at Pecos. The completed ring for 1951 is present under bark at the right. Ring boundaries marked along the edges of the photographs help to identify such structures as false rings for 1911 and 1913 and microscopic or locally absent rings at 1925 and 1934 in specimen 3916 (cf. the other photos at these dates). (From *Tree-Ring Bulletin*.)

method from that used in the 1945 index; since only some 10 percent of the earlier data were incorporated in the later series, the two indices are substantially independent.

Four features of particular interest may be noted in the 850 years of data. Almost the entire thirteenth century was exceedingly dry (the ca-

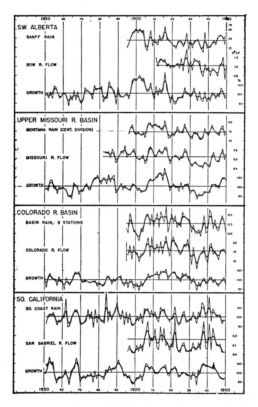

Fig. 2. Yearly rainfall (July–June), water-year runoff (October–September), and annual-growth departures show closely parallel trends in each of four areas of western North America from Banff (52° N) to Southern California (34° N). The river stations, N–S, are at Banff, Fort Benton, Lees Ferry, and Azusa.

tastrophic effect at Hoover Dam of a recurrence of such a major change in climate is obvious). In contrast, the index suggests very persistent storminess during the fourteenth century, of magnitude probably equal to or greater than that during the major wet period in this basin from 1905 to 1929. The last quarter of the sixteenth century seems to have been the driest interval in the last 650 years, of substantially greater severity than the drought near 1900 and during the 1930's. Finally, we call attention to a remarkable change near 1670 from irregular, generally long fluctuations to shorter ones of the order of 20 to 25 years.

One of the fundamental difficulties in interpreting drought-type ring indices in terms of absolute rainfall is the indeterminacy of the scale at the curve limits. The mean trend in growth, fitted to the upper series in Fig. 3, must usually depend on the series itself. Additional data, particularly at the beginning of the record, where the slope of the trend line is relatively steep, may greatly alter its position. Since most published data on ring growth are based on averages of departures in relatively short ring records, of varying length up to three or four centuries, it is evident that important information on climatic changes must even at best be lost in such data. The construction of families of homogeneous curves as in the Colorado River basin provides a partial solution of this problem.

The extension of the Colorado River chronology, by means of pre-Columbian beams from Pueblo ruins, has now been carried to 58 B.C. (Fig. 4). Based on the most sensitive ring records in the archaeological collections of the last 25 years, subregion indices have been derived which, in turn, have been averaged to form a continuous general index. This archaeological extension must, however, be examined with caution as far as the longer fluctuations are concerned, for each subregion represents an overlapping chain of commonly short sequences, which enter the index only as departures from their own trends. In passing, one may mention that the archaeological index seems to eliminate the hope that the major change from drought to flood conditions shortly after A.D. 1300, 1600, and 1900 represents a cyclic recurrence of forecasting reliability.

Two transects containing dendroclimatic histories, one along the Pacific Slope from southern California to British Columbia (Fig. 5), the other from New Mexico to Alberta in the general zone between the Rocky Mountains and the Great Plains (Fig. 6), may be examined for systematic changes of long period from one area to the next. No obvious changes of this nature that are of synoptic value in forecasting appear to be indicated.

In Fig. 5 the southern California index is seen to exhibit tendencies similar to those just noted for the Colorado River basin: the major minimum in the last six centuries occurs in the late 1500's and a tendency to long irregular changes gives way near 1630 to shorter fluctuations of the order of 15 to 30 years. The dates of change-over in the two regions in which this phenomenon is noted are perhaps not so sharply defined as to discourage completely the thought that there may be some evidence here relating to the great dearth of sunspots in the late 1600's.

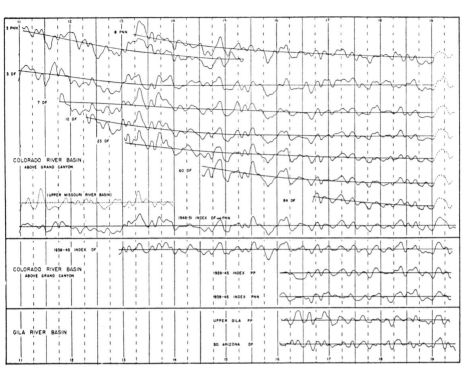

Fig. 3. *Upper panel:* Smoothed mean curves of measured growth in pinyon pine (PNN: *Pinus edulis*) and Douglas fir, sampled in southwestern Colorado, north central Colorado, and northeastern Utah; the chronology tends to approach a stable form as larger numbers of trees — with necessarily later common starting date — are averaged. Growth release affects the record during the recent decades in the older trees, which were selected without regard to site modification by man. The data are summarized as departures from trend in the bottom series in the panel. A very preliminary comparison is possible with the index for the Upper Missouri River basin, in which four trees extend the record preceding A.D. 1400 (cf. Fig. 6). *Lower panel:* Indices for the Colorado River basin and the Gila River basin derived by 1945 for various species. PP: ponderosa pine (*P. ponderosa*). In order to condense the large number of data in this and the following diagrams, 3-year nonoverlapping means of the annual indices were plotted and then graphically smoothed by a weighted running mean of three terms.

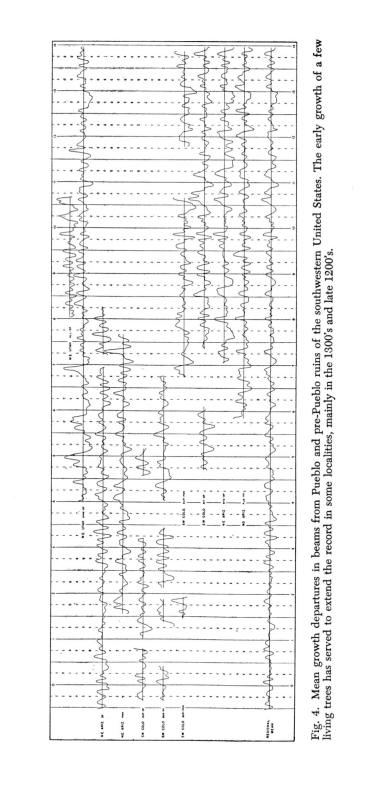

Fig. 4. Mean growth departures in beams from Pueblo and pre-Pueblo ruins of the southwestern United States. The early growth of a few living trees has served to extend the record in some localities, mainly in the 1300's and late 1200's.

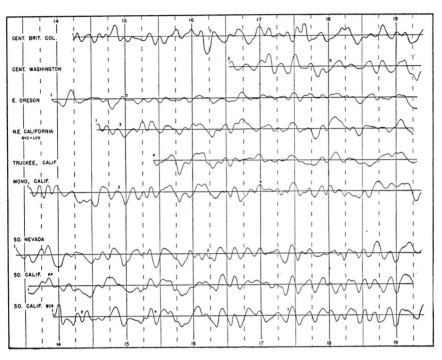

Fig. 5. Regional mean growth departures along the Pacific Slope. The number of *stations*, indicated along the curves, is a rough measure of the weight of the index, all indices representing many trees. The upper two series are based on both Douglas fir and ponderosa pine; the next three, derived respectively by F. P. Keen, Ernst Antevs, and Hardman and Reil, represent ponderosa pine, as do the rest except for the bigcone spruce (BCS: *Pseudotsuga macrocarpa*) index at the bottom of the diagram.

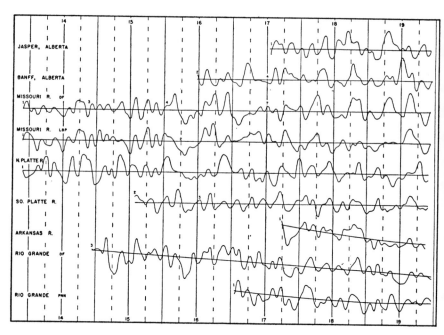

Fig. 6. Regional mean growth indices in Rocky Mountain basins east of the Continental Divide. One index is based on limber pine (LBP: *Pinus flexilis*) and one on pinyon pine; all others on Douglas fir. The number of *stations*, indicated along the curves, is only a rough guide to relative weights; for example, no part of the Missouri LBP series is based on more than ten trees. The lower three curves represent mean measured growth before the removal of age trend; the others, growth departures. The reference line of zero departures for Banff is misplaced slightly.

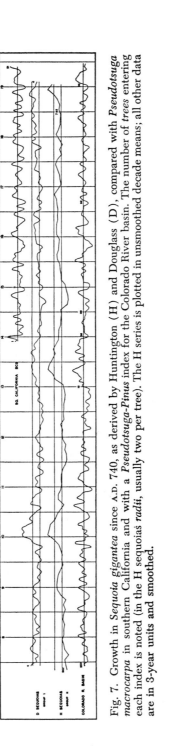

Fig. 7. Growth in *Sequoia gigantea* since A.D. 740, as derived by Huntington (H) and Douglass (D), compared with *Pseudotsuga macrocarpa* in southern California and with a *Pseudotsuga-Pinus* index for the Colorado River basin. The number of *trees* entering each index is noted (in the H sequoias *radii*, usually two per tree). The H series is plotted in unsmoothed decade means; all other data are in 3-year units and smoothed.

Although the earlier centuries of the Missouri River basin index (Fig. 6) are as yet based on a meager set of tree-ring records, the data suggest that a change from short to relatively long fluctuations, the reverse of that which occurred in the Southwest and California, took place near 1570; this date, however, is particularly uncertain. Two characteristics of the Alberta index deserve special mention: the maximum in rainfall near 1900, which appears to have been as great as or greater than any in the past three centuries, and the slight tendency to reversal with respect to the sequences from more southerly regions, especially southern California.

No series in the data just presented compares in length with the chronologies derived by Huntington[6] and Douglass[1] for the sequoias of the southern Sierra Nevada. The Huntington index, often used to estimate the climate of earlier millennia,[7] is briefly reëxamined here. The validity of these data as rainfall records has been questioned,[8] and certainly the relatively lush sequoia forest does not suggest rainfall as a critically limiting factor. Yet we may note in Fig. 7 that the four most sensitive slope and ridge trees precisely dated by Douglass (D, group 1) exhibit a modest tendency to parallel fluctuations in the well-established rainfall index in bigcone spruce of southern California. The upward trend in recent centuries evident in this series and in the Huntington index (group H) appears merely to reflect a natural tendency to select sampling radii on stumps at buttress lobes.

The index by Huntington was obtained by mass decadal counts and measures on stumps from both moist and dry areas and corrected by him, in a rough, empirical fashion, for estimated errors in ring count. His series, based on several hundred trees, shows a good agreement in major maxima with the four exactly dated dry-site trees of Douglass, and comparison with the extended index for the Colorado River basin supports the inference that such maxima are very probably intervals of high rainfall (for example, the stormy fourteenth century). The dry 1200's are also indicated in both sequoia series, though in less pronounced form. It appears likely that in Huntington's average the essentially random fluctuations of moist-site trees canceled out in good measure, and then the trees from drier sites determined the major maxima and minima. (Antevs found that curves derived separately for "dry" and "moist" sites showed essentially identical fluctuations; but this classification by Huntington now appears to be in good part invalid.)

Smaller fluctuations in the plotted portion of the 3200-year Huntington series are perhaps of dubious significance. Work in progress suggests that the early third or so of this series may have much less significance in terms of climatic history than the later data, perhaps a result of cumulative errors in dating and of inhomogeneity of record.

Three general considerations may serve to complete this very brief review. First, though numerous reports have appeared of cyclic variations in tree growth that are undeniably similar to cyclic variations in solar activity, no combination of such cycles seems to be yet established as reliable in forecasting growth and climate. Second, the often-suggested instability of climatic means and distributions, based on only 30 or 50 years of weather records, is here emphasized by the characteristics of the long rainfall index for the Colorado River basin. Finally, the construction of centuries-long indices based on drought-sensitive trees of the world is still in its early stages; much remains to be done even in the relatively well-explored western United States; nevertheless the more reliable growth indices of climate presently available may, I believe, be used with some confidence to derive fairly stable statistical probabilities of drought and flood and also may, in some cases, be used to check, at least partially, the theories of climatic change in the latest millennium.

REFERENCES

1. A. E. Douglass, "Climatic cycles and tree growth," *Carnegie Inst. Wash. Publ. 289*, I (1919), II (1928), III (1936).

2. E. Schulman, "Tree-ring indices of rainfall, temperature, and river flow," *Compendium of Meteorology* (American Meteorological Society, Boston, 1951), pp. 1024–1029. See also *Tree-Ring Bull. 18*, 10–18 (1952).

3. W. S. Glock, "Growth rings and climate," *Bot. Rev. 7*, 649–713 (1941).

4. P. Mikola, "On variations in tree growth and their significance to growth studies," *Commun. Finnish Forestry Inst.* No. 38.5, (1950).

5. B. Huber and W. von Jazewitsch, "Aus der Praxis der Jahrring-Analyse," *Allgem. Forstzeitschrift 5*, 527–529 (1950).

6. E. Huntington, "The climatic factor as illustrated in arid America," *Carnegie Inst. Wash. Publ. 192* (1914).

7. C. E. P. Brooks, "Geological and historical aspects of climatic change," *Compendium of Meteorology* (American Meteorological Society, Boston, 1951), pp. 1004–1023.

8. E. Antevs, "The big tree as a climatic measure," in *Quaternary climates*, *Carnegie Inst. Wash. Publ. 352* (1925).

18

CLIMATIC CHANGES AS INTERPRETED
FROM METEOROLOGICAL DATA

John H. Conover

INTRODUCTION

Until recently few meteorologists believed that we were living in a period of climatic changes that could be substantiated by meteorological data. The changes deduced from such data were often dismissed as random, and it was thought that over longer periods of record they would average out. But the very strict application of the theory of random sampling to meteorological data can be misleading because it rules out the now well-founded idea that behind these observed changes of temperature, precipitation, etc., lie genuine physical processes.

Within the past five years a number of important papers have appeared presenting temperature, precipitation, and pressure changes over the entire world. Brier,[1] Lysgaard,[2] Willett[3] and others have illustrated these changes. In particular, Willett's paper in this volume relates the temperature changes to changes in the global atmospheric circulation.

Several years ago the author became interested in temperature changes at Blue Hill, and the Observatory record was reworked and extended backward an additional 36 years with the use of the nearby Milton Center record. A paper[4] presenting this work emphasized the homogeneity of record rather than the significance of the change. In further consideration of this and more recent work on the increasing mildness of New England winters,[5] the author has become concerned over the acceptance, apparently at face value, of some of the meteorological data used in discussing world-wide circulation patterns.

The present communication is, therefore, divided into three sections — the first illustrating the pitfalls of using nonhomogeneous data; the second showing an example of the study of climatic trends with the best available material, and the third presenting a discussion of the results obtained by others, after consideration of observational and inhomogeneity errors.

ACCURACY AND HOMOGENEITY OF OBSERVATIONAL DATA

1. *Temperature.* In the studies of circulation changes, most authors
have found it necessary to break up the over-all variations into 20- or
30-year periods. When this is done, large areas of the world may be characterized by temperature changes as small as 0.5°F or less; therefore, for
these areas to carry significance, the data must be accurate to about 0.5°F.
Mitchell[6] has broken down the causes of secular temperature trends, both
real and apparent, in great detail. Figure 1, a copy of his breakdown, illustrates the problem. Following the "apparent" change side of the chart, in

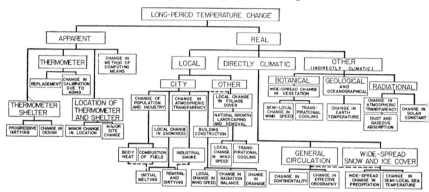

Fig. 1. Factors affecting long-term temperature changes. (After J. M. Mitchell, Jr.)

which we are interested at the moment, we find the "change in the method
of computing means." Unfortunately, corrections for this factor vary with
almost every station. Concerning the thermometers, since calibrations
change with age,[5] it is rather fortunate that thermometers are broken
every 20 years or so. When the site of the thermometer screen is changed,
a correction based on comparative readings must be applied. The dirtying
of the thermometer screen, with consequent overheating during the day,
is gradual and its effect is almost impossible to remove from the data.
Changes in screen design have fortunately been few in the past 50 years,
but here again comparisons are necessary before corrections can be
applied.

Other changes, listed by Mitchell as "local," which should be eliminated as far as possible when global changes are under consideration, are
subdivided under "city" and "other." References covering these types of
changes are given by Mitchell.

From data collected by Mitchell on the mean winter temperatures at
New Haven in the city and at the airport on weekdays and Sundays, it can
be shown that the city has warmed up about 1.5°F over the last 100 years

owing to the combined influences listed in Fig. 1. Other factors listed primarily affect the rural stations. Their effect need not be as direct as, for example, the shading of the thermometer screen, but may result from taller trees, which, in turn, have allowed warm air to accumulate and thereby raise the maximum temperatures. This type of error incidentally points out the advantage of computing means from several or hourly observations rather than from the maximum and minimum temperatures divided by two.

In Mitchell's breakdown it seems reasonable to include the other botanical, geological, and oceanographical factors as part of the climatic change to be isolated, provided they are widespread.

Figure 2, also prepared by Mitchell, shows the magnitude of errors in mean temperature change that might be expected from the above-mentioned influences. The graph is based on a number of investigations which are included in Mitchell's latest and still unpublished work. It is important

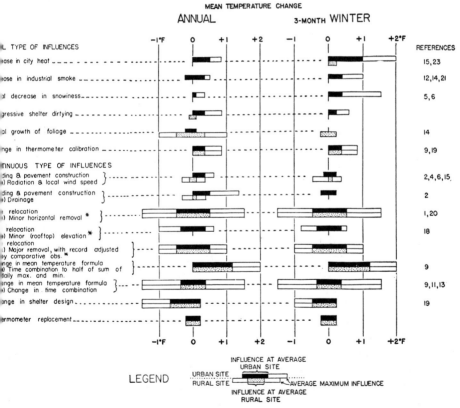

2. The magnitude of mean-temperature errors due to various factors for the period 1850 to present. (After J. M. Mitchell, Jr.)

that the over-all effect of exposure changes is to increase the temperature, the amount being larger in winter than for the year.

2. *Pressure.* The magnitude of the pressure changes experienced over large portions of the globe is also so small that it lies close to, if not within, the observational errors. These errors have not been diagnosed in any detail, but recently a change of 0.007 in.-of-mercury (0.2 mb) over a 2-year period has been detected in one of the standard barometers at Blue Hill. Externally, nothing appears to be wrong with the instrument, and in over 50 years the deviation from the others has never been so large. Means from instruments that may suddenly shift calibration in this way are value-less when global changes appear to be of the order of 0.015 in. in 30 years. Fortunately, at Blue Hill, where four large barometers are checked an-nually, such large errors can be avoided, but not until recently was such a system of standards used over the world.

3. *Precipitation.* The analysis of precipitation data has been more thorough. Changes in gages, exposures, etc. can be detected fairly well by accumulation comparisons. It should be recognized that seasonal and an-nual catches will vary between stations only a few miles apart. The varia-tion between two stations near Blue Hill and about 1 mile apart amounted to 2 percent for the annual and 1 percent for the winter precipitation when totaled over a 10-year period. This variation, of course, changes from place to place over the world. Therefore, it is desirable to have a closer network of precipitation stations than temperature stations for a study of the distribution of changes.

4. *Wind.* Although wind is the basic measure of atmospheric circula-tion, the literature indicates that relatively little has been done with data on wind. C. E. P. Brooks [7] suggested the value of wind analysis; he checked old diaries and was able to determine resultant directions for London, Edinburgh, and Dublin back to 1667. Changes of 45° over long periods were detected. Mitchell [6] attempted to determine what wind directions, if any, contributed the most to the temperature rise at Blue Hill. He en-countered trouble owing to the shelter location during the early period. Wind-direction frequencies can be misleading. For example, when the frequencies of wind direction, observed twice daily, over two 10-year pe-riods centered 20 years apart, were compared, it was found at one station that all the cardinal points increased and the intermediate points de-creased. Such a change could hardly be real. The reason obviously lies in the fact that an observer became careless in reading the wind record. Those who are familiar with the U. S. Weather Bureau triple register can understand why such a tendency could arise. However, when resultant directions of the frequencies are computed, such an error has little effect. Large changes in resultant direction were found, indicating that this par-ticular element is quite sensitive to circulation changes.

AN EXAMPLE OF THE STUDY OF CLIMATIC TRENDS

In order to test the feasibility of correlating changes of wind direction with changes of temperature, pressure, and precipitation, a careful selection of stations was made for periods when the data were readily available. Only stations within the United States were used. The test was made for winter months, including December, January, and February, and the changes were determined for the period 1908–1917 to 1928–1937 (the December of each season belonging to the previous year); thus a 20-year change between the two 10-year periods is represented.

Only stations showing no change in the location of the thermometer shelter or wind equipment were used. These stations were selected from the newly printed station histories found on the back of Weather Bureau annual summaries. With this careful selection of stations it is believed that false changes have been cut to a minimum. Heating from the cities should be about the same for both periods, since the first occurred during a wartime period of industrial activity and the second during a quiet period of depression, thus canceling out the effect of over-all growth.

Figure 3 shows the change in mean winter temperature. The lower

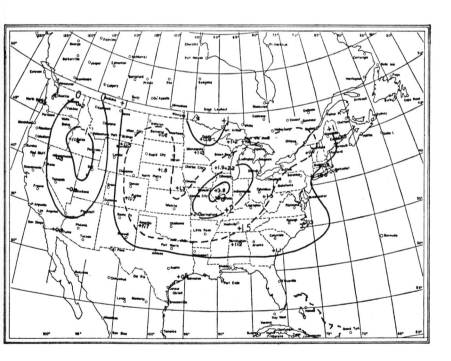

Fig. 3. Winter (D,J,F) temperature change (°F), 1928–1937 minus 1908–1917.

temperatures over the Rockies might be interpreted as a result of greater adiabatic cooling due to the forced ascent of stronger westerlies. In turn, the secondary rise found in the lee of the mountains might be caused by increased foehn winds.

Figure 4 shows the percental change of precipitation of the second period from the first period. In spite of the average variability of precipitation, the large increase along the Gulf and East coasts cannot be dismissed.

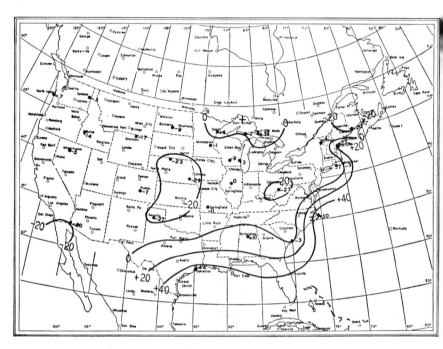

Fig. 4. Winter (D,J,F) precipitation change; percental change, 1928–1937 total from 1908–1917 total.

Figure 5 shows the resultant wind-direction frequencies for both periods. Gordon [8] has shown that over the sea at the several latitudes of the United States the mean angle of inclination of the mean vector wind to the mean isobars is nearly constant (15°). Although this relation has not been tested over land, it is reasonable to expect that the vectors or resultants of exposed stations should bear a nearly constant relation to the mean isobars over the United States. The consistent change to more northwesterly from west-northwesterly directions along the east coast is the most interesting feature of this chart.

These changes in wind direction, as shown in Fig. 5, can be illustrated more clearly by plotting the vector change at each station, as shown in Fig. 6. The vectors represent rising pressure to the right and falling to the left. Now a systematic change appears. The suggestion of increasing westerlies over the northwest from the first to the second period to cause the observed temperature change is not verified by the winds. Local winds caused by topographic effects may have masked a change toward stronger westerlies.

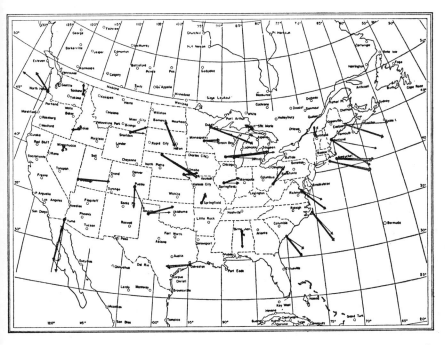

Fig. 5. Winter resultant wind direction frequencies; thin line = 1908–1917 period, heavy line = 1928–1937 period.

Lines representing relative pressure changes have been added. Lysgaard's January pressure-change map of 30 years ending in 1940 minus 30 years ending in 1910 shows a center of 0.5-mb fall over northeastern Montana and centers of 0.5-mb rise over southern New Mexico and Kentucky, with a 1-mb rise over Bermuda. Since the periods in question are not the same and the pressure changes are near the limit of accuracy, no proof of similarity exists; nevertheless, the newly constructed pressure-change map does not disagree with that of Lysgaard. Apparently, rising pressure west and northwest of New England has accentuated the coastal trough, and it may have retrograded slightly. Closer examination of the winds indicates greater variability over this region, which may be interpreted as "more stormy." This is also substantiated by the coastal increase in precipitation and by the decrease in sunshine at Washington and Blue Hill.

Through the use of these charts, greater detail can be extracted from the carefully selected data. For example, Willett's hypothesis that the warming experienced in the United States is a result of the intensification of the Bermuda High remains basically correct. It appears, however, from

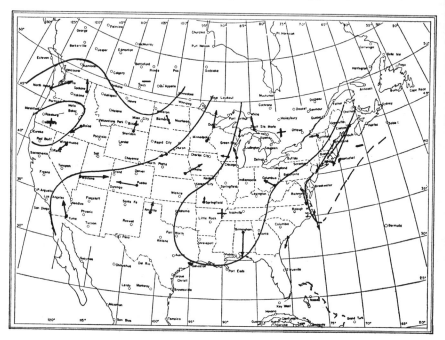

Fig. 6. Winter vector changes in resultant wind direction frequencies, 1908–1917 period to 1928–1937 period; areas of relative pressure changes are outlined.

these charts that the semipermanent High, or offshoot of the Bermuda High, located over the southeastern states also increased, leaving a trough along the coast. Thus the southeast coast did not warm up as much as the center of the country, which was subject to southwesterlies around the stronger inland High. Warming over New England, in spite of more northwesterly winds, suggests that air from the Southwest frequently entered New England from the west.

The colder temperatures over Idaho and Nevada are verified by the increasing northerlies and easterlies over the region.

These details, not shown by previous studies, appear worthy of notice, especially for areas like New England where slight changes in temperature and precipitation can make large differences in snowfall.

SUMMARY OF RECENT CLIMATIC CHANGE STUDIES

In general, little consideration has been given by others to the homogeneity of data before conclusions were drawn. The author has not yet looked into the foreign data, but the United States material is known to be nonhomogenous in many cases.[9] At the time of publication of Clayton's analysis, the details of station histories were all but inaccessible; there was no easy way of sorting good from poor records. It should be pointed out that various manipulations of the data can decrease but not eliminate the effects of inhomogeneities. The computation of changes over short periods and their subsequent addition are valid only so long as no station-change date is crossed or other inhomogeneity involved. With these limitations in mind, the more important change maps of Willett and Lysgaard may be examined.

In general it can be said that the global temperature trends have been upward from about 1885 to at least 1940, with an indication, at least over New England, that the rising trend has decreased over the past 10 to 20 years. Since 1885, the amount of rise has been about 2°F in winter and less than 1°F for the year. The greatest rises have occurred in winter over the Arctic, exceeding 6°F in the 1917–1937 period.

Annual precipitation changes have been positive over the Arctic and North Temperate Zone, in Mexico, La Plata, southern India and southeast Asia, while they have been negative over most of the United States, the northern part of South America, Africa, Malaya, and Australia. Scherhag [10] attributes these phenomena to a strengthening of the atmospheric circulation and consequently of the Gulf Stream. Observational evidence shows that the warming of northern waters lags behind the warming of the atmosphere.

Willett [3] believes that the primary causes of the most significant changes of temperature in the Northern Hemisphere, in terms of the general circulation pattern, lie in the position and intensity of the winter polar anticyclones over Eurasia and North America. This interpretation is borne out by Petterssen [11] in his study of the frequency of cyclones over the North Atlantic and eastern Europe. A decrease in storminess was found over Scandinavia, where pressures have risen, while storminess increased from Newfoundland northeastward and northward. This pattern causes more frequent southwest winds over the eastern North Atlantic and thereby warm-air advection. Petterssen, in the above-cited work, also computed the meridional flow and was able to show that winds flowed into and out of the Arctic more frequently than formerly, thus allowing less time for radiational cooling. Consequently, northerly winds also averaged warmer than before. He also pointed out that the higher wind speeds observed over Scandinavia, as a result of this pattern, tend to increase minimum temperatures by reducing the magnitude and frequency of temperature inversions at the ground or level of observation.

In conclusion, it has been shown that meteorological data definitely indicate climatic changes over parts of the world. Over large areas of the temperate and equatorial regions, however, the changes are of a magnitude approaching the over-all accuracy of the data; therefore they must be viewed with caution. It is suggested that the change maps over the questionable areas be augmented by wind-change charts and that only homogenous data be used for the recomputation of the maps.

The author wishes to thank J. Murray Mitchell, Jr., for his permission to reproduce Figs. 1 and 2, and Sarah H. Wollaston and Lawrence C. Howard, both of the Observatory staff, for the considerable effort put into tabulation work and typing.

REFERENCES

1. G. W. Brier, "40 year trends in Northern Hemisphere surface pressure," *Bull. Amer. Meteorol. Soc. 28*, 237–247 (1947).

2. Leo Lysgaard, "On the present climatic variation," *Roy. Meteorol Soc. Cent. Proc.* (1950), pp. 206–211.

3. H. C. Willett, "Temperature trends of the past century," *Roy. Meteorol. Soc. Cent. Proc.* (1950), pp. 195–206.

4. J. H. Conover, "A century of rising temperatures at Milton, Mass.," presented at the American Meteorological Society Meeting, Washington, D. C., May 1950. Unpublished.

5. J. H. Conover, "Are New England winters growing milder?" *Weatherwise 4*, 5–9 (1951).

6. J. M. Mitchell, Jr., "On the causes of instrumentally observed secular temperature trends" (Thesis submitted in partial fulfilment of the requirements for the B.S. degree, Massachusetts Institute of Technology, 1951), pp. 19–76.

7. C. E. P. Brooks, *Climate through the ages* (Benn, London; McGraw-Hill, New York, 1949), pp. 312–314.

8. A. H. Gordon, "The relation between the mean vector surface wind and the mean vector pressure gradient over the oceans," *Geofisica Pura e Applicata 21*, 49–51 (1952).

9. H. H. Clayton and F. L. Clayton, *World weather records 1931–40* (Smithsonian Institution Publications, Washington), vol. 105 (1947); also vols. 79 and 90.

10. R. Scherhag, "Die Erwärmung der Arktis," *Jour. Cons. Int. Explor. Mer.* (Copenhagen) *12*, 263 (1937). [Referred to by C. E. P. Brooks.]

11. S. Petterssen, "Changes in the general circulation," *Glaciers and Climate, Geografiska Annaler 31*, parts 1–2, 212–221 (1949).

19

CLIMATIC CHANGES OR CYCLES?

Victor Conrad

AN INVESTIGATION I HAVE RECENTLY
finished deals with the recurrence of severe and mild winters.
According to A. Angot, temperature conditions of winter are well characterized by the sum of the negative daily means in centigrade degrees. The
colder the winter, the larger is the total.

The limits between normal and abnormal are usually defined arbitrarily. This procedure is impaired by the fact that the same limits applied,
for instance, to temperature series pertaining to places in different climates
cannot yield reasonable results. Thus, an arbitrarily chosen limit for temperature variations at a place of low continentality could yield too great
a range of normals. For another place of high continentality the same
limit of normals would be much too narrow.

The author, therefore, has recommended the use of the standard deviation, or some other measure of scattering derived from the series in
question, as the limit between normal and abnormal.

Objective limits derived from a measure of scattering, including all
the *normal* values, automatically become narrower with a temperature
series in the more uniform climates, and wider in the more extreme
climates.

Sums of negative daily temperature means, in centigrade degrees, for
the whole winter, recently published by Knoch,[1] give an opportunity to
apply the method of objective limits between normal and abnormal to a
long series of observations (1767–68 to 1946–47). Orders of magnitude
may be mentioned:

(1) The total of daily mean temperatures below freezing is 233 C deg.
(centigrade degrees) for an *average winter* in Berlin, Germany.

(2) The standard deviation is 154 C deg.

Therefore the definitions read:

(a) A *severe* winter is one with a total of daily means below freezing in
centigrade degrees greater than 387.

(b) A *mild* winter is one with a total <79.

(c) Totals between 79 C deg and 387 C deg (below freezing) are called *normal*.

Based on these definitions a list of 29 severe and 25 mild winters is compiled.

With the *probable error* as a limit between normal and abnormal, the definitions would read:

Severe winter: total $>$ 337 C deg
Mild winter: total $<$ 129 C deg

This limit yields a list of 33 *severe* and 56 *mild* ones, since the range of normal winters is narrowed by 50 C deg on either side so that necessarily the number of abnormal winters is increased. We arrive at the simple but important corollary that the number of abnormal winters is dependent upon the magnitude assumed for the limit between normal and abnormal.

Intervals between successive abnormal winters were calculated in order to look for possible cyclic recurrence. On the average, 2.23 normal winters are inserted between two consecutive abnormal winters. The average interval between two consecutive severe winters was found to b 5.10 years, and that between two consecutive mild winters to be 5.42 years.

Since the number of abnormal winters naturally depends upon the magnitude of the limits, the intervals between abnormal winters are subject to the same dependency. Wider limits for normality decrease the number of abnormal events and increase, therefore, the duration of the average intervals. With narrower limits the contrary is the case.

The significance of the average duration of the intervals is, therefore, only a relative one. They are, however, comparable from place to place if the same measure of scattering is used for the determination of the limit between normal and abnormal.

Obviously, average intervals derived from arbitrarily fixed limits are not comparable with each other, for reasons given above. What is valid for the general average interval is also valid for average intervals between possibly periodically recurrent abnormal winters. It is clear, therefore, that the length of cycles found with arbitrary fixed limits is dependent upon the individual numerical definition of these limits; other definitions would yield other periodicities, if any. Objective limits derived from a *measure of scattering* are self-adaptable and flexible and yield comparable, although relative, results.

The series of intervals between consecutive abnormal winters derived from the Berlin series by means of the standard deviation does not stimulate an investigation into cycles. Only the frequency distribution of the numbers of normal winters inserted between two consecutive abnormal winters shows a special feature. Short intervals are by far the most frequent. The frequency is represented by a decay curve. Thus, the frequency curve does not at all give a hint of a periodic tendency for abnormal winters to recur at more or less regular intervals.

Although the Berlin series of below-freezing centigrade totals for 180 winters does not show periodic features, a *remarkable trend of changing temperature conditions* over a long period is revealed. I have divided the entire period into successive decades. The number of mild winters and severe ones in the respective decades was counted. These data show that the difference, number of mild winters minus number of severe ones, is negative, or at most zero, from the decade 1771–1780 through that of 1861–1870. For the decades 1871–1880 through 1921–1930 the reverse is true; without exception the number of mild winters is greater than that of cold winters, decade by decade.

In the period 1770–1870 the number of severe winters was three times as great as that of mild winters; in the period 1871 to 1921 seven times as many mild winters occurred as severe ones.

A further confirmation of these conditions is offered by the following data: In the 69 years from 1871 to 1939, the warm portion of the period, only two severe winters have been recorded, namely 1892–93 and 1928–29. Mild winters, however, were lacking in the 25 years from 1797 to 1821 and in the 32 years from 1834 to 1865.

These facts disclose a decided and clear-cut *climatic secular change* for North Germany. This result may be valuable *per se*, especially because the methods applied are fully objective and because only original series, not deformed by possibly misleading smoothing procedures, are used.

REFERENCE

1. K. Knoch, "Ueber die Strenge der Winter in Norddeutschland nach der Beobachtungsreihe 1766–1947," *Meteorol. Rundschau 1*, 137–140 (1947–48).

20

EVIDENCE OF CLIMATIC CHANGE IN THE GEOLOGIC RECORD OF PLANT LIFE

Elso S. Barghoorn

Pₗₐₙₜ LIFE HAS EXISTED ON THE EARTH for probably more than a billion years. Although this extent of time is essentially inconceivable to the human mind as anything more than an arithmetic expression, it nevertheless provides a chronological framework within which the evolutionary picture may be visualized. The known fossil record of plants from which this picture emerges is a fragmentary, though decipherable, sequence of tangible organic forms, featured by a remarkable progression from simplicity to complexity.

The geologic record yields only the history of morphologic change and tells us nothing directly of the physiologic responses of organisms. These must be inferred or surmised through analogy with known relations of form and function in existing organisms. For example, the extremely thick leaf cuticles and other structural modification of many xerophytic plants can reasonably be interpreted as evidence of adaptations to resist water loss and hence adaptation to arid climate. By the same token, comparable structures in fossil forms may reasonably be interpreted as evidence of arid climate in the past, especially if the degree of taxonomic relation between the living and the extinct is known.

Because of the innumerable and frequently obscure relations between structure and function in higher plants I should like to raise the question whether the increasing morphologic complexity that features organic evolution has not also been associated with a physiologic evolution, the essence of which is an increased sensitivity or susceptibility on the part of the organism to react to physical factors of the environment. Such an assumption applied to plants would certainly aid in explaining the extraordinary cosmopolitan distribution of many ancient groups, over the surface of an earth, which throughout geologic time must have possessed climatic zones, regardless of how different these were from existing geographic zones. There exist today no truly cosmopolitan species of higher plants, and the study of ecology and distribution of living plants is to a great extent concerned with relating geographic ranges to factors of the environment. We are able today to recognize the larger climatic zones, or types of climates, by characteristic flora and fauna. How far back in the geologic record this relation can be extended is certainly an open question. It is, however, basic to our concept that the history of climate may be read in the history of life. Certainly since the appearance of higher plants it seems reasonable to accept the idea that natural selection has been strongly influenced by physiologic demands imposed by the physical environment. Therefore environment participates in the direction of evolution and in the natural selection of anatomic features that we ordinarily think of as the physical evidence of evolution. If we accept these premises we have accepted the idea that climate and evolution are closely entwined, to the extent that knowledge of climate and its history are fundamental to the understanding and interpretation of the paleontologic record. As George Gaylord Simpson[1] has recently pointed out, "search for *the* cause of evolution has been abandoned." However, it seems evident to the writer, as to many others, that climatic change has been a most significant, if not *the most* significant factor in the migration and dispersal of the existing terrestrial flora and fauna, whatever the ultimate causes of initiating biological variation, that is, of evolution, may be.

It seems appropriate at this point, and before surveying the geologic record, to examine the fundamental basis for assuming that plants and their distribution are related to changes in climate. The land plant is a photosynthetic mechanism, thermodynamically concerned with trapping solar energy through the chemistry of photosynthesis. As such, its efficiency, as well as that of the vegetation as a whole, is confined within the physical ranges of protoplasmic activity, especially with respect to availability of water and of heat, to mention only two factors essential for life. Since these physical limitations are thrust upon the plant through the agency of the atmosphere, it necessarily follows that atmospheric conditions — the essence of climate in meteorologic terms — profoundly affect the vital processes of vegetation to such an extent that climate constitutes a major control over growth and survival. In this connection, it may be noted that higher plants as individuals cannot migrate to more favorable environments as most higher animals are able to do. Extreme conditions of temperature or of available moisture consequently serve to limit photosynthetic activity and, therefore, exert control on the maximal tolerance of land plants. Through the operation of natural selection on the inherently variable population there occurs a distribution of forms best suited to meet the limitations of a wide range of physical conditions. In this way climate (and physiography) are geographically correlated with vegetation, in a vague but nevertheless definable interrelation. The closeness of the relation between climate and vegetation is sufficiently well developed, as noted before, to allow the major climatic zones of the earth's surface to be defined by vegetational areas.

Extensions of the relation between climate and vegetation may be made in two directions. One of these lies in quantitative analysis of climatic factors which may operate in delimiting the geographic distribution of constituent members of the vegetation. The other line of inquiry lies in extending known correlations of climate with vegetation into the geologic past. Such extensions into the past records of vegetation comprise the nucleus of botanical paleoecology, though in its broadest terms paleoecology deals with the totality of physical as well as biological evidence of past environments. It is my intention here to present evidence that land plants are probably the most valid and widespread biological indicators of past physical conditions, especially of climate.

There are two basic assumptions for the paleobotanical interpretation of climatic history. The first of these is that plant groups of the past had environmental requirements similar to those which they possess today, the degree of similarity being a function of morphologic, taxonomic, and hence genetic affinity or relationship. The second assumption is that an environmental complex of definable climatic and other physical conditions supports a biotic population which is in general equilibrium with these conditions, and that this population will show no more than minor (specific) changes unless there is distinct alteration of the environmental conditions.

Acceptance of these two principles provides us with an extremely valuable means for examining and interpreting the history of climate, though their bland acceptance by the unwary investigator may lead to erroneous and unfortunate conclusions. For example, morphologically similar but ecologically different forms of variable species may complicate or confuse the issue in that their presumed living equivalents exist today under different environmental conditions. In addition, certain species, and to a greater extent genera, of the living flora commonly exhibit such widespread distribution, and occur in such diverse habitats, that they provide little basis for evaluating environmental conditions.

A further possible objection to the logical basis of paleoecology may be found in the rather startling realization that its working concepts, if too rigidly adhered to, would deny the operation of organic evolution. Organic evolution demonstrates that organisms vary, disseminate, and adapt through natural selection to meet changing environmental conditions. To the botanist concerned with plant evolution, this aspect of the problem may raise a real obstacle to accepting the entire structure of paleoecology, and would necessitate a retreat to considerations dealing largely with extremes of the physical environment and their relation to limiting plant growth in general.

Students of plant distribution and biogeography are frequently skeptical, and justifiably so, about the interpretation of past ecology on the basis of fossil plants. The argument is sometimes advanced that adaptation, that is, evolution, is more rapid than climatic change and that therefore the stratigraphic sequence with which the paleoecologist deals is an evolutionary rather than an ecologic sequence. If this view be accepted, paleoecology becomes a grand delusion of circular reasoning, whereby climate is interpreted in terms of evolution, and evolution interpreted in terms of climate, with infinite concordance of the evidence.

Because of our limited understanding of the actual causes of evolution, certain weaknesses in the methods of paleoecology must be carefully weighed. Perhaps it would be reasonable to conclude that the paleoecologic method when applied to more than major details of climatic history is largely limited to the Cenozoic era in geologic time, during which period fossil representatives of many living groups are known and can be studied in terms of existing ecology and present environmental relations. Accuracy of the method in elucidating the history of climate seems to be inversely proportional to the geologic age of deposits from which the evidence is secured. Ecologic interpretation of ancient and extinct groups of plants will always be subject to uncertainties, and will always require confirming evidence from the physical geology and paleozoölogy.

The over-all geologic record of terrestrial plants seems to provide us with certain basic concepts. I should like to enumerate three.

(1) Higher plants can exist only within certain thermodynamic, physiologic limits imposed by climate. Their remains in richly fossiliferous sediments, or in the form of coal seams, therefore indicate that the climate at the time of deposition was neither too arid nor too cold for vigorous vegetative growth. In this connection, it should be noted that coal seams and other plant-bearing deposits such as are known from high latitudes on the Antarctic continent could not conceivably form today under existing climatic conditions.

(2) Species of plants, even though genetically variable and composed of numerous ecologically different forms, are geographically limited by environmental factors, among which climate is of prime importance. If this were not the case, it would be impossible to decipher any meaning whatsoever in the history of climate deduced from the paleontologic record.

(3) Associations or communities of plants, to an even greater extent than individuals, exist in a dynamic, though not easily definable, equilibrium with climate, in particular with extremes of temperature and moisture. Climatic change can alter the equilibrium and result in the migration

of plant associations, through natural selection and population pressure, to areas resembling climatically their former habitats. Plant associations are not constant populations, but assemblages continually undergoing change by extinction of forms and by evolution of new types. The tendency for plant associations to retain their essential taxonomic identity through extensive latitudinal and longitudinal migrations is one of the most impressive features of the Cenozoic history of vegetation, a fact which early engaged the attention of both Charles Darwin and Asa Gray.

With both the strengths and the weaknesses of paleoecology in mind, it is possible to review more objectively the paleontologic record of plants and its bearing on the central theme of this symposium, the history of climate and climatic change.

More than one-half the total chronologic record of plant life is restricted to marine sediments, and the bulk of this marine record is limited to calcareous algal deposits. Ecologic interpretation of these plant-bearing marine formations, some of great antiquity in pre-Cambrian rocks, is potentially of much significance, especially wherever correlation is possible with associated faunas. Calcareous algae are world-wide in distribution at present, but their quantitative role in carbonate precipitation, owing to the chemistry of sea water, is strikingly greater in warm, shallow seas than in cold marine waters. Occurrence of extensive deposits of stromatolites, now generally agreed to be of calcareous algal origin, in the Pre-Cambrian sediments of the Belt Series in Montana, in the Black Hills of South Dakota, and in the Northwest Territories of Canada [2] provide evidence of former widespread seas over areas that are now in cold temperate and even subarctic regions. In marine sediments of early Paleozoic age, algal reefs are fairly common over many areas of the continents, in both the Northern and Southern Hemispheres. These reefs provide a disconnected but widespread record of invasion of the Cambrian and Ordovician seas into large areas of the present continents. If viewed in terms of present-day ecology, the distribution of early Paleozoic marine algae would indicate extensive poleward spread of warm, shallow seas, a marked contrast to the cold-water floras of many middle-latitude regions today.

From paleobotanic evidence, the climatic history of the present continents begins in the late Silurian and early Devonian. Continental sediments of this time record the most striking transformation known in the paleontologic record of plant life, namely, the emergence of plants from the sea and the establishment of a true land flora. The significance of this step in the subsequent evolution of vascular plants and of animals is of paramount importance. The development of terrestrial animals, in particular the vertebrates, has been greatly influenced by developments in plant evolution, especially among the so-called herbivorous animals. One example suffices to illustrate the interrelation: the evolution and dispersal of grazing animals during Tertiary time are closely associated with the evolution and spread of grasses and grassland environments. It is perhaps reasonable to conclude that the origin of a land flora of vascular plants was a biologic prerequisite for the successful liberation of animal life from the sea, though, as R. J. Russell [3] has pointed out, marine vertebrate animals were certainly not evolving in premeditation of the event.

Early land plants show two outstanding features: first, extreme simplicity of structure and small size; and second, very widespread geographic distribution. Occurrence of abundant Devonian plant life from terrestrial sediments of such widely removed areas as the Falkland Islands, Spitzbergen, and the interior of Asia and North America, to name only a few localities, indicate either an enormous range of tolerance on the part of structurally similar plants, or the presence of far more uniform and milder climate than occurs today. The emergence of Devonian plant-bearing strata from beneath the melting glaciers of Ellesmere Land and Spitzbergen is impressive evidence of climatic change.

Unfortunately our knowledge of early Devonian plants from areas within the present tropics is extremely limited, and it is not possible to attempt a reconstruction of the climatic zones of the earth during Devonian time on the basis of plant distribution. The known distribution of Devonian plants, especially their diversification in high latitudes, suggests that glacial conditions did not exist at the poles, though positive evidence from that most interesting of all land areas in the history of climate, Antarctica, is missing.

By the end of Devonian time land plants had evolved many complex types, some of which were true trees and constitute evidence of the earliest forests. One group of upper Devonian large trees, the genus *Callixylon*, was widespread in what are now such ecologically diverse environments as those of Oklahoma, Indiana, New York State, and western Siberia. The paleobotanic record would indicate a nonglacial climate, with probably great expansions of humid warm temperate regions into higher latitudes during most of the Devonian. Establishment of the terrestrial flora probably in itself constituted a climatic factor, or at least a factor of local importance in climatic change. Covering of the former bare land surfaces of the earth with vegetation contributed influences that did not exist before, such as the accelerated loss of ground water from the soil, effected by absorption and transpiration from plants, and the acceleration of the oxygen-carbon dioxide interchange brought about by enormous new areas of photosynthetic activity. Geologic processes such as erosion and weathering would be very different on an earth devoid of vegetation from what they are on the present continental surfaces, where numerous interrelations exist between vegetation and erosion. Considerations such as these, however, quickly lead us into questions that are beyond the reach of paleontologic evidence and can be answered or thought of in terms of logic rather than discovery.

Despite the lapse of time that separates us from the floras of the Carboniferous, we probably possess today more knowledge of the plant life of that Paleozoic period than of any other period in geologic history until the Pleistocene and Recent. Sedimentary rocks of that time have been given an appropriate geologic memorial in the name Carboniferous, or carbon-bearing, because of the accumulations of plant residues which we recognize as coal. The mining of coal and associated sediments has yielded, as a by-product, great collections of fossil plants and a great variety of information on their structure, classification, and distribution, to such an extent, in fact, that a substantial part of our knowledge of extinct plants is limited to floras of the late Paleozoic, especially the Carboniferous.

A fairly extensive literature exists on the subject of presumed coal-swamp climates and the environmental conditions of coal deposition. Many of the earlier writers were strongly influenced by now outmoded ideas of the geologic history and the age of the earth. The concept of residual initial earth heat, and final cooling to the present glacial climate, was widely held for a surprisingly long period and much influenced thinking even into the twentieth century.

At present, there is no uniformly accepted theory of Carboniferous climate, nor an adequate explanation of the enormous accumulations of coal during this period of geologic time. It is quite probable that the explanation is both physiographic and climatic and is related to the erosional history of the continents. Early Carboniferous floras exhibit a remarkable uniformity in composition with regard to major and minor groups of plants. The geologic record indicates that their migration and the establishment of larger groups was probably world-wide. The widespread dispersal of early Carboniferous (Mississippian) plants is well attested by deposits from both Northern and Southern Hemispheres.

From the paleontologic evidence available, it would appear that there was very slight climatic zonation between high and low latitudes during the major part of the Carboniferous. Very similar floras occur in regions that today show extreme climatic differences, for example, northeastern Europe and the eastern Mediterranean, or Nova Scotia and central Kansas. The earlier Carboniferous floras of the Southern Hemisphere contain many groups of plants also common to Holarctic regions. Even within the present-day tropics there can be found little indication of regional differentiation of the early Carboniferous vegetation. It is probably significant in

connection with Carboniferous climates that the bulk of the world's Paleozoic coals occur in what are now temperate latitudes. The coal-swamp
climate was quite likely one featured by excessive humidity rather than
high temperatures. Peat formation, the first stage in coal deposition, is
more favored in warm temperate than in tropical regions today, although
peat deposits are by no means absent in equatorial regions. It should be
noted that the major part of the Carboniferous coals are derived from
woody plants, and the source vegetation and presumed environment bear
no resemblance to the type of vegetation and conditions that characterize
northern peat bogs; they were, rather, forest accumulations.

One impressive indicator of uniform climate over great areas of the
Carboniferous continents is the general absence of annual growth rings in
coal-swamp trees. The entire question of ring development in woody plants
is one fraught with botanical variables as well as climatic variables. However, the consistent absence of any index of seasonal growth seems difficult
to explain except on the assumption that winter cold and seasonality of
rainfall were absent or at a minimum. In existing woody plants, annual
ring development may occur under nearly uniform climatic conditions, as
in equatorial rainforests. Nevertheless, in climates with distinct seasons,
seasonal effect is almost invariably reflected in pronounced annual growth
rings.

The picture of Paleozoic climate, developed from paleobotanic evidence, would scarcely be complete, or indeed fairly represented, if reference were not made to the climatologic anomaly recorded in plant-bearing
beds of the late Carboniferous (Permo-Carboniferous) of the Southern
Hemisphere. Here there is ample evidence of widespread continental
glaciation of the austral continents including tropical Africa, and also
peninsular India. Associated with geologic evidence of glaciation occur
remains of a depauperate flora characteristically represented in the Lower
Gondwana beds of India. This flora is featured by a small number of
species and a pronounced difference, botanically, from the supposedly contemporaneous coal-swamp flora of the northern land masses. Remains of
plants have recently been found even within the tillites of the Talchir
boulder beds of India,[4] indicating that a flora developed in a rigorous climate certainly in the near proximity of glacial conditions.

Fragments of wood from late Paleozoic austral deposits frequently
show pronounced ring growth as further evidence of seasonal periodicity,
probably winter cold. Contrast between the paleoecologic conditions of
late Paleozoic climates in the Northern and Southern Hemispheres is so
great as to evoke equivalently bizarre explanations. One of these is the
often refuted but continually persistent concept of continental drift, a
hypothesis that unfortunately creates more problems than it sets aside.

Whatever explanation is finally made of the problem of late Paleozoic climate, the available geologic and paleobotanic evidence relating to the period now constitutes one of the great enigmas of paleoclimatology.

Although floras of the early Mesozoic, especially the Triassic period, are poorly known in comparison with those of the late Paleozoic, they provide evidence of a return to more uniform world-wide climate. This is indicated by an increasing cosmopolitanism of certain groups of plants which make their first appearance in the Mesozoic. The rapid development of coniferous trees and other groups of primitive seed plants, which show structural adaptation to arid or semiarid environment, support diverse geologic evidence pointing to well-developed dry or monsoonal climates in temperate latitudes during the early Mesozoic. Triassic coals are not common, but their existence indicates the prevalence of humid meso-phytic forest climates in other parts of the temperate regions, for example, in the south central Atlantic states of the United States. Cosmopolitan dispersal of certain groups of plants and their extension into high latitudes appears to have reached its peak in the Mid-Mesozoic, probably in the early Jurassic.

Jurassic floras, botanically rich in varied types, are known from some of the most northerly land areas of the Arctic, such as northern Greenland and Franz Josef Land, north of the 80th parallel. The most remarkable evidence of the nonglacial climate of polar regions in Jurassic time, how-ever, was discovered on the Third Byrd Expedition to Antarctica. Fossil plants and coal were collected on Mount Weaver, at an elevation of 10,000 feet at latitude 86°58′ S. The plants themselves, interestingly enough, belong to genera known from Jurassic sediments of temperate and even arctic regions of the Northern Hemisphere. The development of coal-forming swamps close to the South Pole. demands an explanation allowing for extraordinary climatic change. Botanically also, Jurassic floras present the curious anomaly of a well-differentiated vegetation developing under the physiologic conditions of the polar night.

With the close of the Mesozoic it becomes possible to refine greatly the paleoecologic interpretation of climate. By Upper Cretaceous time the Angiosperms, the ubiquitous group of flowering plants that now domi-nate the earth's vegetation, had attained great diversity. Many existing genera of trees and shrubs can be recognized in Upper Cretaceous rocks, and by the early Cenozoic a number of associations of genera, surprisingly similar to mid-latitude forest associations in the present living flora, have been described. With the appearance of extant forms providing possible ecologic indices of existing environments, the reconstruction of climatic history becomes far clearer. Because of the extent of detail known at present, it is desirable to present here only the major features of the extraordinary trends of Cenozoic climate which culminated in the last glaciation.

The luxuriant growth of broad-leaf hardwood forests in high Arctic latitudes persisted from the Cretaceous into the Eocene and probably the Oligocene, indicating a prolonged continuation of humid warm temperate, or at least temperate forest climate in polar regions. Evidence for this may be found in both Arctic and Antarctic regions. During the early Cenozoic the northern *mid-latitudes* were covered by a vegetation, the botanical equivalent of which is now largely confined to subtropical and even tropical climates. A striking example of this is the rich and varied flora of the Eocene London Clay, the present equivalent of which is now to be chiefly found in the Austro-Malaysian tropics, or in New England in the Brandon lignite flora of western Vermont, the major equivalent of which now exists in the Atlantic and Gulf coastal plain area. It seems quite unlikely that truly tropical conditions occurred in mid-latitudes during the Eocene. It is more probable that the absence of pronounced winter freezing allowed an unusual extension poleward of tropical plants. Thus the situation was featured by a gentle temperature gradient between high and low latitudes instead of the steep gradient which now exists. Hence the absence of cold, the lethal factor to tropical vegetation, rather than extreme warmth is indicated. Rainfall, however, would have to be far greater than is easily explainable for such high latitudes as 48° to 52° N, probably of the order of 70 to 80 inches per year.

A shift in vegetational belts initiated by gradual climatic change and manifested by migration of forest association apparently began in the late Eocene. By the mid-Tertiary, temperate forms begin to appear in increasing numbers in mid-latitude floras, and with them a sudden influx of herbaceous plants. The appearance and rapid evolution of herbs is primarily a phenomenon of the late Cenozoic and an evolutionary development of great importance to many mammalian groups, including man. Climatic deterioration probably went on at an accelerating rate during the late Tertiary and it is probable that glacial conditions began to develop at the poles in the mid-Pliocene. Later Pliocene floras are essentially modern, though indicative of somewhat warmer climates in terms of the present geographic range of many forms represented. Unfortunately, the total number of Pliocene floras known is regrettably small.

In an attempt to reduce the large volume of paleobotanical data to a graphic representation of Cenozoic paleoecology, recourse has been made to botanical and geographic analyses of 32 of the larger Tertiary floras which have been described from North America (Table 1). The genera of flowering plants in each flora have been segregated statistically into three elements: (1) extant genera which at present occur in the bordering geographic areas of the fossil deposit and hence are designated "native" (Fig. 1); (2) extant genera which are now exotic to the bordering geo-

Table 1. Floras plotted on graph.

1. Woodbine	12. Comstock	23. Mascall
2. Tuscaloosa	13. Goshen	24. San Pablo
3. Ripley	14. Jackson	25. Weiser
4. Vermejo	15. LaPorte	26. Remington Hill
5. Laramie	16. Catahoula	27. Esmeralda
6. Medicine Bow	17. Weaverville	28. Black Hawk Ranch
7. Lance	18. Bridge Creek	29. Mulholland
8. Raton	19. Alum Bluff	30. Sonoma
9. Wilcox	20. Latah	31. Mt. Eden
10. Green River	21. Tehachapi	32. Citronelle
11. Claiborne	22. Calvert	

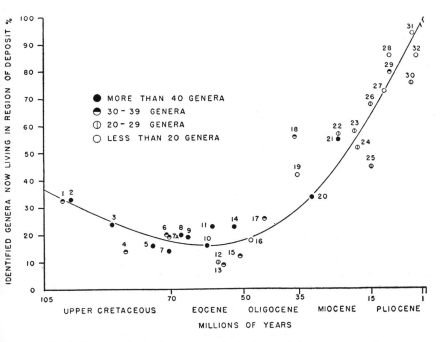

Fig. 1. Graph showing relation between geologic time and the proportion of genera in fossil floras which also occur today in the geographic region of the respective deposits. The higher a point is on the curve the greater the similarity in generic composition to the existing flora. The slope of the curve from the middle Eocene to the Pleistocene indicates the rate of trend toward the modern flora and can be regarded as a curve of climatic change. The age of each flora is that proposed by the author. Data are restricted to higher plants. Numbers refer to floras listed in Table 1.

graphic areas of the deposit (Fig. 2); and (3) genera which are not assigned to a living group and which can be regarded as extinct or botanically unidentified (Fig. 3). The percentage in each category has been computed with reference to the total number and plotted against geologic time. The increasing percentage of the "native" generic element in succeedingly younger Tertiary floras is quite striking. It should be emphasized that it

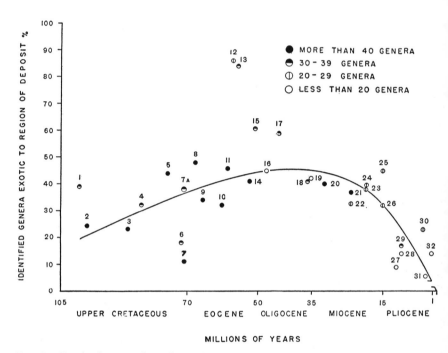

Fig. 2. Graph showing the relation between geologic time and the proportions of genera which occur in the respective deposits but are now exotic to the geographic regions of the deposits. The higher a point is on the curve, the greater the difference in generic composition from the existing flora. The exotic element is composed largely of genera now limited to warmer temperate or subtropical regions. The exotic genera rapidly decline in the later Tertiary owing to retreat southward of the warmer elements of the various floras. The data are not the direct inverse of Fig. 1 because of the unidentified or extinct elements in the fossil floras. Numbers refer to floras listed in Table 1.

is the "native" element in which accuracy of botanical identification is greatest.

From the relation shown it is apparent that American early Tertiary floras were consistently featured by a large exotic element and that this exotic element begins to decline in the late Eocene and Oligocene. By the later Tertiary, continuing to the Pleistocene, the influx of genera native at present to the respective geographic areas increases at an almost exponential rate.[5]

The relation demonstrated here seems clearly to indicate climatic change and vegetational migration. The changing composition of successive floras is not due primarily to evolution of new types but rather to migration of associations of plants. The most significant feature of the Cenozoic migration of vegetation is the steady retreat of the temperate

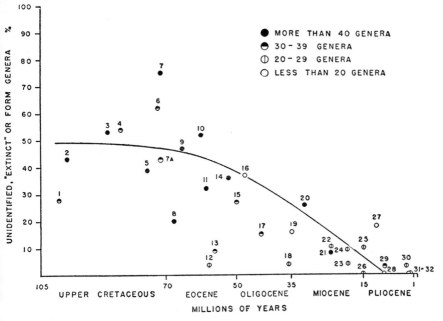

Fig. 3. Graph comparable to Figs. 1 and 2 but showing the changing percentages of unidentified or "extinct" genera. The percentage of this element in fossil floras is highly variable, owing to the uncertainty of assigning certain forms to recognized living genera. It is significant, however, that the percentage of unidentified forms drops sharply in post-Eocene deposits, a fact which emphasizes the rapid modernization of angiosperm floras, both geographically and biologically, in the later Tertiary. Numbers refer to floras listed in Table 1.

forest flora from Arctic regions and the concomitant retraction of the early Tertiary tropical elements of mid-latitude floras into the present marginal tropics. The curve of floristic change may therefore be translated into a curve of climatic change. If this interpretation be accepted, it appears that the great trend of Cenozoic climate which culminated in Pleistocene glaciation began in the mid-Tertiary, probably more than 20 million years ago. Pleistocene glaciation itself, of which present climate is in many respects an extension, may then be regarded as a geologic and climatologic event the antecedents of which extend over a fair segment of recent geologic time and is not to be viewed as a sudden change in the history of the earth's climate.

Evidence for interpreting climatic history from paleobotanic history is drawn from such wide and varied sources, both stratigraphic and geographic, that this survey is more an abstract than a detailed analysis of the geologic record of plants. However, certain conclusions emerge from the paleontologic record as a whole. Perhaps the most outstanding conclusion to be drawn is that, throughout the past several hundred million years of earth history, plant distribution demonstrates a far more uniform and less intensified latitudinal zonation of climate than now exists on the continents. The greater part of climatic history, evidenced by extinct floras and their distribution, appears to have been characterized by more equable distribution of temperature and probably also of rainfall. This geologically "normal" climate has been altered at long intervals by far briefer periods of polar ice and glaciation of the continents, even into middle and lower latitudes. In view of the geologic record of plant distribution in the past, especially in high latitudes of the Arctic and Antarctic, it is apparent that the present climate of the earth is not a logical point of departure for interpreting past ecologic conditions of the present land surfaces, nor probably in the shallower seas of the continental slopes. Detailed studies of the morphologic and taxonomic relations of fossil assemblages and additional information on the ecologic tolerance of living plants are greatly needed in further clarifying the paleoecologic record of climatic change.

REFERENCES

1. G. G. Simpson, "Periodicity in vertebrate evolution" (Symposium on distribution of evolutionary explosions in geologic time), *Jour. Pal.* 26, 359–370 (1952).

2. C. L. Fenton, "Algae of the Pre-Cambrian and Early Paleozoic" (Symposium on paleobotanical taxonomy), *Amer. Midland Naturalist* 26, 259–264 (1946).

3. R. J. Russell, "Climatic change through the ages" in *Climate and Man, Yearbook of Agriculture* (Washington, 1941), pp. 67–98.

4. M. N. Bose, "Microfossils from the Talchir Boulder Bed," *Jour. Indian Bot. Soc.* 29, 1–46 (1950).

5. E. S. Barghoorn, "Age and environment: a survey of North American Tertiary floras in relation to paleoecology," *Jour. Paleontol.* 25, 736–744 (1951).

21

THE RECORD OF CLIMATIC CHANGES AS REVEALED BY VERTEBRATE PALEOECOLOGY

Edwin H. Colbert

THE NATURE OF THE EVIDENCE

THE RECORD OF CHANGES IN THE earth's climate during past geologic ages can be derived from various lines of evidence, and of these the history of the vertebrates, as revealed by their fossil remains, is of particular importance. In the first place, the evidence afforded by the backboned animals through geologic time is important because it covers a vast expanse of earth history. True, the record of the vertebrates is not quite as extensive in time as that of the invertebrate animals, but the difference is not great. These two lines of evidence, combined with those of paleobotany and of stratigraphy, cover the whole time span during which there is a record of life on the earth.

The evidence of fossil vertebrates is important also because it covers the widest possible range of ecological environments. Vertebrates have lived at all levels in the oceans, and at almost all levels on the land. They have lived in continental waters and in upland environments of exceeding dryness. They have lived in the air. Because of these wide ecological adaptations the vertebrates can be used in conjunction with all other forms of life, both plant and animal, in the interpretation of past climates.

The vertebrates are useful too because many of them have been very sensitive to climatic conditions, and therefore to the changes in climates. In this respect they may, of course, be compared with the invertebrates and with plants. In all forms of life the ecological tolerances vary greatly from group to group, often down to the species level, so that when the evidence is properly evaluated and weighted it is frequently of the utmost importance because of the implications that can be drawn from it concerning climatic conditions in past times.

In the discussion of the problem at hand attention should be called to the use of the word *implications*. It must be realized that the evidence of the vertebrates as it bears upon past climates is for the most part indirect evidence. We assume that ecological conditions (and by extension, climatic conditions as well) were thus and so because of the presence of certain animals in the sediments. This assumption rests upon a basic precept that must be accepted at the outset, if our interpretation of past climates upon the evidence of vertebrate paleoecology is to have order and validity. The precept is that within wide limits the past is to be interpreted in terms of the present. Of course this maxim is commonly accepted in the fields of geology and paleontology — so much so that it is generally taken for granted — but it is being emphasized here because it is of unusual significance in the present study.

In line with this assumption we suppose that animals of the past were more or less similar to their modern relatives in physiologic requirements, and hence in their ecological tolerances. Consequently we assume that fishes, amphibians, birds, and mammals of the past were more or less like their modern relatives in their life processes, in their habits, and in the environments within which they were contained. From this we are then able to draw conclusions as to the environments and the climates in which certain animals lived by a comparison of environments and climates in which their modern relatives live.

Of course such a method of interpretation must be used with great caution and with as much insight as possible, because animals are never identical in their needs. But it is reasonable to suppose, for instance, that the temperature limitations under which reptiles of the past lived would be roughly similar to temperature limitations for modern reptiles; and to extend the argument to greater detail, it is reasonable to think that the ecological conditions favorable to crocodiles in the past would be more or less similar to ecological conditions under which modern crocodilians live. On the other hand, the possibilities of closely related animals living in strikingly different environments must always be kept in mind. One need only cite the limitations of modern elephants to tropical and subtropical climates as compared with the extensions of some of their closely related cousins, the extinct mammoths, into arctic realms. Examples such as these call attention to the need for careful interpretation of fossil evidence.

In the attempt to interpret past climatic conditions from the vertebrates, evidence other than that of the fossils is used whenever possible. In many instances such evidence is lacking or, if present, is of little value, but in other cases there is material that, when taken in conjunction with the evidence of the fossils, throws considerable light on the ecologic conditions in which the animals lived.

The physical characteristics of the sediments are often helpful. Thus the nature of the rocks may indicate whether the animals that they contain lived in fresh or salt water, in muddy rivers and estuaries, or in clear lagoons, in swamps or uplands, in deserts or regions of much vegetation. Of course the nature of the sediments is not so important in an interpretation of verebrate life as it is for the invertebrates, especially the marine invertebrates, since the vertebrates are generally rather independent animals that can move from one place to another. Even so, the sedimentary record must be carefully analyzed as an adjunct to the study of the fossil bones.

Very commonly — possibly in a majority of cases — invertebrates and plants are not found along with the vertebrates, but when they are they may supplement the backboned animals in an interpretation of the ecological conditions of the time and place being studied. Also, such things as fossil footprints, raindrop impressions, mudcracks, and so on should be mentioned. The list might be extended. Again it is necessary to insert a word of warning. In using fossil vertebrates and the correlative evidence of sediments, plants, footprints, and the like, one may fall into the error of reasoning in a circle. Ecological conditions may be inferred from the presence of certain vertebrates in the sediments and in turn the presence of the vertebrates may then be interpreted in the light of the inferred ecological conditions. This is a danger that must be kept in mind, and generally it will not trap the alert paleontologist. Various lines of evidence can quite legitimately supplement each other, back and forth, without introducing the pitfall of circular reasoning. Only the unwary are apt to be caught.

METHODS OF COMPARISON

In practice, the interpretation of probable past climates from the evidence of fossil vertebrates rests largely upon a study of the distributions of vertebrates during past ages. In following such a study attention is given not only to the occurrences of various types of vertebrates in the sediments of the earth, but also to the distribution of entire faunas, since the conclusions that are to be drawn from a complete fauna may often have greater validity than those based upon single genera or species. Faunas and the elements that compose them are studied in space and in time, in their distribution over the surface of the earth and in their succession through the strata that constitute the sedimentary history of the earth. In each geologic period, and so far as possible within the subdivisions of each period, the assemblages of animals and the individual animals themselves are analyzed for the information that they may give as to the environments in which they lived. What were the conditions of temperature, of humidity, of light, of periodic variations, and of air and water currents that prevailed when the animals and the faunas to which they belonged were living? To answer these questions, contemporaneous animals and faunas of the past are compared with each other, and as far as is possible they are also compared with related animals and with similar faunas living at the present time. When close relations do not exist, some attempt is made to draw analogies from which reasonably valid conclusions can be established.

All of this results primarily in a restoration of local environments, and from the composite relations of many environments broad conclusions as to general climatic conditions can be reached.

The test of these conclusions rests in part upon the manner in which they accord or fail to accord with the general climatic picture of the past that has been drawn upon the basis of all the data available. If the evidence of vertebrate paleoecology is more or less in accord with other lines of evidence, it would seem probable that all the data, and the conclusions drawn from these data, are valid. If serious discrepancies are apparent, then it becomes necessary to evaluate the various lines of evidence bearing upon the problem of past climates. In this case the error may rest either with the evidence of the vertebrates, or at least with the interpretation of such evidence, or it may be that the vertebrates throw new light upon the problem at hand and show that some of our previous concepts have been at fault.

Perhaps at this place it might be well to outline the general sequence of climates during past geologic ages, as developed from many lines of evidence. As set forth by Brooks in his definitive text, *Climate Through the Ages*, the succession from Cambrian to recent times is as follows:

Pleistocene	Glaciation in temperate latitudes
Pliocene	Cool
Miocene	Moderate
Oligocene	Moderate to warm
Eocene (including Paleocene)	Moderate, becoming warm
Cretaceous	Moderate
Jurassic	Warm and equable
Triassic	Warm and equable
Permian	Glacial at first, becoming moderate
Carboniferous	Warm at first, becoming glacial
Devonian	Moderate, becoming warm
Silurian	Warm
Ordovician	Moderate to warm
Cambrian	Cold, becoming warm

The striking thing about this table is the preponderance of warm and moderate climates that prevailed through the greater part of earth history since Cambrian times. According to Brooks's analysis, the Paleozoic era began with cold climates, but from then until the present, the history of the earth has been characterized by warm and moderate conditions except for two major glacial interludes — one in the late Paleozoic and one in the Pleistocene.

How does the evidence of the vertebrates accord with this picture? To check this, let us now turn to a brief survey of vertebrate paleoecology.

THE EVIDENCE OF MIDDLE PALEOZOIC VERTEBRATES

The record of climatic changes as based upon the evidence of extinct vertebrates begins with the Silurian period. It is certain, of course, that the vertebrates originated long before Silurian times, and they must have been well established in the faunas of the Cambrian and Ordovician, but in those distant days they were very likely small unarmored animals that would not be preserved as fossils in the sediments. Indeed, isolated scales from sediments of Ordovician age give undisputed proof of the fact that primitive vertebrates were then living on the earth — probably in streams and ponds.

Adequate remains of early vertebrates first appear, however, in sediments of Silurian age, so it is at this stage of earth history that the vertebrate record really begins. And while the Silurian record is definite, it is not, for the most part, abundant, nor is it very widely spread. Consequently, we must look to the sediments of Upper Silurian times, to those of the stage known as the Downtonian, and especially to the rocks of the following Devonian period, to find the fully documented beginning of vertebrate history. For this reason our discussion will begin with the Devonian period, a geologic age that represents about the middle point of Paleozoic history.

The Devonian period has often been called the "Age of Fishes" because of the abundance of early aquatic vertebrates in many Devonian faunas, and also because of the dominant position that these early vertebrates enjoyed at that time. This was the period of the first great evolutionary radiation of vertebrates. Primitive jawless vertebrates, the ostracoderms, abounded in many faunas over the world. Contemporaneous with them were the armored placoderms, representing an "experiment" in vertebrate evolution that was destined to early failure. In addition to these early vertebrates, which cannot properly be designated as "fishes" (as we generally use the term), there were the early ancestors of our modern fishes, primitive sharks, ancestral bony fishes, early lungfishes, and the important crossopterygian fishes that were to give rise to the first land-living amphibians. At the very close of Devonian times the first amphibians appeared, and the vertebrates came ashore and invaded a new environment.

The Devonian vertebrates represent for the most part animals that lived in continental fresh waters, or in relatively shallow estuaries that led to the sea. This evidence, along with correlative facts, seems to indicate that the vertebrates had their origins in fresh water and went through some of their early history in such a habitat. It was only at a later date that they invaded the oceans.

This view is especially important in the attempt to interpret past climates, since it gives evidence of continental conditions. And in the interpretation of climates the development of life on the continents and along the continental borders must be given particular attention, since this is perhaps a more accurate guide to past climates than is the development of marine life. There is no intention at this place to decry the importance of the marine evidence; certainly marine invertebrate faunas are very important because of their wide distributions, and especially because of the sensitivity of many marine organisms to temperatures. Yet as we know from experience, the ocean is a vast world of its own, less affected by climatic changes than the land. Life on the land, even the life of continental waters, is bound to be more sensitive to changing conditions in the atmosphere than life in the oceans.

Devonian vertebrates are especially well known from northern Europe and from North America, and in these regions various faunas have been found that represent a succession of life through the period, which in Europe extends down into the Downtonian stage as well. In Europe the "Old Red Sandstone" of Scotland is rightly famous, and fossils from this extensive deposit have been collected for much more than a hundred years. In addition to the Scottish region, Devonian vertebrates are known from the Shetland and Orkney Islands, from the Baltic states, from Germany, and from Russia. They are even found as far north as Spitzbergen.

The arctic occurrence of Devonian vertebrates is further illustrated by the presence of very important faunas in eastern Greenland, where the earliest amphibians, of upper Devonian age, are found. Devonian vertebrate faunas can be traced from Greenland to the south, through Quebec and into New York and Ohio. To the west they are found in Wyoming and Arizona.

Our knowledge of Devonian vertebrates in other parts of the world is scanty, but well-known faunas are found also in New South Wales, Australia, and even Antarctica.

From this it can be seen that the early vertebrates were widely distributed, and it is reasonable to think that if the fossil record were more complete we would know many numerous faunas in other regions between the extremes of Greenland and Australia where now the record is blank. At any rate, it is safe to assume that Devonian vertebrates were of almost world-wide extent, and because of the close relationships that characterize the individual elements of the various faunas, it is reasonable to suppose that the environmental conditions under which these faunas lived were roughly the same.

Most of the Devonian "fishes" were obviously the inhabitants of rather shallow waters, living either in continental streams or ponds or in estuaries and bays along the edges of the continents. These faunal occurrences give evidence of a warm-water environment, where the conditions of life were controlled to a large extent by the climates that were prevalent over continental areas. Because of this it is reasonable to assume, on the basis of vertebrate evidence, that the Devonian period was a time of widely spread equable climates, a period of uniformity over most of the earth's surface.

A striking character of the Devonian vertebrate faunas is the prevalence in them of air-breathing or choanate fishes; of lungfishes and crossopterygians. The presence of these fishes in such relative abundance in many of the Devonian localities is a clear indication that the waters in which they lived were subjected to frequent periods of great reduction or drying up. This conclusion is reached by analogy with the recent lungfishes. (The one known species of modern crossopterygian is a specialized marine form, and properly it cannot be used in an interpretation of the habits of the fresh-water or estuarine Devonian lungfishes.) The recent Australian lungfish (the most primitive of the modern forms) is able to withstand periods of drought, when the streams or ponds in which it lives become much reduced and the water foul, by coming to the surface and breathing air. The South American and African lung fishes are able to bury themselves in the mud, to withstand several months of complete dryness as air-breathing vertebrates.

Evidently environmental conditions were advantageous to air-breathing fishes in Devonian times, and this would point to the fact that, while climates may not have been arid, there were probably dry seasons, during which bodies of fresh water became considerably restricted. Indeed, the periodic alternations of wet and dry seasons can be correlated closely with the rise of the amphibians from crossopterygian fishes. It was the urge in these fishes to venture from one pool of water to another during dry seasons that marked the first steps in the invasion of land by the vertebrates — a process that was to culminate in the appearance of the amphibians.

It is interesting that the first amphibians known to us have been found in the upper Devonian sediments of eastern Greenland. Modern amphibians have very definite limits of temperature tolerance, and taking into account the anatomical and physiological characteristics of this class of vertebrates one can only assume that the same was true of the amphibians of past ages. Therefore the presence of early amphibians in the upper Devonian of eastern Greenland leads to the conclusion that this part of the world enjoyed relatively warm climatic conditions in middle Paleozoic times, when the earth climatically was a relatively uniform planet. Gradations in climate from equator to the poles were probably very gradual and were not marked by extremes. It is probable also that the temperature differences between seasons were not so strikingly varied as they are at the present time.

THE EVIDENCE OF UPPER PALEOZOIC VERTEBRATES

The invasion of the land by vertebrates, which began with the close of the Devonian period, was thoroughly established in the next phases of geologic history, that is, in the lapse of time that is designated abroad as the Carboniferous period and in this country as the Mississippian and Pennsylvanian periods. The amphibians evolved along various lines of adaptation in Mississippian times, and this evolution continued into the Pennsylvanian. The first reptiles — derived from certain amphibians — appeared in this latter period.

This period was the time of the great coal forests in the Northern Hemisphere. There is abundant evidence from the sediments and from paleobotany to show that during the Carboniferous (to use the European term as a comprehensive designation for all of this portion of Paleozoic history) great tropical swamps covered extensive portions of the Paleozoic continents, and in these lush, swampy forests the early land-living vertebrates abounded. Climates must have been warm and moist throughout a great part of Carboniferous times to support the abundant vegetation of ancient club mosses, lepidodendrons, horsetails, and ferns that constituted the forests of those distant days, and such climates and environments were most conducive to the development of the early cold-blooded tetrapods, the amphibians, and reptiles.

These early amphibians and reptiles are known mainly from North American and European localities. They are found, for instance in England and Scotland, and in Bohemia and France, while on this continent they have been found in the Allegheny region of Pennsylvania, West Virginia, and Ohio, in Illinois, in New Brunswick, and in Nova Scotia. The resemblances between some of the faunas of North America and Europe are very close, and indicate not only closely parallel climatic conditions in these separate regions, but very probably a land connection that allowed a relatively rapid diffusion of animals from one region to the other.

The evidence of the vertebrates indicates that climates of the Carboniferous continued without much break from those of the Devonian. As in the earlier period the climates of the earth were in general rather uniform. Tropical floras and the animals that one might expect in such associations of plants lived at fairly high latitudes — as far north as 45°. Geologic evidence indicates that there were mountain uplifts toward the end of Carboniferous times, and these were accompanied in the Southern Hemisphere by extensive glaciations. Profound as these events may have been, they seem not to have affected the late Carboniferous faunas of the Northern Hemisphere to any appreciable degree. Amphibious and primitive reptiles continued to prosper in the swamps and streams of northern Europe and America; evidently environments were not greatly changed in those regions.

The Carboniferous was the period of amphibian dominance. Perhaps the picture as we see it is somewhat unbalanced as a result of facies developments. Thus, the Carboniferous vertebrates that are especially well known are those of the coal-forest deposits, and hence they represent the animals that were living in the swamps of those days. Perhaps there were numerous reptiles living in upland regions that have not been preserved in the fossil record. While this is a distinct possibility, the evidence seems to indicate that reptiles were generally small and minor elements of the faunas of that day. Certainly Carboniferous environments were favorable to amphibian life.

With the advent of Permian times, however, there were definite changes in climates and environments, and in the land-living vertebrate faunas. The mountain-making and the southern glaciations that had been initiated in late Carboniferous times continued, reaching a climax in the early part of the Permian period. The world was becoming a planet characterized by varying climates and environments. All of this favored the emergence of the reptiles, which then became the dominant animals of the earth, even though there was probably some active competition between these animals and some of the largest and most aggressive of the amphibians.

The one great advantage that the early reptiles enjoyed over the amphibians with which they were contemporaneous was the method of reproduction. The advent of the reptiles was marked by the appearance of the protected amniote egg — an egg capable of development away from water, and this was an event of great importance in the evolution of the vertebrates, for it completely emancipated the land-living tetrapods from dependence upon the water. The amphibians were forced to return to the water to breed, because the unprotected amphibian egg could develop only in a liquid medium, but with the appearance of the amniote egg the reptiles were able to reproduce and live entirely on dry land. Consequently, these animals became much more independent than the amphibians had been, and many new ecological possibilities were made available for their evolutionary development. One must keep this important fact in mind in connection with the uplift of continental masses in Permian times.

Permian vertebrate faunas, with reptiles the dominant and in most cases the most abundant animals comprising the assemblages, but with amphibians generally present in goodly numbers, are also known from many continental regions. Lower Permian faunas are abundantly represented in the so-called red beds of Texas and adjacent states, while closely related faunas are found in Europe, especially in France. Middle Permian faunas are found in some parts of Europe, while upper Permian assemblages are known from Scotland and from the Zechstein of Germany. There is a remarkable series of Permian deposits on the Dvina River in northern Russia, containing a succession of faunas ranging from middle through upper Permian age, and beyond. The famous Karroo series in South Africa carries vertebrate faunas that begin with the middle Permian and extend through the remainder of this geologic period and on into the Triassic. Permian faunas are found in other regions of Africa as well, and in addition in Asia and Australia. Some Permian vertebrates have been found in Brazil. This survey gives an idea of the world-wide extent of the land-living tetrapods in Permian times.

In many regions the Permian continental sediments in which vertebrates are found are marked by their striking and often brilliant red colors. Many theories have been advanced to explain red beds, and it would be fruitless to discuss them here. There is much reason to think, however, that the continental red beds of Permian age represent in many instances a deposition of sediments under conditions of alternating moist conditions and drought. The evidence of the vertebrates would seem to be in accord with such an explanation.

In view of the distribution of vertebrate faunas this theory of Permian climates is more logical than the idea of widely spread desert conditions that has been invoked by so many students of geologic history. It is hard to reconcile the indications of abundant reptilian and amphibian faunas with permanent desert environments. For instance, the Permian faunas of Texas, New Mexico, and Oklahoma contain mixed assemblages of fishes, amphibians, and reptiles. Although some of the reptiles in these faunas may have lived very well under desert conditions, it is difficult to imagine the amphibians as existing very far from water — at least for a part of each year — while the presence of fresh-water fishes certainly is an indication of streams and ponds. Even some of the reptiles must have lived in close proximity to water, as is indicated not only by the morphological evidence of the animals themselves, but also by the nature of the sediments in which they have been preserved. Therefore one comes to the conclusion that these animals lived in a region where water was near at hand during a part of the year, even though some months may have been rather arid. In this connection Olson has recently suggested, upon the basis of his long and careful studies of Texas faunas, that some of the early Permian animals of North America lived in a delta region. The resemblance of some of the European faunas of early Permian age to those of North America suggests that environmental conditions in the Old World may have been rather similar to those of Texas and adjacent regions.

When we come to look at the Permian vertebrates of the Karroo series (South Africa), a somewhat different picture emerges. Here we find a preponderance of reptiles, many of them of large size, and most of them obviously active in a reptilian way. Amphibians are much less evident in the Karroo faunas than they are in the early Permian faunas of Texas or of France. In the Karroo assemblages there are numerous large herbivorous reptiles, and associated with them are many carnivorous forms. Here is an ecological relationship of herbivore and carnivore that has been paralleled many times among later land-living tetrapods. In fact, Watson has compared the Karroo reptiles with the plains-living mammals of Tertiary times, and has suggested that South Africa in the Permian period was not unlike North America in the days when herds of camels and horses, with their attendant predators, roamed the high plains. The parallel is an apt one. Because of the resemblance of the Dvina faunas of Russia to the Karroo faunas, it is reasonable to think that in northern Europe similar conditions were typical of middle and upper Permian times.

From such evidence it is apparent that the environmental conditions under which the continental Permian faunas lived were varied, but were marked on the whole by their "upland" nature. Evidently there were different types of climates and it is quite probable that there were marked alternations of seasons.

What about temperatures? Here the evidence of the Permian reptiles is particularly important. Many large reptiles are known in the Karroo faunas in South Africa at a latitude of about 30° S, while Permian tetrapods are found at similar latitudes in South America and in Australia. Large Permian reptiles closely related to the South African forms are found along the Dvina River of Russia just below the Arctic Circle, at a north latitude of about 65°. Therefore one is led to the conclusion that in much of the Permian period temperatures were similar over a broad belt of the earth, extending up and down toward what we now call the Arctic and Antarctic regions. Temperatures over this broad belt of the earth must have been warm to temperate, but never very cold.

The reason for this assumption is founded upon our knowledge of reptilian physiology and temperature tolerances. Modern reptiles have varying temperatures that correspond roughly with the temperatures of the environments in which they live. Their temperature tolerances cover rather narrow ranges, and it is not possible for them to survive body temperatures that go above or below the limits of their ranges of tolerance. In this modern world of definite climatic belts all reptiles find the environments most suitable to them in the tropical, subtropical, and temperate regions of the earth, while the large reptiles inhabit only the tropics and subtropics.

The large crocodilians and turtles, and the largest lizards and snakes, find the optimum conditions for life and growth in a band around the equatorial part of the earth and bounded north and south more or less by the 30th parallels of latitude. North or south of this tropical and subtropical band the winters are too severe for such large reptiles; they are unable to protect themselves against the cold. The smaller reptiles that live in the more northerly and southerly regions exist through the winters by burrowing into the ground or by retiring into subsurface dens, where they endure several months in a stage of suspended animation.

It is reasonable to think that the large reptiles of Permian times were not markedly different from large modern reptiles in their physiological requirements. Consequently, the presence of various reptiles as large as big dogs, sheep, ponies, and even oxen in the faunas of South Africa and northern Russia is an indication that temperatures in these widely separate regions were warm to moderate, but never really cold. Varied as the climates may have been because of seasonal changes and the alternation of wet and dry periods, the earth enjoyed comparatively uniform temperatures during most of the Permian period. There was an interlude of southern glacial climates at the beginning of Permian times, but the effects of this cold period had disappeared by the middle Permian, when large reptiles extended their ranges into the southernmost tip of the African continent.

THE EVIDENCE OF LOWER MESOZOIC VERTEBRATES

The Permian is represented at the present time in many regions by red beds, and the same is true of the Triassic. In fact, continental red beds are especially characteristic of the beginning of Mesozoic history, and they can be found in widely separated parts of the earth, in western North America and along the Atlantic seaboard, in Scotland and central Europe, in South Africa, in Yunnan and other parts of western China, in India, and in southern Brazil. As in the case of the Permian sediments, many geologists have interpreted these widely distributed Triassic red beds as indicative of broad desert regions at the beginning of Mesozoic history, but again, as in the case of the Permian sediments, the included faunas indicate that moist conditions were prevalent in many regions. It would seem that the Triassic was a time of alternating wet and dry seasons, which led to the oxidation of iron in the accumulating sediments and the production of the characteristic red colors.

The labyrinthodont amphibians that were so prominent in the Permian faunas continued into the Triassic period, where they went through a final stage of evolution marked by extreme adaptations for life in the water. Therefore, wherever Triassic labyrinthodonts are found, it seems safe to assume that there were streams and ponds in abundance, and climates must have been fairly moist. The distribution of the Triassic labyrinthodonts is remarkably wide. These large and highly specialized amphibians are found in all of the continental regions, as far north as northern Russia and as far south as South Africa, southern Argentina, and eastern Australia. Moreover, they extend beyond the continents to the north, to eastern Greenland and to the island of Spitzbergen. Consequently, their latitudinal extent is from 80° N to about 40° S. This spread is indeed a very broad belt, for which fairly uniform conditions must be assumed. The labyrinthodonts, as said, lived in moist environments, and it must be supposed that the temperatures of their habitats were moderate.

The evidence of the Triassic reptiles is similar to that of the labyrinthodont amphibians. Reptiles in the faunas of that geologic period are, like the amphibians, widely spread, from northern Russia and Scotland on the north to South Africa and southern Brazil on the south, with many localities in between. It has already been pointed out how temperature tolerances of reptiles are such that these animals are unable to exist in regions of extreme temperatures unless they are able to protect themselves by going underground or by seeking refuge in temperate waters. Therefore the presence of large Triassic reptiles at high and low latitudes is a pretty clear indication that temperatures were moderate over much of the earth's surface at the beginning of Mesozoic history. Such large reptiles would have been unable to seek protection underground, and therefore the environments in which they lived were never really cold. It is probable that tropical, subtropical, and warm temperate climates extended from the equator toward the poles, with climatic variations brought about mainly by the alternation of wet and dry seasons.

It will be remembered that the Karroo series of South Africa was cited in connection with the discussion of Permian vertebrates. This series of sediments continues from the Permian into the Triassic, seemingly with no major break; here is one locality on earth where we can see a merging of Paleozoic and Mesozoic history as a single, continuous story (which, of course, would be true of the entire geologic record if we had it completely preserved). Large reptiles were present in the Permian phases of the Karroo series, and they continued into the Triassic portions of South African history. For instance, the dicynodont reptiles, many of considerable size, continued into the Triassic, while some of the mammallike Triassic theriodonts were good-sized reptiles. Early dinosaurs appear in the Triassic of South Africa, as they do at the beginning of Mesozoic history in other regions such as central Europe, North America, and western China. The presence of these first dinosaurs, some of them 20 feet or more in length, is an indication of mild climates and an abundant food supply.

The dicynodont reptiles, which were so characteristic of the Karroo of South Africa, spread to many other parts of the world in Triassic times, and gigantic dicynodonts are found in southern Brazil, in the Chinle Triassic sediments of North America, and in China. We might mention also the Triassic phytosaurs — crocodilelike reptiles of large, and often of gigantic, size. They are found in western and eastern North America, in central Europe, and in central India, and in all of these regions the phytosaurs are remarkably similar to each other.

All of this evidence from the early Mesozoic land-living vertebrates supports the concept of moderate temperatures throughout the world in Triassic times. There is additional support for the picture of Triassic climates as here drawn from marine reptiles of the Triassic. In this geologic period the first ichthyosaurs or fishlike reptiles arose, to commence a line of reptilian evolution that was to continue through the extent of Mesozoic times. Certainly the ichthyosaurs must have been warm-water animals, and it is interesting to see that these animals lived not only in such latitudes as central Europe, western North America, and Timor, in the East Indies (almost on the equator), but also in the extreme north, in Spitzbergen.

THE EVIDENCE OF MIDDLE AND UPPER MESOZOIC VERTEBRATES

With the close of Triassic times and the opening of Jurassic history there were broad areas of desert conditions in some parts of the world. For instance, the early Jurassic continental sediments of the southwestern United States are marked by extensive exposure of eolian sandstones that could have been deposited only as great desert dunes. As Jurassic history progressed, however, these arid conditions, wherever they had been established, gave way to generally moist climates.

The evidence would seem to indicate that most of the Jurassic period was a time of uniformity seldom equaled in the history of the earth. Lands were generally low and frequently covered with swamps, while there were extensive marine incursions over the continents. Climates must have been very uniform and benign, because this was a period of luxuriant vegetation and a trend to giantism among many of the reptiles that dominated the earth and the seas.

Vertebrate faunas of Jurassic age are not so numerous nor are they so widely distributed as are the faunas of Triassic or of Cretaceous age. Perhaps this is partly because of continental submergence and the advancement of shallow-water seas over the continental platforms. Certainly our knowledge of land-living Jurassic tetrapods is restricted for the most part to the upper Jurassic, and to a few areas. In this respect it should be mentioned that the fossil record of marine reptiles from the Jurassic is as widely distributed as the record of land-living vertebrates.

There are two great upper Jurassic faunas, one, the Morrison fauna from western North America, the other, the Tendaguru fauna from East Africa. These faunas are remarkably similar to each other, and they are characterized by the prevalence in them of gigantic dinosaurs. In both of these faunas there are many huge, plant-eating sauropod dinosaurs, armored stegosaurs, and the smaller herbivorous camptosaurs; and balanced against these plant-feeders, the giant carnivorous theropod dinosaurs, the predators of those distant days. There are other reptiles as well — crocodiles and turtles being especially noteworthy — but the dinosaurs are dominant. The presence of such great numbers of large dinosaurs in the Morrison and Tendaguru faunas is an indication of the prevalence of swamps in which the sauropods lived and of the luxuriance of vegetation on which these dinosaurs fed, which in turn is an indication that climates were very mild, and for the most part probably tropical or subtropical. The occurrence of such similar faunas in North America and East Africa betokens the wide spread of tropical conditions over much of the land surface of the earth.

In England and Europe the upper Jurassic sediments contain not only the large dinosaurs so characteristic of this period of geologic history, but also giant ichthyosaurs and plesiosaurs, which were marine reptiles. Evidently in this part of the world there were low islands or restricted land areas with seaways between them, thus bringing about the deposition of land-living and aquatic reptiles in the Jurassic sequence. Again, it would seem reasonable to suppose that the climates were essentially similar to those of North America and Africa.

As for marine vertebrates, it should be pointed out that ichthyosaurs and plesiosaurs have been found in the Jurassic of eastern Greenland at a north latitude of some 70° or more. Another point that should be made here is that in the Jurassic Solenhofen limestones of Germany are found the skeletons of pterosaurs or flying reptiles, and the remains of the first birds as well. Studies of the limestones indicate that they were probably deposited in a coral lagoon, which would indicate tropical seas as far north as 50° during the Jurassic period. Jurassic limestones in England are also interpreted as having been formed by coral reefs.

From all of this evidence one can picture the Jurassic period as a time of extraordinary climatic uniformity over much of the earth, when tropical and subtropical conditions extended far toward the polar regions. It was probably a period during which there was little differentiation of seasons, in contrast to the preceding Triassic period.

The transition from Jurassic to Cretaceous times was marked by the beginnings of mountain uplifts that were to bring an end to the uniformity of middle Mesozoic environments and initiate the varied conditions that were to mark in ever-increasing measure later geologic history. Intense mountain foldings, the Nevadan Revolution, took place along the Pacific border of North America. Continental uplifts began that were to continue through the Cretaceous period and beyond. Of course these changes were gradual, so that in effect the beginning of Cretaceous times was on the whole much like the closing stages of Jurassic times.

That the Cretaceous period was a time of uplift is indicated by the extensive land-living vertebrate faunas characterizing this phase of geologic history, especially toward the end of Cretaceous times. Cretaceous sediments containing land-living tetrapods are found at various localities on all of the continental land masses, and as exploratory work continues additional localities come to light with each passing decade. Consequently, our knowledge of Cretaceous tetrapods is much more extensive and varied than is the information we have about the Jurassic amphibians and reptiles. In this respect it should be pointed out that much of what we know about the Cretaceous land-living vertebrates is based to a large degree upon faunas of upper Cretaceous age.

Faunas containing Cretaceous land animals are found as far north as northern Europe and western Canada and as far south as South Africa, Australia, and Patagonia. Moreover there are many faunas from the continental land masses in between these limits of latitude. The marine reptiles of the Cretaceous period, notably the ichthyosaurs, plesiosaurs, and mosasaurs, were as widely spread across the face of the earth as the land-living forms — an indication that warm seas extended far into the northern and southern latitudes of the globe. From this it is evident that environmental conditions were sufficiently uniform to allow the successful existence and evolution of great reptiles over a large part of the earth's surface.

There is, however, ample evidence from the reptiles that the earth in Cretaceous times, especially in the upper Cretaceous, was a more varied planet that it had been during the Jurassic period. For instance, none of the dinosaurs of the Cretaceous attain the extreme size seen in the Jurassic sauropods, even though in some lines, such as that of the giant carnivorous dinosaurs, the culmination of phylogenetic size was not reached until the end of the Cretaceous period. Sauropods continued into Cretaceous times, but in this later geologic period they were reduced in bulk as compared with their Jurassic forerunners. Most of the other dinosaurs of the Cretaceous, especially the dominant ornithischians, were only moderately large as compared with the Jurassic giants. This change would indicate that environmental conditions probably were not so favorable to giantism as in the preceding geologic period, which in turn means that the climates were perhaps not so uniformly tropical or subtropical and plant life not so luxuriant as they had been in Jurassic times.

While the consideration of plants is not rightly within the scope of the present discussion, it might be pointed out at this place that one of the great events of the Cretaceous period was the modernization of floras. It was during this stage of geologic history that the angiosperms made their appearance, so that the forests, which hitherto had consisted of comparatively primitive ferns and gymnosperms, now assumed a modern aspect by reason of the varied deciduous trees composing them. The presence of angiosperms in Cretaceous floras is an indication, it has been suggested, of alternating seasons. The occurrence in Alaska and Greenland of such plants as figs, breadfruit, palms, and cycads leads to the conclusion that subtropical and temperate climates extended far beyond the middle portions of the earth during these final stages of Mesozoic history.

Not only did the flowering plants give a modern appearance to Cretaceous life, but also some of the land-living animals, contemporaries of the dinosaurs and pterosaurs, were essentially modern in form and relationships. In this category we find the crocodilians, turtles, lizards, and snakes, all of which had their beginnings in the earlier phases of Mesozoic history, and all of which survived the end of the Cretaceous period to live into modern times. Also the first placental mammals appear in Cretaceous sediments. This is significant, because it represents the beginning of evolutionary radiation among the animals that were to be freed from the old reptilian dependence upon external temperatures. Cretaceous mammals were comparatively insignificant, but they set a pattern for vertebrate life that was to develop after conditions were no longer favorable for the continuation of the dinosaurs and the other dominant reptiles of the Mesozoic.

To sum up, the evidence of Cretaceous vertebrates shows that the end of the Mesozoic era was a time of rather varied climates, possibly with a definite alternation of seasons, but with cold climates as we know them either very much restricted to the polar regions or completely nonexistent. The wide distribution of giant Cretaceous reptiles shows that temperature conditions favorable to ectothermic vertebrates were general over most of the continental regions of the earth. To our modern eyes it was still a world of genial climates.

THE EVIDENCE OF LOWER CENOZOIC VERTEBRATES

The transition from Mesozoic to Cenozoic times was one of the great crises of earth history. Mountain uplifts constituting the so-called Laramide Revolution had begun with the close of the Cretaceous period, and these continued into Tertiary times to build the great mountain chains of the modern world. Because of these crustal disturbances, and very likely because of other factors as well, climates and environments were affected to such an extent that there was a great change in the life of the earth, especially among the land-living vertebrates. A wave of extinction swept away the many reptiles that had been dominant in Mesozoic times, leaving only the crocodilians, the turtles, the snakes and lizards, and a few rhynchocephalians to carry on the history of reptilian life. The mammals that had been so insignificant during the Cretaceous period suddenly expanded with explosive effect, to occupy the various ecological niches that had been vacated by the once-dominant reptiles. Modern birds appeared in all their variety. From this point on the land and the air, and to some extent the sea as well, were to belong to the warm-blooded vertebrates, the birds and mammals.

This fact introduces a complication in our attempt to interpret past climates from the evidence of the vertebrates. As has been shown, the amphibians and reptiles are especially valuable to the student of environments because of their temperature limitations. The distribution of extinct faunas containing large reptiles is an indication of the possible distribution of warm climates in past times.

But the mammals and birds, being endothermic, are not such effective indicators of the conditions under which they lived. True, we know that certain mammals and birds at the present time are confined to tropical areas, while others live in the polar regions of the earth. By analogy, it can be assumed that extinct forms closely related to modern tropic-dwelling mammals (or birds) also lived in such environments, and of course the same line of reasoning can be extended to inhabitants of other climatic belts. But there are pitfalls here, as pointed out earlier in this communication. Modern elephants are tropical and subtropical animals, but their close relatives, the extinct mammoths, were temperate and arctic animals. The same is true of modern rhinoceroses and some of the extinct rhinoceroses. Modern musk oxen are arctic mammals, but it may well be that some of the extinct musk oxen lived in temperate regions.

The picture is complicated still further by the fact that many mammals and birds have very wide ranges. For instance, the modern puma or cougar of the Western Hemisphere ranges from the snows of Canada to the tip of South America, while his cousin, the Old World leopard, extends from northern China to the southern part of Africa. Among the migratory birds, individuals cover vast expanses of latitude twice each year. All of these facts must be kept in mind when evaluating the distribution of animal life during Cenozoic times.

There are still the amphibians and the reptiles, especially the latter, to aid the student of past climates during the Cenozoic. These animals were as much at the mercy of their environments as their Mesozoic relatives and forebears. And the student of Cenozoic faunas is of necessity guided to a considerable extent by the associations of the animals with plant life of that time.

Even though the extinction of the dinosaurs and the sudden appearance of many groups of mammals were almost instantaneous events in terms of geologic time, the actual processes of extinction and replacement by new forms must have been slow in terms of years. It is hard to believe that climates at the beginning of the Cenozoic were widely different from those that characterized the close of Mesozoic times, although there is evidence of some cooling during the early stages of Cenozoic history.

The mammals of the Tertiary period that one finds in middle and northern latitudes are of the sort that one might expect in warm climates, although again it must be repeated that this criterion is to be used with great caution. In early and middle Tertiary times there were various herbivorous animals living in the middle and even the northern latitudes, and they must have depended for their sustenance upon rather luxuriant vegetation of the type that one would expect in moist subtropical or temperate forests. Such were the early horses, rhinoceroses, and tapirs, so widely spread in Tertiary times, the ubiquitous mastodonts, and other large browsing animals like the amblypods and titanotheres. These animals in themselves are not definitive, but taken in conjunction with the paleobotanical evidence they contribute to a concept of fairly uniform temperatures extending in a wide belt around the earth. The evidence is reinforced by the frequent presence of crocodilians in association with such mammals.

Consequently we come to the conclusion that although climates were gradually changing, the earlier part of the Cenozoic era was still marked by much of the uniformity that was so typical of Mesozoic times. There must have been varied environments at this stage of earth history, and there were probably variations in climatic conditions. But in spite of environmental and climatic differences from place to place, the definitely zoned climatic belts, so familiar to us at the present time, apparently did not exist.

EVIDENCE OF UPPER CENOZOIC VERTEBRATES

It is not until upper Cenozoic times that the evidence for an earth with climates more or less like those known to us begins to emerge. This is apparent for the most part from clues other than those afforded by the vertebrates — from paleobotanical evidence, from direct evidence of the sediments, and so on. But the vertebrates do give some help on this problem.

The climates of the earth were still fairly warm as late as the beginning of the Pliocene period. In sediments of that age there are alligators found in the northern Great Plains of North America, which means that temperatures must have been at least warm-temperate at that time. On the whole, however, the mammalian faunas of late Miocene and Pliocene times give an indication of the development of varied environments and zonation in climates. In the later stages of the Tertiary period we can see the development of steppe forms, of animals that lived upon the high plains where temperatures at times were certainly severe. Plains-living horses and many kinds of deer and antelopes are prominent in the faunas of that time. This may be in part an expression of facies developments, but nevertheless it is an indication too of the fact that climates were becoming more extreme than they had been, perhaps since late Paleozoic times.

Near the end of the Pliocene there are indications of definite climatic cooling in the Northern Hemisphere, intimations of the first great glacial advance of Pleistocene times. These indications come from evidence other than that of the mammals, but the mammals none the less are in accord with such evidence.

The history of climates during the Pleistocene period is so well known that it needs little elucidation here. It is well authenticated by the glacial evidence, and there is not much that can be added from the evidence of the mammals. There were clearly four glacial advances in the Northern Hemisphere, with interglacial periods of warmth and moisture. The mammals of that time receded and advanced with the glaciers, so that during periods of glacial maxima boreal forms like musk oxen and mammoths, woolly rhinoceroses and reindeer, lived in latitudes that are now temperate. In the periods of glacial retreat the mammals advanced to the north, so that horses and antelopes lived in Alaska. We are now living in an interglacial period in which glaciers are still diminishing, and there is evidence even in recent times of the movement of mammals from one region to another. It is a mere detail, but an interesting one, that certain mammals like the armadillo and the cacomistle, generally considered as "southern" in North America, are now spreading their ranges to the north.

With the advent of Pleistocene times the patterns of climatic succession and climatic variations as we know them became set. The climates of the earth became sharply zoned, from the tropics of the equator through the temperate zones to the boreal climates of the poles. Definite alternations of seasons were established — wet and dry seasons in the equatorial regions, hot and cold seasons in the higher latitudes. But this climatic pattern, so generally accepted by us, is far from typical in the history of the earth; in fact, the present climates of the world make up an atypical pattern, quite at variance with what has held through much of geologic history.

CONCLUSION

So far as past climates can be interpreted from the record of fossil vertebrates, it would appear that during much of earth history the world has enjoyed uniformly warm, equable climates over most of its surface. There have been digressions from this pattern of uniformity at times, and various complications in it, but the general picture of past vertebrate life is that of warmth-loving animals living over wide ranges of latitude, from the southern tips of the continental land masses through the middle latitudes to regions as far north as the Arctic Circle.

The earliest vertebrates of middle Paleozoic times are found in many northern regions where climates are now severe. Yet these early vertebrates must have been the denizens of warm or temperate — certainly not cold — waters.

At the close of the Devonian period the first known amphibians appeared in eastern Greenland. These animals certainly lived in other regions as well, although still unrepresented in the fossil record, but their presence in a land so far north is an indication of the mild conditions that must have prevailed over much of the earth at that time. The story is continued through upper Paleozoic times, when first the amphibians and then the reptiles become well established in characteristic faunas from the equator to far northern and southern regions. In late

Carboniferous and early Permian times the climatic conditions probably became more extreme than they had been, and it seems likely that varied, if not rigorous, climates continued through the Permian into the Triassic period. Yet even so, the Triassic was sufficiently warm that amphibians and reptiles, notably sensitive to temperature conditions, lived as far north as Spitzbergen and Greenland and as far south as the extent of the southern continental land masses.

Middle and upper Mesozoic times were periods of relatively great uniformity, when climatic and environmental conditions were favorable to the development of giant reptiles that spread over the face of the earth. In the Cretaceous period, however, there were subtle but definite changes in environments, leading finally to the extinction of the great reptiles that had been dominant since late Paleozoic times, and leading to the establishment of the mammals as the dominant land animals.

In early Cenozoic times it is probable that there was some cooling, but climates were not greatly different from those typical of late Mesozoic days. During the course of later geologic history definite changes took place. Climates became zoned to a greater degree than they had been zoned before, and environments showed great variations from the equator to the poles. To such changes in climates the mammals and the birds readily became adapted, but the ectothermic amphibians and reptiles, being unable to adapt themselves completely to climatic extremes, were restricted in distribution. These events marked the emergence of the modern pattern of climates, and of the distribution of animals in relation to these climates, to culminate in the world as we know it today.

BIBLIOGRAPHY

E. Antevs, "The climatologic significance of annual rings in fossil woods," *Amer. Jour. Sci.* (5) 9, 296–302 (1925).

W. J. Arkell, "On the nature, origin and climatic significance of the coral reefs in the vicinity of Oxford," *Quart. Jour. Geol. Soc.* (*London*) 91, 77–108 (1935).

E. W. Berry, "The past climate of the North Polar region," *Smiths. Misc. Coll.* (Washington, 1930), vol. 82, no. 6.

W. H. Bradley, "The varves and climate of the Green River epoch," *U. S. Geological Survey Professional Paper*, 158-E, pp. 87–110 (1929).

C. E. P. Brooks, *Climate through the ages.* McGraw-Hill, (New York, 1949).

E. C. Case, *The environment of vertebrate life in the late Palaeozoic in North America* (Publ. No. 283, Carnegie Institution, Washington, 1919). *Environment of tetrapod life in the late Palaeozoic of regions other than North America* (Publ. No. 375, Carnegie Institution, Washington, 1926).

R. W. Chaney, "Tertiary forests and continental history," *Bull. Geol. Soc. Amer.* 51, 469–488 (1940).

E. H. Colbert, R. B. Cowles, and C. M. Bogert, "Temperature tolerances in the American alligator and their bearing on the habits, evolution, and extinction of the dinosaurs," *Bull. Amer. Mus. Nat. Hist. 86*, 327–374, pls. 36–41 (1946).

A. P. Coleman, "Late Palaeozoic climates," *Amer. Jour. Sci.* (5) 9, 195–203 (1925).

E. Dacqué, *Grundlagen und Methoden der Palaeogeographie* (Gustav Fischer, Jena, 1915).

W. C. Darrah, *Textbook of paleobotany* (Appleton-Century, New York, 1939).

C. O. Dunbar, *Historical geology* (Wiley, New York, 1949).

H. Gerth, "Das Klima des Permzeitaltern," *Geologische Rundschau 40*, 84–89 (1952).

H. V. Ihering, "Das Klima der Tertiarzeit," *Zs. Geophys. 3*, 365–368 (1927).

P. D. Krynine, "The origin of red beds," *Trans. New York Acad. Sci.* [2] 2, 60–68 (1949).

W. D. Matthew, *Climate and evolution* (Special publ., New York Acad. Sci., vol. 1, 1939).

E. C. Olson, "The evolution of a Permian vertebrate chronofauna," *Evolution 6*, 181–196 (1952).

A. S. Romer and B. H. Grove, "Environment of the early vertebrates," *Amer. Midland Naturalist 16*, 805–856 (1935).

A. S. Romer, *Vertebrate paleontology* (University of Chicago Press, Chicago, 1945).

C. Schuchert, "The palaeogeography of Permian time in relation to the geography of earlier and later periods," *Proc. 2d Pan-Pacific Sci. Congr.*, pp. 1079–1091 (1923).

G. C. Simpson, "Past climates," *Proc. Manchester Lit. Phil. Soc. 74*, 1–34 (1929); "Possible causes of change in climate and their limitations," *Proc. Linn. Soc. London* (Session 152), 190–219 (1940).

C. A. Süssmilch, "The climate of Australia in past ages," *Jour. Prog. Roy. Soc. N. S. Wales 75*, 47–64 (1941).

J. H. F. Umbgrove, *The pulse of the earth* (Martinus Nijhoff, The Hague, 1947); *Symphony of the earth* (Martinus Nijhoff, The Hague, 1950).

D. M. S. Watson, "The Beaufort beds of the Karroo System of South Africa," *Geol. Mag.* [N.S.] 10, 388–393 (1913).

D. White, "Upper Palaeozoic climate as indicated by fossil plants," *Sci. Mon. 20*, 465–473 (1925).

S. Weidmann, "Was there a Pennsylvanian-Permian glaciation in the Arbuckle and Wichita mountains of Oklahoma?" *Jour. Geol. 31*, 466–489 (1923).

F. E. Zeuner, "The symposium on palaeoclimatology at Cologne, 7th-8th January, 1951 and summary of the contents of the second klimaheft of *Geologische Rundschau*," *Geologische Rundschau 40*, 192–193 (1952).

22

PALEOLIMNOLOGY AND CLIMATE

Edward S. Deevey, Jr.

Paleoecology is one of those hybrid sciences that requires, in these days of intensive specialization, coöperation between specialists. Coöperation in research does not come about by fiat, at least outside of wartime, but must consist of voluntary association, suggested by common interests and justified by concrete results that are recognized as such by the collaborating workers. To the geologist, who is constantly seeking to interpret ancient environments, the value of the ecologist's contribution is obvious: an ecologist who knows the species of molluscs or foraminifera and can diagnose the environments in which they live is a handy man to have around. It is not so obvious that the ecologist's role in the partnership is not the docile one of a captive authority. His chief aim is the understanding of how organisms and their habitats are interrelated, and no such understanding can be achieved without considering the history of the biotic community or eco-system. In the study of lakes, which are the eco-systems that lend themselves most readily to the kind of analysis that does not lose sight of their essential wholeness, the geologist and the ecologist can collaborate most happily. One knows that the present is the key to the past, the other knows that the past is the key to the present, and each can think of the other as the captive expert.

Unfortunately this pleasant intellectual symbiosis has not really come into being. Instead, there is a divergence of viewpoint about lakes that is as natural, considering the specialized training received by geologists and ecologists, as it is regrettable. Perhaps this review will help to reconcile some of the differences, but it must be admitted that they exist, and that they partially explain the inadequacy of evidence on the subject in hand. As practiced by ecologists, paleolimnology has paid too little attention to climates of the geologic past; in the hands of geologists, paleolimnology has seldom achieved an understanding of lake dynamics that a limnologist can regard as satisfactory.

This review must confine itself to evidence of former climate provided by lakes as lakes. This is a severe restriction, for fossils of terrestrial plants, preserved in lake and bog sediments, offer a fuller climatic record than the sediments themselves. Only the barest summary of this historic framework is given here, because it has been the subject of several recent reviews.[1, 2, 3]

LATE WISCONSIN STRATIGRAPHY

General Remarks. The Blytt-Sernander scheme, based originally on megascopic plant remains in north European bogs, called for a fourfold division of postglacial time: Boreal, Atlantic, Sub-Boreal, Sub-Atlantic. An immense amount of study of fossil pollen in the same or similar bogs, begun by von Post,[4] has refined the stratigraphy, so that a larger number (8 to 12) of pollen zones is now established for nearly every country of northern Europe. A minor but confusing consequence of the refinement is that the Boreal, as now understood, was not particularly boreal, but had summer temperatures as high as or higher than today's.[5] The Blytt-Sernander names are retained for phases that were warm and dry, warmer and moist, warm and drier, and cooler and moister, respectively. Pre-Boreal phases are distinguished as "Late Glacial" if there is evidence (such as pollen of tundra plants) that glaciers lingered in the near vicinity, and "Postglacial" if there is no such evidence. The formal term "Pre-Boreal" applies to the earliest "Postglacial" (transitional) phase.[3]

Tables showing stratigraphic equivalence of zones have been prepared, most recently by Jessen[6] and Fries.[7] An arrangement of typical pollen sequences is given in Table 1. Like all such tables, this one is oversimplified, because horizontal lines represent stratigraphic equivalence and not contemporaneity in absolute time. The European chronology is based on a combination of archaeologic evidence and varve counting, and is generally accepted; but pollen zones record migrations of plants in response to the shifting of climatic belts, and are certainly not contemporaneous everywhere, even within a limited area such as northern Europe. An idea of the temporal variation concealed in such a table may be got from some radiocarbon dates[8] which show a 3000-year delay in the movement of "pine pollen time" from southern Connecticut to northern Maine. Fortunately this difficulty is almost certainly less acute for the later climatic phases.

Alleröd Interval. A second weakness of this particular table is its possible overemphasis on the value of Zone L2 in Maine. The Aroostook County borings[9] are the first in North America to penetrate deposits of a tundra phase (a boring in Upper Linsley Pond, Connecticut, described by Deevey and Potzger[10] and discussed by Flint[11] may also show a tundra zone). The existence of tundra at that time seems undeniable, but the warmer phase within the tundra time is less certainly real, since it rests on one to three samples in four profiles. Its tentative correlation with the pre-Mankato Alleröd (= Two Creeks) horizon has nevertheless been shown by Flint[11] to fit extremely well with other evidence that nearly all of New England and the Hudson Valley south of Fort Edward lies outside

Table 1. Stratigraphic arrangement of certain European and American pollen sequences, their climatic interpretation, and their dates as used in Europe.

		MAINE *(DEEVEY)*		IRELAND*(JESSEN)*	DENMARK*(JESSEN)*		SWEDISH ZONES	EUROPEAN DATES		*CLIMATE*
POSTGLACIAL	SUB-ATLANTIC	C3	HEMLOCK, SPRUCE RETURN; BEECH MAXIMUM	VIII	ALDER-BIRCH-OAK	IX	BIRCH-SPRUCE-PINE	I / II	*A.D.* 1000 / 0 / *B.C.*	*SWEDISH RECURRENCE SURFACES* -I / -II / -III / -IV	COOL, MOIST
	SUB-BOREAL	C2	OAK MAXIMUM; HEMLOCK, BEECH AT MINIMUM	VII*B*	ALDER-OAK	VIII	OAK-BIRCH	III / IV	1000 / 2000 / 3000	-V	WARM, DRY
	ATLANTIC	C1	HEMLOCK MAX.; OAK, BEECH	VII*A*	ALDER-OAK-PINE	VII	MIXED OAK; LIME	V / VI	4000 / 5000		MOIST; THERMAL MAXIMUM
	BOREAL	B	PINE MAXIMUM; BIRCH FALLS	VI	HAZEL-PINE	VI	ALDER-ELM	VII	6000		WARM, DRY
	PRE-BOREAL	A3	FIR-BIRCH	V	HAZEL-BIRCH	V	PINE-BIRCH-HAZEL	VIII			COOL
		A2	SPRUCE MAXIMUM	IV	BIRCH	IV	BIRCH	IX	7000		
		A1	BIRCH; NAP FALLS								
LATE-GLACIAL		L3	NAP HIGHER	III	YOUNGER SALIX HERBACEA	III	YOUNGER DRYAS	X	8000		COLD; GLACIAL ADVANCE
		L2	NAP LOWER; SPRUCE, BIRCH	II	BIRCH	II	BIRCH	XI	9000		WARMER; ALLERÖD = TWO CREEKS INTERVAL
		L1	NAP HIGH	I	OLDER SALIX HERBACEA	I	OLDER DRYAS	XII	10000 *B.C.*		COLD; GLACIAL ADVANCE

the Mankato drift border. At localities near but beyond the limits of the Mankato ice, the vegetational sequence during "Late Glacial" time should have been: tundra — forest tundra — tundra, and, as in the European sections of Alleröd type, this is what the Aroostook County profiles show. Equivalence of the Two Creeks and Alleröd horizons has been discussed by Flint and Deevey [8] on the basis of radiocarbon dates.

A new map of European pollen profiles showing Alleröd layers has been published by Gams.[12] Unfortunately the evidence does not yet permit a decision as to how far beyond the ice margin the glacial influence was felt, because a typical Alleröd sequence in central Europe does not immediately tell us which ice sheet was involved in the oscillation from cold to warmer to cold. Proof of such a sequence comes from places as far from the Scandinavian Ice Sheet as Romania and the Cantal in France, and there it implicates the Alpine Ice Sheet, but the waning of the latter cannot yet be correlated in detail with the substages of the Weichsel glaciation. All that can be said is that Alleröd localities in northern Germany are at least 100 miles from the nearest glacier margin.

In North America, where the absence of a counterpart of the Alpine Ice Sheet poses a slightly different problem, the matter has scarcely been studied. A few pollen profiles located on pre-Mankato drift show indications of chilling associated with a later glacial substage,[13, 14] but most of them do not. In some of the latter cases it is possible to doubt that the deepest levels have been analyzed. Incomplete study cannot be the whole explanation, however, for in southern New England, where the drift is probably of Tazewell age,[11] pollen profiles of the oldest mineral sediments show no trace of the cooling one might expect from the Cary (?) glacial readvance to a position less than 20 miles away. It is possible that the pollen record in the southern Connecticut basins did not begin until after the Cary maximum; if that is so, some evidence of cooling ought to be associated with the Mankato ice. There is none. Perhaps the reason is that the ice in Mankato time was too far away (200 miles) to exert an influence on the climate of southern New England. This hypothesis would be more attractive if the extraordinary pollen sequence from Singletary Lake, North Carolina,[15] did not record two maxima of conifer pollen of which the later is almost certainly of Mankato age. This is a puzzle that can only be solved by further work. What seems certain is that there was an essential difference between American and European regions marginal to the ice sheets in Mankato (= Fennoscandian) time. Forests appear to have lived much nearer the ice in North America, so that an abundance of forest tree pollen masked the evidence of tundra.

Recurrence Surfaces. In northern Europe, where many bogs have been drained and exploited for fuel, peat stratigraphy has attained a refinement undreamed of in North America. Studies of megascopic plant remains reveal striking changes in bog ecology. In typical sections there is at least one conspicuous level that marks the drying and stabilization of a former bog surface, above which lies a younger body of peat formed under much moister conditions. One such cycle of regeneration occurs in so many bogs at the same horizon (as dated by pollen analysis and by archaeologic remains) that it can only mean a return to a moist climate. In fact, several cycles of stabilization and regeneration can sometimes be discerned in the same section.

The first recurrence surface to be noticed was called the *Grenzhorizont* by Weber.[16] It marks the culmination of dry conditions in the Sub-Boreal and the beginning of the Sub-Atlantic "climatic deterioration," and roughly coincides with the transition from Bronze Age to Iron Age in northern Germany. In a fundamental contribution Granlund [17] established the existence of five different surfaces in Swedish bogs. As many as nine have been recognized by some workers.[1, 18, 19] Not all are equally well developed, or even present, in any one bog. By pollen and archaeologic evidence Granlund dated the two major surfaces (II and III) at A.D. 400 and 600 B.C. (the latter corresponding to the classic *Grenz*). A later one (I) around A.D. 1200 and two earlier ones (IV and V) about 1200 B.C. and 2300 B.C. completed Granlund's series.

The recent work of Godwin [20] and Clapham and Godwin [21] may be consulted for an account of British recurrence surfaces and for references to the continental literature. Nothing in any way comparable has yet been worked out in North America, but it is clear from sections published in the literature of economic peat geology [22-27] that cycles of drying and bog regeneration are not unknown in North America.

Thermal Maximum. The complex postglacial pollen stratigraphy in northwestern Europe and northeastern North America would not be expected to be applicable on a world-wide scale. Much of its complexity arises from climatic fluctuations involving moisture, not temperature, and these cannot have been totally unrelated to the physiographic history of the Baltic and Great Lakes regions. This history is partly one of crustal movements following glacial unloading, and even if regional parallelism applies to eastern North America and western Europe, it can hardly extend much farther afield. For this reason we must look to temperature changes for guidance in long-range correlations.

If temperature alone is considered, postglacial climatic changes both in Europe and in North America can readily be reduced to a consistent scheme: increasing warmth, maximum warmth, decreasing warmth. For the segment of time legitimately called "postglacial" in some districts and "postpluvial" in others, Antevs [28] suggested the term "Neothermal." Within that time, which according to Antevs began about 7000 B.C. (8000 B.C. ± 1000 years seems a reasonable guess), the "warm, dry middle period" or "climatic optimum" seems to have prevailed from approximately 5000 B.C. to 600 B.C. Antevs called it the "altithermal"; Flint and Deevey [8] prefer the term "Thermal Maximum." It may have begun everywhere about 5000 B.C., as it did in Europe with the formation of the Littorina Sea,[29] or it may have begun somewhat earlier, in Boreal time. The Thermal Maximum may be said to have come to an end when Matthes' [30, 31] "Little Ice Age" began. Matthes suggested a date of 2000 B.C. on the basis of evidence that modern descendants of Lake Lahontan and other pluvial lakes in the western United States are no older than 4000 years.[32] The date of 600 B.C. is a well-documented figure for the end of the Sub-Boreal in Europe, marked by Granlund's Recurrence Surface III (see above). Flint [11] suggested that the Cochrane glacial substage [33] is the Canadian counterpart of the "Little Ice Age," which would mean, among other things, that the James Bay peat deposits [34] are not "interglacial" but probably belong to the Thermal Maximum. The time since 600 B.C. seems too short for the advance and retreat of the Cochrane ice, and it is worth remembering that there are several older recurrence surfaces in European bogs that might represent the beginning of the Little Ice Age.

In regions where neither glacial nor pluvial conditions prevailed, or at least cannot be proved to have occurred in Mankato (= Fennoscandian) time, the lower boundary of "postglacial" or "postpluvial" time is uncertain. What is clear is that a thermal maximum was so widespread as to appear universal, and that it was followed by what von Post [1] called "final period revertence." A series of pollen diagrams selected by von Post to demonstrate this situation is reproduced in Fig. 1. Data discussed by von Post came from New Zealand,[35, 36] Argentina,[37, 38] Hawaii,[39] and Laborador.[40] The Argentine evidence seems especially weak, and its presentation was marred by Auer's attempt to equate minor irregularities in the Nothofagus (southern beech) pollen curve to those in a birch pollen curve from Finland. The Hawaiian sequence is also hard to assimilate to von Post's scheme, because the middle phase was one of *increased* moisture, and "revertence" was toward *drier*, not cooler, climate. A recent study of pollen profiles from Tristan da Cunha [41] fails to show conclusive evidence of revertence, but local difficulties of interpretation are admittedly great.

Von Post's threefold division of Late Pleistocene time seems likely to endure, despite the temptation to use it as a Procrustean bed. Evidence of a Thermal Maximum exists in the form of high strandlines on stable seacoasts (Stearns,[42, 43, 44] Fairbridge [45, 46]), as well as in the occurrence of marine molluscs of nonarctic character in various parts of the Arctic.[47]

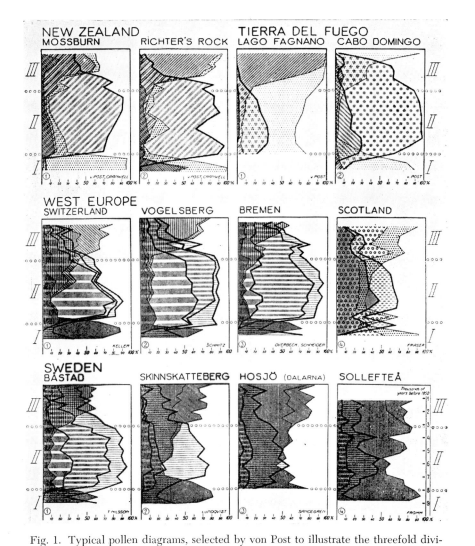

Fig. 1. Typical pollen diagrams, selected by von Post to illustrate the threefold division of "postglacial" time into phases of increasing warmth, maximum warmth, and decreasing warmth. Areas bordered by thick lines represent "mediocratic" ("middle period dominant") warmth-loving plants; areas bordered by thin lines represent "terminocratic" or cooler-climate species dominant in Zones I and III. From Selling (Fig. 29).[39]

Most of the world's deserts seem to have been drier than today at some time in the recent past; this is true of Australia,[48, 49] Egypt,[50, 51] Palestine,[52, 53] Kenya,[54] and South Africa,[55] and there is abundant evidence from North America. This evidence is not all of equal value; where the existence of warm or dry conditions is certain their age is usually problematical. Deserts are not all alike, and it is not yet clear whether the sequence of climates in subtropical deserts and regions of Mediterranean climate was the same, or even whether one would expect it to be the same, in tropical savanna regions. For a defense of the view that one would expect meteorologic conditions in the tropics and in subtropical Asia to have been out of phase, see the discussion by Mayr.[56] The correlation between pluvial ages in middle latitudes and in the tropics is considered in a later section.

Summary. In well-studied regions, that is, in moist-temperate Europe and North America, and in the semiarid western United States, "post-glacial" or "postpluvial" time can be divided into three phases: increasing warmth, maximum warmth, decreasing warmth. These phases may well have been contemporaneous all over the world. Superimposed on them were fluctuations in moisture. In their major outlines, at least, these fluctuations were approximately synchronous in western Europe and eastern North America, the middle phase of Thermal Maximum being divisible into dry (Boreal), moist (Atlantic) and dry (Sub-Boreal) episodes. The time of maximum temperatures lasted from about 5000 to about 600 B.C. Less important cycles of alternating drought and moisture, stratigraphically recorded by recurrence surfaces in bogs, are known to have been approximately synchronous in Europe since about 2300 B.C., and should be looked for elsewhere. In the United States and in northern Europe the whole series of events postdates the last glacial (Mankato, Fennoscandian) substage, and radiocarbon dates suggest that the last pluvial episode in the western United States was contemporaneous with the Mankato maximum (about 8000 B.C.). Near but outside the Mankato and Fennoscandian end moraines a temporary phase of warm (that is, nonglacial, mainly forest tundra) climate is recorded — the Alleröd (= Two Creeks) interval, dated at or just before 9000 B.C.

Most of the evidence summarized here comes from bogs. In their earlier stages, at least, most bogs were lakes. We may now examine the history of events within the lakes themselves for clues to the relation between paleolimnology and climate.

ONTOGENY OF LAKES

Linsley Pond. Not many lacustrine embryologies are available for comparison, but Linsley Pond, Connecticut, appears sufficiently typical to serve as a base for discussion. Figure 2 shows the principal features of the postglacial stratigraphic sequence, and Fig. 3 attempts a synthesis of events as inferred from four borings.[57] Analogy with the embryology of organisms suggests that *growth* and *differentiation* are the fundamental

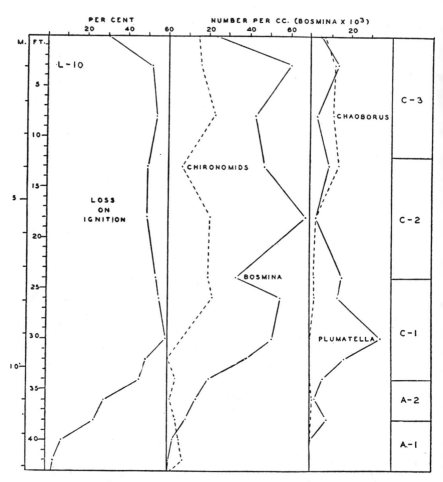

Fig. 2. Percentage loss on ignition and microfossils per cubic centimeter of wet sediment in Boring L-10 (water depth 13 m) in Linsley Pond, Connecticut. From Deevey (Fig. 1).[57]

processes going on, and suggests furthermore that it will be difficult to separate them in analysis. In the developing lake the *quantities* of most things, notably the total organic matter in the sediments but also including remains of zoöplankton and bottom animals, increased in a way that suggests growth, whereas the *kinds* of animals and plants changed systematically in a way that can be called differentiation.

Of outstanding theoretical importance is the course of organic matter as a function of time. The depth scale is a time scale, though certainly not a uniform one; and if the percentage of organic matter in the sediments is plotted against time in the standard way, with time as the independent variable (Figs. 4 and 5), it is obvious that this growth, at least in its early part, was identical in form with the sigmoid growth of organisms and populations. Evidently the original, organically sterile lake basin, while receiving large amounts of inorganic sediment from the thinly vegetated hills of glacial drift, approached its modern eutrophic condition at an accelerating tempo. This acceleration resembles the autocatalytic process

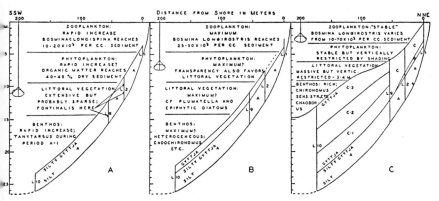

Fig. 3. Summary of ecologic conditions in Linsley Pond, Connecticut, (A) during the spruce-fir phase, (B) at the time of maximum organic matter, and (C) at present. Estimated transparencies shown by Secchi disks at the left of each figure. The vertical dimension is exaggerated 10 times. From Deevey (Fig. 7).[57]

that is so obvious and so mysterious in other kinds of growing things. As the living communities — plankton, bottom fauna, rooted vegetation — gradually succeeded in utilizing the available chemical nutrients with maximum efficiency, the acceleration decreased to zero, and a stage of equilibrium set in. Subsequent departures from equilibrium are apparent from the irregularities of the curves, and are not yet fully understood; for the present they may be ignored as less interesting than the fact that equilibrium was attained.

From a maximum of epiphytic diatoms[58] and of statoblasts of the (presumably epiphytic) bryozoan Plumatella (Fig. 2), it is inferred that early in the equilibrium stage the rooted vegetation grew at greater depths than today; hence the transparency must have been greater. Plankton production may have been as great then as at any time later, but the lighted zone in which plankton production exceeded consumption was thicker; subsequently the planktonic algae have restricted their own production by shading themselves as the volume of the lake became smaller and the nutrients, as well as the plankton, became more concentrated. This growth process could go on without increasing the delivery of or-

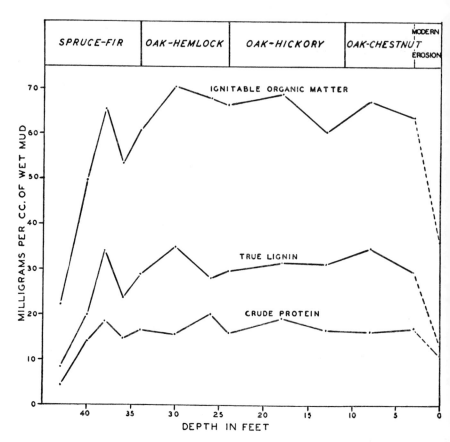

Fig. 4. Crude protein, true lignin, and ignitable organic matter per cubic centimeter of wet mud in Linsley Pond, Connecticut, Boring L-10. The abscissa gives time as an inverse function of depth. These curves give relative measures of organic deposition on the basis of Assumption 1 (constant rate of sedimentation of unit thickness). After Hutchinson and Wollack (Fig. 3).[59]

ganic matter to the sediments, in somewhat the same way as the growth of a man continues long after the upper limit of mass has been attained. In other words, the equilibrium was a steady state and not a true equilibrium.

In order to make the apparent time scale correspond more nearly to the true one, Hutchinson and Wollack [59] made two alternative assumptions: (1) that unit volume of sediment was deposited in unit time, and (2) that unit mass of inorganic matter was deposited in unit time. Figure 4 corresponds to Assumption 1, but the true state of affairs undoubtedly lies closer to Assumption 2, shown in Fig. 5. This leads to a picture of the growth of total organic matter, and of the crude protein and lignin fractions, as stretched out over time. A rough calculation that uses this as-

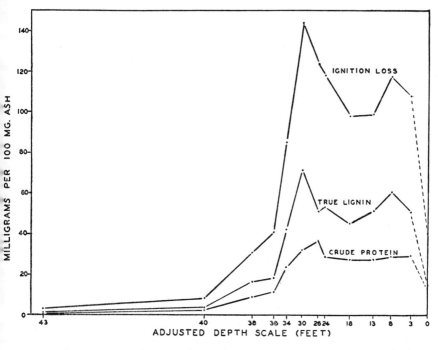

Fig. 5. Crude protein, true lignin, and ignitable organic matter per 100 parts of ash in Linsley Pond, Connecticut, Boring L-10, plotted against a scale proportional to the total ash deposited, and inverted to show time as an inverse function of depth. These curves give relative measures of organic deposition on the basis of Assumption 2 (constant rate of sedimentation of unit mass of ash). After Hutchinson and Wollack (Fig. 4).[59]

sumption, and attempts to deduce the length of the sedimentary record in years, was made from the number of Bosmina carapaces in the sediments and the estimated annual production of this clacoceran in the modern lake.[57] This is an application of the method that Lohmann [60] used to calculate rates of deposition of deep-sea sediments from their content of coccolithophores. The results suggest a total time span of between 11,000 and 16,000 years. That is, in terms of radiocarbon dates, the origin of

Linsley Pond antedated the Mankato maximum and may be older than Cary; the agreement is probably fortuitous, but on Flint's new interpretation [11] the lake should be older than Cary.

Turning to differentiation, the striking fact is that the ancestral Linsley Pond had a qualitatively rich tendipedid bottom fauna of the type ("Tanytarsus fauna" of the older literature, properly called Calopsectra fauna [61]) characteristic of deep lakes with ample amounts of oxygen in deep water. The modern lake, whose depths are practically devoid of oxygen in summer, has a Tendipes (= Chironomus) fauna. It is difficult to say when this condition set in, on account of the great diversity and small numbers of tendipedid fossils identified. It probably occurred at the time of pollen zone C2, when the phantom midge Chaoborus first appeared in numbers.

From the transition from a Calopsectra to a Tendipes lake one infers that the oxygen supply in deep water was depleted during summer stagnation, but the inference itself is equivocal. This is because limnologists mean either of two different things when they describe a lake as oligotrophic or eutrophic, and the quantity of oxygen in deep water does not permit a choice between the possibilities. Once thermal stratification sets in, shallow lakes exhaust their oxygen supply more quickly than do deep lakes of the same basic productivity, simply because events are confined within a smaller volume. On the other hand, some lakes are fundamentally more productive than others, owing to differences in amount or availability of nutrients. Productivity is so difficult to measure that it has seldom been possible to distinguish the *morphometric* from the *edaphic* factors underlying the concepts of oligotrophy and eutrophy.

Linsley Pond became shallower automatically as it filled with sediments, and that could be the only reason it became more eutrophic. However, the senescent Lyd Hyt Pond in the same drainage basin also started life as an "oligotrophic" Calopsectra lake, although its original depth was only 11 meters, 4 meters shallower than Linsley Pond today. It therefore seems unlikely that shoaling alone was responsible for the depletion of oxygen in Linsley Pond as it changed from a Calopsectra lake about 26 meters deep to a Tendipes lake about 18 meters deep. An absolute increase in productivity, that is, an edaphically controlled eutrophication, seems to be implied. To that extent, then, the process of differentiation is separable from that of growth, and the sequence oligotrophy → eutrophy may be considered the normal course of lake ontogeny, regardless of the form changes accompanying sedimentation.

What has this ontogeny to do with climate? Broadly speaking, if the climate had not warmed up, Linsley Pond would still be an ice-bound, sterile lake of the excessively oligotrophic type. Apart from this, it seems that changes within the lake itself were relatively independent of fluctuations, either of temperature or of moisture, in the climate outside. The truth is that few of the fossil animals identified have sufficiently narrow thermal requirements to tell us much about prevailing temperatures, and, being aquatic, they can tell nothing about moisture. In Sodon Lake, Michigan, Cain and others [62] found that *Valvata sincera*, a northern species which is the only aquatic mollusc in the older sediments that does not live in the lake today, had its maximum abundance during the time of the pine-pollen zone. One Linsley Pond fossil, the bryozoan *Pectinatella magnifica*, is also a stenothermal species, and it made its first appearance before the time of the pine zone. As early as spruce-fir time, then, the summer surface temperature reached 18°C to 20°C, but these temperatures would not be surprising in a small lake in the taiga today.

The rare and highly distinctive cladocerans *Chydorus faviformis* and *C. bicornutus* should be mentioned, for although their present geographic distribution is almost unknown, their zonal distribution as fossils in Linsley Pond (and in Upper Linsley Pond and Oyster Pond, Massachusetts, according to unpublished studies) suggests that they are warm-water indicators. Like other cladocerans [63] they may occur almost anywhere in postglacial sections, but they are much more abundant in sediments of Zone C2. Daphnia, the most familiar cladoceran, is unknown from Linsley Pond, but occurs in Alleröd lake deposits in Europe [64] and even in interglacial deposits in Denmark.[65] Water fleas are not particularly good indicators of climate, but they are so abundant in lake deposits that they can be treated statistically, like pollen grains, and when this is done on a wide scale in combination with zoögeographic studies the results may be of great interest.

So far as the character of the whole Linsley Pond biocoenosis can show, the steady, and at first steadily accelerating, growth process continued while the Cary ice approached within 20 miles of the lake. Even if we assume that ice or permafrost occupied the basin in Cary time, and that the sedimentary record did not begin until after the Cary maximum, there is no trace of the Mankato advance to the Saint Johnsbury–Fort Edward line,[11] about 200 miles to the north. Still less is there any indication in the lacustrine record of fluctuations of moisture implied by pollen zones C1, C2, and C3. No such indication would be expected, of course, apart from changes of lake level, of which there is no evidence, but the failure to respond to temperature changes between deglaciation and the time of the pine zone is more surprising. Obviously, Linsley Pond was more of a thermostat than the upland environment from which the pollen was derived.

Windermere. Of the other noncalcareous lakes for which paleolimnologic data are available, the best known is Windermere in the English

Lake District.[66,67] The older sediments of this lake show a typical late-glacial sequence, Zone II — a layer of "detritus silt" intercalated between layers of varved clay — being the first Alleröd deposit discovered in the British Isles. The postglacial development indicates growth of the bio-coenosis, recorded, as in Linsley Pond, by a perfectly sigmoid curve of organic matter with a long and remarkably constant equilibrium phase. The fossils, however, suggest little in the way of climatic change since the time of Zone IV. Even the Alleröd zone yields no *lacustrine* evidence of warming, for its fossils are dominantly terrestrial plants. The typical sequence was found only in shallow water, and a deep-water equivalent of the silt appears to be lacking. Some cladocerans were found in Zone II organic deposits at an intermediate depth, but "the species of Entomostraca recorded from that layer all occur in the main bed of organic material, that is, in the [postglacial] brown mud above the clay. They are also living in the lake at the present day." [68]

Pyramid Valley Swamp. The idea that the sequence ologotrophy → eutrophy is a kind of homeostasis, independent of climate within wide limits, finds some support in the otherwise rather puzzling history of Pyramid Valley Swamp, South Island, New Zealand. Two moist phases separated by a dry interval are recorded at this locality, and although the pollen stratigraphy is incomplete, such a sequence naturally suggests the three postglacial zones of Cranwell and von Post. The earlier moist phase is represented by a peaty soil. The later one saw the formation of a lake, or rather a shallow pond, some features of whose history are shown in Fig. 6 (from unpublished studies by the author). The sediments are highly calcareous, and total organic matter has therefore to be represented by organic nitrogen. Sigmoid growth was the dominant process during the history of the lake, and departures from equilibrium, though suggested by the fluctuations of organic nitrogen content, seem to have had no consistent effect on the animals, for molluscs, Cladocera, ostracods, and tendipedid larvae all display rather uniform changes in total numbers. The pond eventually filled in to make a swamp in which large numbers of moas were trapped.[69-71] This filling is recorded at the top of the section, where the marl gives way to a slightly less calcareous deposit that is poorer in fossils, and then to a humus layer, the latter not being represented in the profile of Fig. 6.

If the whole of the lacustrine sequence belongs to the moist third phase of Cranwell and von Post, as unpublished pollen studies by Harris suggest, the inception of the lake was the result of climatic change, but the details of its history record nothing but lake ontogeny. There is, however, some indication that the latest climatic trend in parts of New Zealand was toward drier climate, and it may be that this is the meaning of the increased silting and the return of the ostracod Darwinula at the top of the section.

Bogs. Some paleolimnologic information can be gleaned from the innumerable sections published by pollen stratigraphers. The majority of these sections are of bogs, so that the chief paleolimnologic problem they raise is that of the origin of dystrophy — the peculiar "pathological" condition that supervenes when a harmonic lake turns into a bog.[72] The inception of dystrophy means that allochthonous organic matter, delivered as lake peat or *dy*, reaches the lake in such quantities that the lake's metabolism is overbalanced, and instead of reworking the dy into a less humic

PYRAMID VALLEY SWAMP NEW ZEALAND

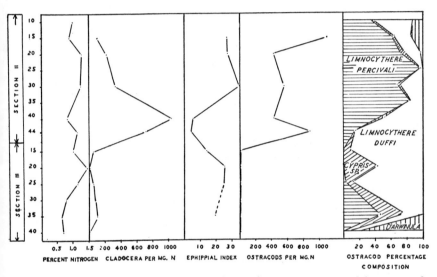

Fig. 6. Some chemical and microfossil analyses of a shallow extinct lake, Pyramid Valley Swamp, South Island, New Zealand. The ephippial index gives the number of ephippia (resting eggs) per cladoceran per milligram of organic nitrogen in the mud, and suggests that the middle phase was climatically most favorable for cladocerans.

gyttja the lake permits it to accumulate virtually unchanged. The dy is strongly reducing, so that the oxygen curve of a dystrophic lake looks like that of a eutrophic lake, but tendipedid larvae and other ooze browsers are excluded from the bottom and the bottom fauna consists almost entirely of Chaoborus.[73] The plankton is also likely to suffer impoverishment, and to be restricted to acid-water types and to those zoöplankters that can stand the presence of humic colloids. The peculiar biota persists until the lake is completely filled in and is succeeded by a *Flachmoor* (nonraised bog).

No systematic paleolimnologic study, including chemical and micro-fossil analysis, has ever been made of a dystrophic lake. For his studies of lake sediments in their regional as well as historic aspects, Lundqvist [74] devised a semiquantitative classification, based on microscopic examination, that permits the recognition of dy in profiles. Pure dy seldom occurs, however, and the most abundant component of even the most dystrophic lake sediments is coarse-detritus gyttja. As this sediment is formed wherever plant remains are deposited too rapidly for oxidative destruction, it is usually impossible to see the initiation of dystrophy in profiles; the usual picture is one of normal lake development (clay or silt grading upward into algal gyttja), followed by a gradually increasing proportion of un-decomposed coarse detritus toward the top of the profile.

Such a picture may mean nothing but shoaling as a result of harmonic lake development. On the other hand, it may imply rise of the water table, swamping and peat formation on the adjacent upland, and delivery of greatly increased quantities of raw peat to the lake. A lake without outlet is somewhat more likely to have its metabolism overthrown in this way than one that is drained. Such a combination of circumstances was of widespread occurrence in Europe at the time of the "Sub-Atlantic climatic deterioration." There is evidence that it occurred several times in the history of lakes near Woods Hole, Massachusetts.[75] But dystrophic conditions do not necessarily imply increased precipitation and decreased temperature, and careful investigation is needed to learn what climatic or other significance they may have.

The origin of raised bogs (Hochmoore) is not a strictly limnologic problem, for these remarkable structures often arise in shallow depressions that previously contained no lakes and grow radially by paludification of the surrounding upland. Vertical and radial growth of a raised bog is made possible by the capillary quality of Sphagnum peat, but an excessively maritime climate is a prerequisite. The climatic sequence discernible in the stratigraphic record of European bogs, with their cyclic stabilization and regeneration,[17] has already been discussed. The fossil plant associations that provide this record are semiterrestrial, or at least not lacustrine, and so their description falls outside the scope of this review. It should be noted, however, that bog stratigraphy is on the whole richer in climatic implications than is that of harmonic lakes. Bog sediments are known from all divisions of postglacial time in Europe, as well as from the Alleröd interval, and an extensive bog system of Boreal age now lies on the bottom of the North Sea.[76] The major episode of bog formation began in Atlantic time, and its resurgence in Sub-Atlantic time seems to have been a quietly spectacular event over much of northwestern Europe.

There are two groups of animals whose remains are found in bogs and provide confirmatory evidence of climatic change. These are the beetles, studied by Henriksen [77] (see discussion by Deevey [2]), and the testaceous rhizopods, studied by Harnisch.[78] Like the plants with which they are associated stratigraphically, these animals are partly terrestrial and partly aquatic; the proportions of the two kinds fluctuated with postglacial changes of moisture, while inferences about temperature can be drawn from the geographic ranges of the various species. The most informative single species of animal, however, belongs to neither of these groups; it is the tortoise *Emys orbicularis,* whose remains in Danish bogs have been studied by Degerböl and Krog.[79]

Seasonal Cycles. In view of the relative constancy of the lacustrine climate, which follows from the thermal properties of water and which is amply demonstrated by the insensitivity of Linsley Pond and Windermere to known postglacial climatic changes, it may seem surprising that the small differences between summer and winter can often be detected in lake sediments. Two rather different kinds of seasonal record have been found in lake deposits. One, reflected in the classic late-glacial varves, is the result of freezing and thawing of a nearby glacier, and consists of a series of spring-and-summer coarse (silt) layers, each of which grades upward into a fine (clay or silt) layer laid down in quiet water, presumably under the ice of a frozen lake. Because sediments of this type are mainly allochthonous, they are less interesting to the paleolimnologist than the autochthonous, seasonally laminated gyttjas that usually involve an alternation of light-colored calcareous and darker organic layers. The less interesting glacial varves are exposed in sections, and as they are therefore better known they will be discussed first.

The discovery that the laminations called varves provide a record of glacier retreat was made and fully exploited by De Geer, who summarized his life's work in a volume published in 1940.[80] The paleolimnologic interpretation of varves has not always been satisfactory in all its details, particularly in the assumption [33] that glacial lakes must have been isothermal. Antevs' latest views [81] have profited by the important hydrographic studies of Johnsson [82] on Lake Klämmingen, and permitted an attempt to reconstruct the hydrography of Steep Rock Lake, Ontario, in terms of increasing stability of thermal stratification with distance from the ice tongue. This interpretation seems nevertheless to rest more on deduction than on sedimentary evidence in the varves themselves.

The *proof* that varves are annual is credited to Johnston,[83] who based his case on a calculation of the annual load of sediment delivered to Lake Louise, Alberta, where varves are still forming. The calculated thickness agreed reasonably well with the observed thickness, about $\frac{1}{6}$ inch. Johnston was aware of but did not discuss an earlier study of the sediments of this lake by Wilcox,[84] who found the laminae to be approximately 0.01 inch thick when dry. This discrepancy should be resolved; it seems possible that the varves examined by Wilcox were old, while those studied by Johnston were recent, dating from a time of increased glacier melting in the present century. It is unfortunate that varved deposits are generally so unfossiliferous that a more convincing proof of their annual nature is not easy to achieve.[85]

Cycles in varve deposition other than the annual one have not been given the study they deserve. De Geer claimed that the sunspot cycle is not shown, but never published enough data to permit an independent decision. Douglass [86] applied his periodograph method to a varve sequence from the Connecticut valley, and reported that the 11-year sunspot cycle is absent, and is replaced, as it was in tree rings during periods when sunspots were essentially absent, by the 10-year "dearth cycle." Cycles of 8.8 and 20 years' length were also reported. Varve sequences are only one of several sorts of periodic phenomena urgently demanding study by statistical methods that have only recently become available.[87]

A discussion of the role of turbidity currents in the formation of varves has recently been given by Kuenen,[88] and is based on evidence that varves can be produced in a laboratory model.[89] That the coarser members, at least, were often deposited from a current flowing along the bottom of the glacial lakes was inferred by De Geer from their increased thickness on the upstream side of irregularities of the basin floor.

Annual laminations are apparently much rarer in fossiliferous postglacial sediments than in late-glacial silts. Apart from some inadequately described Russian examples,[90–92] which were said to provide a complete record of most or all of postglacial time, the most notable series of laminated gyttjas was reported from the Faulensee near Spiez, Switzerland, by Welten.[29, 93] The laminae consist of a light-colored summer layer of marl-gyttja and a dark organic layer formed in winter. The proof that the couplet is annual is fourfold, being based on cyclic changes in (1) size of the largest $CaCO_3$ crystals, (2) total quantity and (3) percentage composition of pollen, and (4) diatom abundance. As a record of the sedimentary history of ten thousand years, the Faulensee sequence suffers from incompleteness, so that some interpolation is necessary, but it remains unmatched for its elegance and for the care with which it was studied.

Annual laminations in other modern lakes are mainly confined to the youngest deposits. This is certain in the Zürichsee [94, 95] and in Third Sister Lake, Michigan,[14] and probable in McKay Lake, Ontario.[96] Whether the light-colored member of the annual couplet is composed of marl, as in the Zürichsee and McKay Lake, or of inorganic silt or clay, as in Third Sister Lake, it seems that human disturbance has been responsible for the

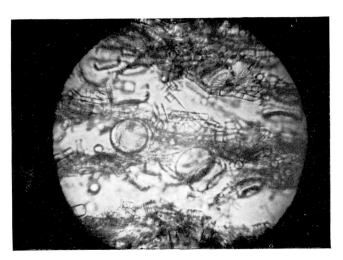

Fig. 7. Photomicrograph of a thin section of laminated sediments from Douglas Lake, Michigan. The organic matter has been burned out, so that the darker layers appear light in the photograph, and are separated by layers of diatom skeletons. Photograph by I. T. Wilson.

change in conditions that permitted the preservation of the laminae. That is, it seems likely that eutrophication, arising from domestic pollution, has so restricted the oxygen supply in deep water that the bottom fauna has been excluded and thus prevented from reworking the seasonal deposits. Cultural eutrophication of the Zürichsee has been thoroughly documented.[97-99] In this lake it has gone so far as to produce permanent stagnation (*meromixis*), and while Third Sister Lake has not yet reached this stage and may be too shallow to do so, meromixis is probably a normal prerequisite to the preservation of laminae.

Not all laminae observed in lake deposits are annual. The brown oxidative microzone that forms on a black gyttja when it is brought to the surface of the lake also forms *in situ* during circulation periods when reducing conditions in deep water give way to oxidizing conditions. Variations in oxidation-reduction potential in narrow layers within and just above the mud have been studied systematically, both in the lake and in laboratory models, by Mortimer.[100] The brown color is generally due to ferric hydroxide, the black to ferrous and manganous sulfides. When Linsley Pond mud is allowed to stand in an aquarium, three layers can sometimes be seen: under the brown surface layer there is a light-gray intermediate layer of uncertain chemical composition, which grades downward into the typical black reduced layer. Under certain conditions, not yet fully understood, these layers migrate downward to give a multiple lamination (according to preliminary observations by J. H. Vallentyne). The same phenomenon has been observed in laboratory studies of mud from Lake Haruna, Japan,[101] and the "red" layers were proved to be richer in iron than the intervening gray layers. Sugawara attributed the lamination to the Liesegang mechanism, though this is more a description than an explanation.

If the Liesegang layers are stable as sediment forms above them, it seems likely that some such process is responsible for the indistinct lamination encountered in the sediment cores of Douglas Lake, Michigan, by Wilson.[102] Thin vertical sections of several of these laminae can be mounted on microscope slides, and as shown in Fig. 7 the light-colored layers are rich in diatoms, while the intervening dark layers are less so. The estimate of 103,000 of these laminae in the postglacial sediments of Douglas Lake is so high that it is obvious that the layers are not annual. Wilson supposed that they are approximately semiannual, reflecting circulation (and diatom flowering) periods in spring and fall, alternating with stagnation in winter and summer. Even so, the count of 51,500 years must overestimate the length of "postglacial" time. Clearly these remarkable laminae deserve further study.

Calcium Deposition. Seasonal lamination of organic lake deposits is rare, but when it occurs (that is, when absence of bottom fauna permits its preservation), it usually involves calcium carbonate as one member of an annual couplet. This suggests that calcareous lake deposits are likely to be exceptionally sensitive to climatic variation. Calcareous sediments, varying in composition from marl-gyttja to almost pure marl, cannot occur unless there is a certain amount of lime in the drainage basin. Whether or not limestone is the country rock, however, much of the Middle West and of Europe is mantled by glacial drift that is rich in lime, or was so when it was fresh. Some of the lime that was leached from the drift is now to be found in the lakes.

Deposition of marl is a biochemical process.[103] Photosynthesis by algae and rooted plants removes carbon dioxide, and some of these plants can also remove bicarbonate ions as such. If this removal is continued, the acidity of the water may decrease to such a point that the solubility product of calcium carbonate is exceeded, and the lime precipitates. The precipitation is favored by high temperature, owing to decreased solubility of gaseous carbon dioxide. The role of bacteria in the precipitation has often been discussed [104] and is apparently minor, though variable. Conditions are most nearly ideal for marl deposition in summer in shallow water over weed beds in a hard-water lake. Such lakes often have a littoral girdle of marly sediment; below the thermocline, where temperature is low and carbon dioxide is often enriched, the sediments are less calcareous.[105, 106]

One of the few hard-water lakes whose postglacial history is known is the Grosser Plöner See, Holstein, where Groschopf [107] has shown that deposition of the marl girdle in shallow water was largely completed by the end of Atlantic time. In deep water also, though the sediment is a marl-gyttja and not marl, the maximum of carbonate deposition fell in Boreal and early Atlantic time. In smaller, shallower lakes, which may be supposed to have warmed up earlier, the maximum may have occurred in pre-Boreal time, as Tidelski [108] has shown.

While postglacial warming explains the inception of calcium deposition, it cannot explain the existence of a maximum that was followed by a decline. Such a maximum is of rather general occurrence, to judge from numerous sections of lakes and bogs. Well-studied American examples are Cedar Bog Lake, Minnesota,[109] and Sodon Lake, Michigan.[62] Marl also lies a short distance below the modern organic deposits of Lake Mendota.[110] The decline of marl deposition in such lakes seems not to imply cooling, but rather a decrease in the supply of calcium. It happens that nearly all marl-forming lakes that have been studied lie in deep glacial drift, and their lime is derived from that source, often by way of groundwater seepage, and not from bedrock by way of streams. As the drift was gradually leached of its available carbonates, and as exchange between

lake water and ground water was impeded by a sediment seal, the supply
of lime gradually diminished. This is Groschopf's interpretation of events
in the Grosser Plöner See, and it is probably of wide application.

A good example of the sensitivity of carbonate deposition to climatic
change appears to be shown by Tippecanoe Lake, Indiana (Fig. 8). Pollen
analyses of a deep-water boring in this lake were reported by Potzger and
Wilson,[14] while Wilson and Opdyke[111] published proximate chemical
analyses of the same profile. The interpretation of the stratigraphy is the

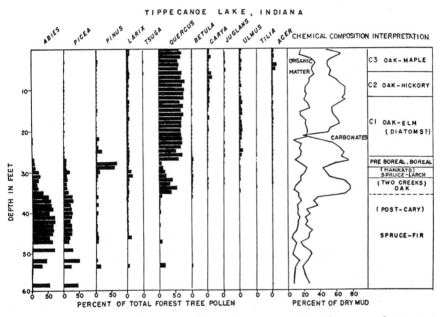

Fig. 8. Pollen diagram and proximate chemical composition for a deep-water boring in
Tippecanoe Lake, Indiana, drawn from data of Potzger and Wilson[14] and Wilson and
Opdyke.[111] The interpretation of the stratigraphy is the writer's.

writer's, and may seem daring, but the concurrence of the otherwise
anomalous early oak-pollen phase with a maximum of carbonate deposition strongly suggests the Two Creeks interval (the lake is situated on
Cary drift). The pollen sequence is peculiar in several other respects,
notably in the compression of pre-Boreal and Boreal zones, but the second
minimum of carbonate content, falling as it does high up in the deciduous
forest segment of the profile, would require a special explanation on almost
any interpretation of the stratigraphy. The purely *ad hoc* assumption that
it represents a maximum of diatomaceous rather than inorganic silica,
however reasonable, must be reckoned a weak point in the hypothesis.

Conclusions. The lacustrine biocoenosis has an internal stability comparable in its homeostasis to that of an organism, and normal ontogeny proceeds from oligotrophy to eutrophy. Within wide limits this development is independent of climate. An exception has to be made for the biogeochemical processes involved in carbonate deposition, for these are responsive to temperature. In at least one lake, Tippecanoe Lake, Indiana, whose origin antedates the Mankato glacial sub-age, the Two Creeks interval and the subsequent Mankato chilling appear to be recorded by a maximum and a minimum of carbonates. Seasonal changes in temperature are sometimes recorded by annual lamination involving a summer marl layer and a winter organic layer, but such laminae do not usually survive the ooze-browsing activities of bottom animals.

Raised bogs, which are nourished by atmospheric precipitation rather than ground water, are more sensitive to climatic changes than lakes or the nonraised bogs that sometimes succeed them, but their stratigraphy is well understood only in northwestern Europe.

Few of the lakes whose ontogeny is known by stratigraphic methods antedate the Mankato, or at the earliest the Tazewell glacial subage. For evidence of climates of the earlier Pleistocene we must depend on studies, mainly geomorphic, of ancient lakes in semiarid regions.

CLOSED LAKES AND THE PLEISTOCENE RECORD

Introduction. Outside glaciated regions, a major portion of the Pleistocene record of climatic variations consists of evidence that closed basins, now containing shallow permanent lakes or no lakes at all, formerly held large and deep bodies of water. No such basin records a complete Pleistocene history, because for the most part the basins themselves are the product of crustal movements within the Pleistocene, and most of those that have been well studied give evidence of tilting and deformation, recent enough to have disturbed the high strandlines. For this reason the paleolimnologic record, so far as it is based on strandlines, postdates the middle Pleistocene, and the history of the earlier Pleistocene, where it can be read at all, depends on deposits that have been uplifted and largely removed by erosion, and that may have no genetic relation to the basins in which they are now found. Knowledge of lower and middle Pleistocene lacustrine deposits is scanty, however, not so much because they are fragmentary as because the economic motive for their study has been lacking. Subsurface exploration for oil has penetrated many magnificent series of lower Pleistocene lake beds (such as the Tulare formation,[112] up to 2000 feet thick, in the Central Valley of California), but to a petroleum geologist such deposits are little more than an uninteresting overburden.

The concentration on geomorphic evidence in the study of the later

Pleistocene history of closed basins has had unfortunate consequences. Few geologic features are easier to see than old shorelines in a desert basin, but to work out a lacustrine history from them is a complicated and difficult task for which few geologists have had the necessary time and patience. As a result the record of pluvial ages of the Pleistocene suffers from too much reconnaissance and too little detailed field work.

Two major questions about Pleistocene climates can be answered, eventually if not now, by the lacustrine history of closed basins. They are (1) what was the temporal relation between glacial and pluvial ages? and (2) to what extent did similar Pleistocene events occur in the tropics and in high latitudes? The answer to the first question has been reasonably clear for some time, from evidence in western North America. The second question, which has a more fundamental bearing on the world-wide picture of Pleistocene meteorology, and hence on the causes of an ice age, cannot be answered at present, and can never be answered solely on the basis of work in temperate latitudes. Therefore the evidence from western North America will be treated first, but more summarily.

Western North America. Despite a good deal of search, proof that high lake levels were contemporaneous with glacial advances remains unsatisfactory. The latest Wisconsin glaciers, of presumably Mankato age, seem not to have descended the mountain sides so far as the highest levels of the pluvial lakes, either in the Bonneville [113] or Mono [114] basins. What the field evidence shows is that the Bonneville shoreline and the highest Mono Lake shoreline were carved after, though probably not long after, the deposition of earlier Wisconsin moraines. From the fact that the Bonneville shoreline is replaced by deltaic deposits between the lateral moraines of Little Cottonwood glacier, Gilbert [115] inferred that the moraines are younger than the shore. Blackwelder argued that the deposition of the deltas prevented the cutting of a shoreline, and that the moraines could have been contemporaneous with the Bonneville lake level. So they could have been, but the whole correlation between glacial ages and pluvial ages rests on just such supposititious evidence. We seem to be forced back to the assumption that the two high-water stages recorded for pluvial lakes nearly everywhere [116] should have been of Early Wisconsin (Iowan-Tazewell) and Late Wisconsin (Cary-Mankato) age. This assumption has little more than prior probability to recommend it, although of that it has a great deal.

As Flint [116] pointed out, the unsatisfactory picture of pluvial ages is the result of overemphasis on strandlines to the neglect of the sedimentary histories of pluvial lakes. The lake deposits are generally accessible only by boring in the floors of the basins, and while this has been done in many of them as a by-product of geologic prospecting for borax and potash, the materials recovered have never been properly studied and in most cases even the well logs have been destroyed. The 104-foot boring in the floor of Death Valley [117,118] is not quite unique, as Flint [119] called it, for drilling operations in the Black Rock desert north of Pyramid Lake have been discussed by Hutchinson,[120] and Gale [121] mentioned a 985-foot boring in Carson Sink. Gale [122] also gave an incomplete log of a 628-foot well drilled in the floor of Searles Lake, and there are doubtless many other similar records. All that can be inferred from the available information, however, is that lakes in the Basin-and-Range Province underwent several cycles of flooding and desiccation. The evidence that Lake Manly, in Death Valley, had three major stages [118] is inadequate, for the writer counts eleven salt beds of approximately equal thickness.

Investigators of deposits in pluvial-lake basins will probably profit from the demonstration [123] that closed lakes in arid regions may be distinguished from open lakes by the much higher calcium:silica ratio in their sediments. According to unpublished analyses, the recent dry phase in the southern Mexican plateau, barely discernible in pollen profiles from Lake Pátzcuaro,[124] is much more easily demonstrable by a maximum in the abundance of calcium in the same sediments. For a discussion of late-Pleistocene events in Mexico, see deTerra [125] and especially Sears.[126]

The number of fossils known from lacustrine deposits in the western United States is pitifully small. Vertebrates, mainly birds, are extraordinarily abundant in the sediments of Pleistocene Winter Lake, Oregon,[127] but they are not particularly enlightening. Fishes from Lake Lahontan and Lake Manly beds have been discussed by Miller, [128] and Hubbs and Miller [129] dealt with the biogeography of the Great Basin and adjacent areas in a comprehensive paper, but aquatic fossils other than a few fishes and molluscs are totally unknown. Evidence from modern geographic distribution of species, however exciting to the biologist, is defective in that it cannot reveal complex physiographic histories; all the remarkable facts recounted by Hubbs and Miller could probably be explained by a single pluvial episode.[2] To say this is not to discount the value of biogeographic evidence, for where the whole fauna consists of pluvial relicts, as it does in the Basin-and-Range Province, indications of former hydrographic connection are sometimes clearer from biogeographic than from physiographic data.

The fishes of Pyramid Lake have proved particularly useful in reconstructing the later history of Lake Lahontan. That such modern descendants of pluvial lakes as Walker and Winnemucca Lakes in the Lahontan basin and the modern Owens Lake have re-formed, following a postpluvial phase of desiccation, was suspected by Russell [130] and emphasized by Antevs [131] on evidence presented but misinterpreted by Jones.[32] The objection to a continuous postpluvial history is that the ages of the lakes, calculated from their salinities, come out around 4000 years. Hutchinson [120] showed that freshening by Russell's mechanism (complete desiccation, with deflation or burial of the resulting salt beds), though highly probable as a general explanation, cannot apply to Pyramid Lake, which retains several of the endemic lacustrine (not spring-living or stream-living) fishes. This lake must therefore be supposed to have kept itself fresh by overflow into an adjacent basin.

Despite the lack of critical evidence, the correlation proposed in Table 2 seems reasonable. [28, 116, 132]

Table 2. Proposed correlation of glacial and pluvial sequences in western U. S.

Bonneville Basin	Lahontan Basin	Sierra Nevada Glacial Sequence	Mid-continental Glacial Sequence
	Some lakes re-formed	Little Ice Age	Cochrane
	Most lakes dry		*Thermal maximum*
Provo shore (reoccupied) *	Dendritic lake	Tioga	Cary-Mankato
Stansbury shore	Thinolite lake		*Brady*
Bonneville-Provo shores	Lake Lahontan (lithoid phase)	Tahoe	Iowan-Tazewell
Pre-Bonneville desiccation	Pre-Lahontan desiccation		*Sangamon*
Pre-Bonneville high level		Sherwin?	Illinoian

* Unpublished evidence from Danger Cave, where dung and wood have been dated by radiocarbon at 11,300 years ago,[133] suggests that the Provo shore was not reoccupied, and that the Stansbury shore should be equated to the Mankato substage.

Very similar late-Pleistocene sequences of pluvial and interpluvial stages and substages have been worked out for various basins in Asia and North Africa. In North America, important new evidence is also coming in from the Winter Lake [134] and Klamath Lake [135] basins. No attempt will be made here to assimilate this evidence, because, even were it more complete than it is, it would not lead to any great advance in our knowledge of world-wide Pleistocene climates. This position follows from the fact that pluvial conditions in temperate latitudes are an expectable consequence of continental glaciation. As high pressure developed over the ice sheets, storm tracks in the zone of westerly winds would be expected to have

taken more southerly courses, and thus to have encroached on the subtropical zone of high pressure that produces most of the world's deserts.
From a study of the relative areas of pluvial lakes in the western United
States, Meinzer [136] concluded that though the rain-bearing air masses
shifted southward during pluvial ages, there was no absolute increase in
the amount of moisture, so that Arizona and New Mexico were about as
moist during pluvial ages as Oregon is today, but no moister. In other
words, swollen lakes between 30° and 40° North Latitude can tell us
nothing about the meteorologic pattern in the tropics. To find out more
about this problem we may take for granted a middle-latitude correlation
such as that of Table 2, and turn to equatorial Africa.

Equatorial Africa. In spite of Solomon's protest [137] that "the Pluvial
Hypothesis rests on very slender foundations," evidence is gradually accumulating to confirm and amplify the conception of Wayland [138] and
Leakey [54] of four major pluvial ages during the East African Pleistocene,
separated by interpluvial ages with climates at least as dry as today's. The
temptation to use paleolithic artifacts as guide fossils has caused even
more trouble in Africa than in Europe, but it now seems to be possible to
make some sense of the vertebrate assemblages, and a careful study of
these [139, 140] permits a fourfold division. It is necessary to make use of
negative evidence, since the faunal breaks are much better shown by disappearance of older types than by the appearance of new ones. This situation is what one expects of the Pleistocene, but it violates the principles
on which Tertiary stratigraphy is based, and therefore makes a vertebrate
paleontologist uncomfortable. The essential features of the sequence are
indicated in Table 3.

It is impossible at present for the unprejudiced observer with no experience of African stratigraphy to decide whether this sequence really means
what it implies: a remarkably close correlation between glacial and pluvial
stages. It will be noticed, for example, that *faunal* evidence of interpluvial
ages is so scanty that it is omitted from Table 3, which is taken from
Leakey's summary.[140] The earlier Pleistocene formations have been deformed and cut by faults, and crustal movements have produced changes
in stream regimen that simulate climatic changes in their lithologic results.
Far too little detailed geologic work has been done in the region, and
African Pleistocene formations are hardly ever "mappable units," but are
recognized solely as beds in sections. With all these difficulties it is probably best to pass hurriedly over the earlier Pleistocene, and turn to the
eastern Rift Valley, where former lake levels of Upper Pleistocene age lie
relatively undisturbed.

Evidence of high levels is abundant in the basins of Lakes Nakuru,
Naivasha, and Elmenteita. At least two pluvial ages are recorded, with

desiccation or intense crustal movements, or both, intervening. The earlier (Kamasian, presumably Upper Kamasian or Kanjeran in Leakey's latest terminology) deposits antedated the formation of the Rift Valley in its modern aspect, and are unconformably overlain by deposits of the Gamblian pluvial stage; the latter is supposed to have had two moist phases, and·to have been followed by two "post-Pleistocene" moist phases, the Makalian and the Nakuran.[141] Neither the stratigraphic nor the geomorphic evidence is notably enriched by Nilsson's [142] confusing account, according to which numerous high strandlines fall into groups indicating five "Last Pluvial" and two "postpluvial" phases of successively decreasing

Table 3. Pleistocene faunal sequence in equatorial Africa. (After Leakey.)

Faunal Stage	Beds Represented	Fauna	Pluvial Stage
4	Gamble's Cave, many others	No extinct genera, few extinct species	Gamblian
3	Olduvai Bed IV Kanjera Olorgesailie	Sivatherium, Stylohipparion, Hippopotamus gorgops persist; Paleoloxodon recki the only surviving elephant; Deinotherium, Anancus, Metaschizotherium extinct	Kanjeran (= Upper Kamasian)
2	Olduvai I, II Laetotil lower Rawi?	Deinotherium, Anancus, Archidiskodon, Metaschizotherium persist; Stegodon, Stegolophodon, small hippos extinct	Kamasian
1	Kanam East, Kanam West, Kaiso Omo	Stegodon, Hippopotamus kaisensis, small hippos, small elephants present	Kageran

intensity, during which most of the higher strandlines were tilted to the south. Nilsson's descriptions inspire no confidence that the features measured are really strandlines, let alone that they can be correlated from one transect to the next.

All the evidence, geomorphic, paleontologic, and archaeologic, strongly suggests that the Gamblian pluvial stage is a reality, and that its date is approximately Wisconsin. Its middle dry phase is of uncertain validity and is not mentioned by Leakey in his latest correlation tables,[140, 143] but what appears certain is that pluvial conditions ended in a phase of widespread aridity, when eolian sands were deposited and lacustrine deposits were deeply weathered to laterite soils. The ages of this dry episode and of the ensuing Makalian moist phase are problems of major importance in the correlation of the African sequence with events elsewhere. If the Gamblian pluvial corresponds to the last glacial stage, the Makalian moist phase had no counterpart in Europe or North America, unless it was the moist climate of Atlantic time that accompanied the breaking-in of the Littorina Sea in the Baltic basin. The pre-Makalian dry phase was too dry, and the Makalian was too moist, to suggest this correlation, and if it were proved it would conflict with the fact that there was no postpluvial moist phase in middle latitudes earlier than the Little Ice Age. In other words, tropical Africa would seem to have responded rather differently to postpluvial changes of moisture, and this would raise serious questions about correlation between earlier pluvial and glacial ages.

On the other hand, if the Makalian moist phase corresponded to the Mankato or Cary substages, or to both of them, the parallelism between Africa and middle latitudes would be more complete than has yet been realized, even by Leakey, who is one of the strongest advocates of parallelism. The pre-Makalian dry phase would then correspond either to the Cary-Mankato or to the Tazewell-Cary interval, or (what is more probable) to each of them in turn at different places. On general grounds a Tazewell-Cary date seems more likely, but there are archaeologic reasons for preferring a Cary-Mankato date in the eastern Rift Valley.

The type section at Gamble's Cave II, Elmenteita,[141] has at its base a beach gravel assigned to the "second maximum" of the Gamblian pluvial age, when the ancient lake stood about 510 feet above the 1929 level (5776 feet) of Lake Nakuru. A series of occupation levels representing the Upper Kenya Capsian (formerly called Aurignacian) culture overlies the gravel, and is in turn overlain by eolian sand and then by the occupation level of the Elmenteitan culture. The assignment of the Elmenteitan culture to the Makalian moist phase is based on its occurrence elsewhere in the basin in lacustrine deposits that reach as high as 375 feet above the modern lake, but no higher. At still lower altitudes, in deposits that reach as high as a 145-foot beach, the Nakuran (Neolithic) culture was found.

Both the Upper Kenya Capsian and the Elmenteitan cultures must be classed as Mesolithic, broadly speaking; both contain pottery. The Capsian may be as old as Cary, but is hardly likely to be older, even in Africa. On the other hand, there appears to be no reason, apart from archaeologic correlations that no longer have the force they seemed to have in 1931,[144] for assigning a date later than Mankato to a Mesolithic culture with so strong an Upper Paleolithic cast as the Upper Kenya Capsian. The Makalian lake therefore appears to have been of Mankato age, and as the only "postpluvial" lake postdated a Neolithic culture, Brooks's dating of this, the Nakuran, phase at 850 B.C. still seems reasonable.

Such a correlation is not in conflict with evidence from the Faiyûm depression.[145] Although many aspects of the Faiyûm sequence are still controversial,[146, 147] it seems that the highest levels of the Birket Qarun (classical Lake Moeris) were not climatically controlled, but reflected a connection with the Nile.[148] Caton-Thompson and Gardner agreed that the "Neolithic lake," whose strandline now stands at 206 feet above the modern lake, was formed by overflow from the Nile, but maintained that pauses in its fall after its isolation, particularly those at 180 and 140 feet above the modern lake, must have been the result of increased precipitation. Sites related to the last of these levels range in age from Late Neolithic to Old Kingdom. If moist, this phase resembles the Nakuran, for although the "Old Kingdom" antedated 850 B.C. by a considerable time, the 140-foot lake was later, and could have existed any time later, than the youngest sites that lie above it.

The highest "Neolithic" level, on the other hand, appears to have been genuinely Neolithic, for wheat and barley seeds from two of the "Upper K" granaries related to this level have given radiocarbon dates close to 4000 B.C.,[133, 149] and an even older figure would not have been surprising.[150] As the 206-foot lake was not the result of a moister climate, and as the "Paleolithic lake" deposits at higher altitudes are older than the Gamblian pluvial age, nothing in the Faiyûm precludes a Mankato date for the Makalian pluvial sub-age.

The evidence of widespread increase in moisture following the Mesolithic Natufian horizon in Palestine, as summarized by Bate,[52] mainly refers to the Nakuran phase, but some of it could refer to the Makalian. There is no direct evidence of either phase at the Natufian sites, but the implication of the fossil vertebrates is that Palestine was relatively dry in Natufian time; its assignment to the Cary-Mankato interval would fit all the facts so far as they are known.

On the other side of Africa, in Angola, Leakey[143] has made a brief reconnaissance of the diamantiferous alluvial deposits in the Lunda district, with highly interesting results. Kalahari sands, here found far north of the modern Kalahari Desert, were deposited in an intensely dry episode in the interval between the Kanjeran (= Upper Kamasian) and Gamblian pluvial ages. The Gamblian deposits contain the Upper Paleolithic Sangoan culture. Several (probably two) post-Gamblian episodes of stream aggradation, followed by lateritization and deposition of reworked Kalahari sand, seem to be recorded. The latest coarse stream gravels yielded wood dated at 14,500 years, while a soil surface, developed on the gravel and covered later by redeposited Kalahari sand, was occupied by a late

Upper Paleolithic people called Lupemban; wood found in association with this culture gave an age of 11,200 years.[133] In Angola, then, it would appear that the post-Gamblian moist phase, which Leakey regarded as equivalent to the Makalian, was probably double, the earlier part being of Cary age.

Despite the regrettable necessity of relying on archaeologic correlation, therefore, the climatic sequence in equatorial Africa during Wisconsin time strongly resembles that in North America (Table 4). The major glacial and pluvial sub-ages seem to have been Early Wisconsin and Late Wisconsin; there are suggestions that each was double, and the principal climatic break seems to have fallen between them (except possibly in East Africa). Resemblance to the climatic sequence during the last glacial age in Europe is equally strong, but cannot be discussed here. Are we justified in believing that pluvial ages in the tropics were synchronous everywhere with glacial and pluvial ages in middle latitudes? Unfortunately, not yet.

It can be argued [151] that because North Africa is the only large subtropical land mass lying north of the equator, meteorologic conditions in equatorial Africa are peculiarly likely to vary in sympathy with conditions in the Northern Hemisphere. If Africa is a special case, as it seems to be, convincing proof of climatic parallelism on a world-wide scale must come from South America. So far it has not yet done so, though there are indications that it will.[152] Glacial and pluvial episodes in the high Andes have long been known, but the best and most recent study [153] of the Titicaca basin, which should be of critical importance, tells us only that Lake Balliván was preglacial. Although Newell preferred a Pliocene date for the ancient lake, he admitted the possibility that it was early Pleistocene. The definitive study of pluvial lakes in South America (and elsewhere) remains to be made.

In tropical as in temperate regions, pluvial histories as known at present depend far too much on geomorphic rather than stratigraphic evidence. Special mention should therefore be made of Gardner's important study [154] of the lacustrine molluscs of the Faiyûm deposits. One of the endemic species, the bivalve *Corbicula vara*, was found to be characteristic of the "Paleolithic lake," and to vary in form in a way that strongly suggests the influence of wave action increasing toward the southern, more exposed, end of that large and deep body of water. Both the "Paleolithic" and the "Neolithic" lakes had mainly fresh-water species, and the chief evidence of dry phase intervening between them is the occurrence, at a low altitude in deposits of the higher, older lake, of the brackish-water *Hydrobia peraudieri*.

Stratigraphic sections along the margins of lake basins are seldom satisfactory, because shallow-water deposits and puzzling littoral facies are the chief materials exposed. Borings in the floor of the Naivasha basin or in the Faiyûm depression would probably yield more information in proportion to their cost than all the expeditions that have been sent to equatorial Africa. It is even more important to investigate South American paleolimnology in this way.

Table 4. Suggested correlation of late-Pleistocene events in parts of Africa with the North American glacial sequence. Other correlations are possible, and the table is intended merely to clarify the discussion in the text.

NAKURU-NAIVASHA BASIN	ANGOLA	FAIYUM	NORTH AMERICAN GLACIAL SEQUENCE
NAKURAN	MODERN STREAM CUTTING	140-FOOT LAKE 180-FOOT LAKE	COCHRANE
	2ND REDEPOSITED KALAHARI SAND	4000 BC "NEOLITHIC LAKE"	THERMAL MAXIMUM
MAKALIAN ELMENTEITAN	STREAM CUTTING		MANKATO
	9000 BC SOIL SURFACE LUPEMBAN		9000 BC TWO CREEKS
UPPER GAMBLIAN CAPSIAN	12500 BC "MAKALIAN" FINAL SANGOAN		CARY
	1ST REDEPOSITED KALAHARI SAND		BRADY
LOWER GAMBLIAN	"GAMBLIAN"	"PALEOLITHIC LAKE"	IOWAN-TAZEWELL
	KALAHARI SAND		SANGAMON
KAMASIAN	KANJERAN	"PALEOLITHIC LAKE"	ILLINOIAN

The classic instance of a migrating lake is Lop Nor, in Sinkiang.[155, 156] The mechanism responsible, according to the Swedish geologists, is aggradation of the bed of the impermanent Tarim River to the point where the river slips off its own deposits and reconstitutes the lake in another part of the basin, which has meanwhile been lowered by deflation. Implications of a changing climate can be read in this story, but to do so in the present state of our knowledge requires special pleading. The parallel-aligned lakes of northern Alaska [157] present an equally fascinating and unsolved problem.

The Alaskan lakes are exceedingly numerous in an area of more than 25,000 square miles on the coastal plain, centered on Point Barrow. Their shapes vary from lanceolate to broadly ovate, and their long axes depart little from a line approximately 15° west of north. They have been little studied except from the air, but aerial photographs show clearly that many of them have been or are now migrating over the tundra. In some places several generations can be discerned, since dry lake beds now occupied by polygonal soil still retain their shore outlines; in some cases coalescence, either to north or to south, has led to overlapping basins, while in others as many as three approximately concentric basins are visible with a fourth generation of nonaligned lakes occupying parts of the older basins.

Many of the parallel-aligned lakes, particularly those on the northernmost and presumably youngest part of the coastal plain, are only about a meter deep, but others contain a deep basin, probably at least 15 meters deep, set inside a larger shallow one, not necessarily concentrically. It seems likely that this arrangement has something to do with postglacial climatic changes in the Arctic, for evidence is accumulating [158] that there have been two recent episodes of thawing of permafrost in various parts of Alaska. The later is the modern one, coinciding with the well-known warming of the Arctic that has been going on for about the last hundred years; the earlier is perhaps to be assigned to the postglacial Thermal Maximum, although Taber regarded it as interglacial. Permafrost is locally absent or lies deeper below modern lakes than it does under the upland areas, but it is not known whether this is a cause or a result of the existence of the lakes. Until this question is settled two possibilities remain open for the explanation of the two-cycle history of the deeper lakes.

According to one view, the deep basin came first, as a result of thawing; refreezing led to a rise of the water table, and the latest thawing produced an expanded lake that is still growing over its shallow littoral shelf. It seems equally possible that the shallow basin was produced first, and that the deeper basin collapsed inside it as a result of the later thawing, the greater depth of the second-cycle basin being the result of greater depression of the permafrost layer under the preëxisting lake. Either hypothesis may be invalidated if crustal movements have been involved, as they may well have been in the southern part of the coastal plain adjacent to the Brooks Range. Preliminary studies of a two-cycle lake near East Oumalik by D. A. Livingstone (unpublished) tend to favor the second hypothesis, but do not rule out the first. As shown in Fig. 9, this lake is migrating northward, and the ages of the oldest bushes growing on it show that the floodplain to the south has been uncovered

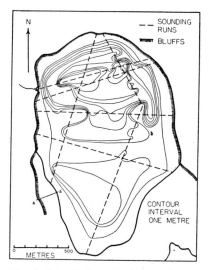

Fig. 9. Morphology of a lake near East Oumalik, in the southern part of the Arctic Coastal Plain of northern Alaska. From unpublished work by D. A. Livingstone.

within the last hundred years, but as the deep-water sediments have proved unfossiliferous the only evidence that the deep basin is younger than the shallow one is that it underlies the younger part of the modern lake.

The obvious inference from the alignment and the elongate shape is that the lakes are migrating downwind. The winds at Point Barrow are dominantly northeasterly, not northwesterly, however, and the hypothesis that the axis of orientation originated at an earlier time when the pre-

vailing wind direction was different conflicts with the apparent youth of
the lakes and their continuing coalescence in the direction of their present
axes. It is probable, then, unlikely though it seems at first sight, that the
elongation and migration of the lakes take place at right angles to the
wind.

It is an odd fact that another spectacular group of parallel-aligned
basins, the Carolina "Bays," has an axis of orientation that is almost
identical with that on the Arctic Coastal Plain. These basins, the subject
of an elaborate study by Johnson,[159] are almost certainly older than the
Arctic ones, but are also of Pleistocene origin. Paleolimnologic studies
by Frey,[15] only the botanical parts of which have been published, when
taken together with radiocarbon dates, show that one of the bays, Singletary Lake, is older than the Mankato substage and may have been formed
as early as Iowan time. Flint, in a work in course of publication by the
U. S. Geological Survey, gave a full account of Pleistocene basins on the
northern Great Plains that are aligned on a bearing approximately 45°
west of north, and concluded that their origin must be ascribed to deflation in a more arid climate. The same conclusion was reached by Hutchinson, Pickford, and Schuurman [160] for the pans of the Transvaal, South
Africa, and by Judson [161] for basins in the southern High Plains. Parallel
alignment of basins need not have arisen at the time the basins were
excavated, but could have been imposed on them subsequently. It seems
clear that the alignment is the result of prevailing winds, but whether
these were northwesterly, as Odum [162] suggested in the latest discussion
of the Carolina Bays, or from some other direction, is one of many unanswered questions about such basins.

PRE-PLEISTOCENE LAKES

Apart from the magnificent work of Bradley [163, 164] on the Eocene
Green River formation, Tertiary paleolimnology cannot be said to exist
and it is accordingly impractical to discuss the relation between lakes
and pre-Pleistocene climates. Innumerable lake deposits have been de-
cribed in a voluminous literature, but it is hardly ever possible to find
out from the descriptions what a limnologist needs to know. This situation
comes about because the deposits have mainly been studied as sources
of fossils, and until recently paleontologists tended to regard the sediment
as an annoying "matrix," to be disposed of as expeditiously as possible.
It may be worth while to list a few of the approaches to the study of
ancient lakes that seem essential if paleolimnology is ever to come into
being.

1. *How deep was the lake?* Temperate and tropical lakes deeper than
a few meters develop seasonal or permanent thermal stratification, and

even moderate organic production can then lead to reducing conditions in the hypolimnion. Minerals such as pyrite can then be formed whose presence in the rocks may be diagnostic of a deep lake with an oxygen-free hypolimnion. Even delicate organic molecules, such as those of pigments and protein derivatives, may be spared subsequent destruction, as they have been in lignites. Oil shales are especially favorable sediments in which to look for such evidence of depth, but lake sediments that are economically unpromising have seldom been subjected to organic chemical analysis.

The climatic inferences that can be drawn from a knowledge that a lake was thermally stratified may often be trivial, but they were not so in the case of the Green River lake, with its seasonally laminated organic deposits whose preservation implies a tropical lake (in Forel's sense, that is, a lake whose surface temperature never falls below 4°C). The few really large and deep tropical lakes that have been studied have proved to be meromictic or permanently stagnant below a certain depth, and the absence of oxygen in deep water should exclude bottom animals and thus favor the preservation of laminated sediments. The geologic implications of laminated sediments have been discussed in a thorough review by Korn.[165] The discovery that ancient water temperatures can be inferred from the oxygen 18 content of carbonates[166,167] opens a whole new division of paleoecology, of which only the marine aspects have so far been considered.

2. *How large was the lake?* Most stratigraphic work has been devoted to marine sediments, and while the shores of ancient lakes can be reconstructed by tracing facies changes, this has seldom been done. What can be inferred if one knows or can guess at the area and volume of an extinct lake? Something about current systems and other hydrographic conditions, useful in interpreting the facies changes. More than this, however, one might be able to estimate the heat budget of the lake. To do so would be comparatively simple, for lakes whose area and depth exceed certain minimum values acquire a constant amount of heat under unit area, and this constancy applies within wide latitudinal limits provided only that the seasons are well defined.

The importance of establishing the annual heat storage, conjectural as it might be, is that the effect of a large lake on the climate of its surroundings is not negligible, particularly if the lake lies in an intermontane basin, as Hutchinson [168] has shown for the Pang-Gong Tso. How significant this effect may have been in the geologic past is difficult to say, but it seems possible that some of the small climatic differences between the Green River basin in Eocene time and the most nearly comparable region today (Georgia and Alabama), reflect the influence of the Green River lake itself. It should be noticed that a means of computing "potential evapotranspiration" from the mean monthly temperature is now available,[169] so that it would probably be possible to go much farther than Bradley [170] was able to go in deducing the Eocene climate.

If an ancient lake is known not to have had an outlet, and if its volume and the area of its drainage basin can be estimated, it is possible to make deductions about the rainfall of the time. Moreau [171] has done this for East Africa at the time of the Gamblian and post-Gamblian pluvial phases, with the primary aim of determining the area covered by forest during the time when certain birds were acquiring their present ranges. Although in his latest comprehensive paper on African climates Moreau [172] wisely restricted himself to nonquantitative arguments, it should eventually be possible to make quantitative deductions about rainfall in pre-Pleistocene time.

3. *Did the lake have an outlet?* From alternations between saline and organic layers in parts of the Green River section, Bradley not only was able to prove repeated desiccation but believed that its rhythmic occurrence kept in tune with the precession of the equinoxes. Salt layers are unequivocal evidence of drying, but where they are absent it still may be possible to decide whether an ancient lake was closed or open. Variations in the calcium content of sediments have been mentioned above as one form such evidence might take, but there are probably others, both mineralogic and chemical. The conditions under which such pseudomorphic minerals as thinolite are formed have not been adequately studied, and this is only one of many unsolved and neglected problems of paleolimnology.

It should be emphasized that all the approaches mentioned are of a nonbiologic sort, and call for sedimentologic studies of a kind paleontologists would not ordinarily make. Biologic data are certain to play as great a part in Tertiary paleolimnology (for a Mesozoic example see Soergel's study [173] of a Triassic pond in Thüringia), but this approach is so obvious as not to require discussion. Fossils alone are of little use to the paleolimnologist, however, particularly when they are fossils of terrestrial plants, listed as a "flora" without reference to the internal stratigraphy of the lake deposits in which they occur and only compared with other floras for evidence of homotaxy. What is needed is an ecologic interpretation of *all* features of the ancient lacustrine environment — a technique for which the only available term is *biostratonomy*.[174] It is impossible to extract much limnologic information from such accounts as those of Scudder [175] on the Florissant formation, or of Heer [176] on the Miocene lake at Oeningen, and there appear to be no modern studies of these highly interesting lakes, at least as lakes.

Information about ancient lakes, from which inferences can be drawn about former climates, falls into two classes, geomorphic and stratigraphic. Geomorphology tells us little more than that a lake existed; stratigraphic studies of its deposits are necessary for a reconstruction of its history. Unfortunately, most paleolimnology is of the geomorphic sort.

Large deep lakes in closed basins in semiarid regions provide most of the evidence of pluvial ages during the Pleistocene. It is likely but not yet certain that pluvial ages in the equatorial zone were synchronous with glacial ages in the temperate zone, the best evidence of which consists of two radiocarbon dates from Angola. This fact gives eloquent testimony of the power of radiocarbon dating to solve problems of Pleistocene correlation, for sixty years of glacial geology has not yet established beyond doubt the equivalence of glacial and pluvial ages near 40° North Latitude, where the probability of such equivalence is inherently far greater. As the Makalian moist phase in East Africa seems to have been of Mankato age, and not "postpluvial," a plausible correlation between glacial and pluvial episodes can be worked out on a world-wide scale, at least within Wisconsin time.

More than this can hardly be expected so long as the paleolimnologic data are mainly geomorphic. Earlier Pleistocene lakes are not so easily recognizable from physiographic evidence, for their strandlines have been blurred by erosion where they have not been obliterated by crustal deformation. The study of pre-Wisconsin (and, *a fortiori*, of pre-Pleistocene) lakes is a stratigraphic problem, easily amenable to attack by modern methods but hardly touched as yet. Between Eocene time, for which Bradley's work on the Green River lake gives a satisfying picture with many climatic implications, and the Cary sub-age of the Late Wisconsin, when "postglacial" histories of many modern lakes began, almost nothing is known of lakes except that they existed. The Florissant (Oligocene), Oeningen (Miocene), and Tulare (Early Pleistocene) lakes are cited as examples deserving careful study, not merely for their fossils, for the biologic approach to paleoclimatology has not been neglected, but for their chemistry, lithology, and mineralogy. The pluvial lakes of the Pleistocene should also yield far more information when borings are made into their deposits than is now available from knowledge of their strandlines.

What little is known of the ontogeny of modern lakes suggests that at best lakes are poor indicators of climatic change. The existence of thermal stratification in lakes of temperate latitudes means that temperatures in the same lake may range from arctic to tropical, and most lacustrine organisms that occur as fossils in sediments are too eurythermal to serve as indicators. Moreover, the lacustrine eco-system has a homeostasis that arises in part from the thermal properties of water and in part from a little-understood tendency for biotic communities to maintain internal stability. As a result, such minor climatic changes as the fluctuations of moisture that were superimposed on the long-period temperature variation during post-Mankato time had no visible effect on lake development. This is true even when the variations of moisture are clearly shown by terrestrial fossils (such as pollen grains) embedded in the lake sediments. Responses to the temperature swings are almost as hard to discern in the sedimentary records as the fluctuations of moisture; and in some cases glacial sub-ages seem to have come and gone, leaving no trace that can be seen in the histories of lakes that lie not far beyond the limits of glacial readvance. Under some circumstances, however, fluctuations of temperature may be recorded by variations in the intensity of carbonate deposition, as would be expected from the fact that seasonal lamination, in the rare instances when it is preserved in organic lake sediments, usually consists of alternations in carbonate content.

Paleolimnology has been too little studied anywhere to warrant sweeping generalizations, and nearly all of our information comes from lakes situated near universities in the temperate United States and Europe. When something is known of lakes in the tropics and in the Arctic, the concept that lake development is insensitive to climatic change may prove illusory. The most interesting arctic lakes yet discovered occur in countless numbers on the coastal plain of northern Alaska. In their ovate shape, in the extraordinary parallel alignment of their long axes, in the two cycles of basin formation that are evident in their morphology, and in their apparent youth and their tendency to migrate over the tundra (all features that can be seen from the air), these lakes present a variety of unsolved problems whose solution will throw light on many relations between limnology and climate.

REFERENCES

1. Lennart von Post, "The prospect for pollen analysis in the study of the Earth's climatic history," *New Phytol.* 45, 193–217 (1946).
2. E. S. Deevey, "Biogeography of the Pleistocene. Part I: Europe and North America," *Bull. Geol. Soc. Amer.* 60, 1315–1416 (1949).
3. Franz Firbas, *Spät- und nacheiszeitliche Waldgeschichte Mitteleuropas nördlich der Alpen* (Gustav Fischer, Jena, 1949), Band 1, *Allgemeine Waldgeschichte*.
4. Lennart von Post, "Om skogsträdpollen i sydsvenska torfmosselagerföljder," *Geol. Fören. Stockholm Förh.* 38, 384–394 (1916).

5. E. Werth, "Zur Kenntnis des postglazialen Klima- und Vegetationswechsels," *Deutsch Bot. Ges. Ber.* 46, 328–339, pl. 10 (1928).

6. Knud Jessen, "Studies in late Quaternary deposits and flora-history of Ireland," *Roy. Irish Acad. Proc.* 52B, 85–290, pls. 3–16 (1949).

7. Magnus Fries, "Pollenanalytiska Vittnesbörd om senkvartär Vegetationsutveckling, särskilt Skogshistoria, i nordvästra Gotaland," *Acta Phytogeog. Suecica* 29, 220 pp.; German summary, pp. 173–207 (1951).

8. R. F. Flint and E. S. Deevey, "Radiocarbon dating of late-Pleistocene events," *Amer. Jour. Sci.* 249, 257–300 (1951).

9. E. S. Deevey, "Late-glacial and postglacial pollen diagrams from Maine," *Amer. Jour. Sci.* 249, 177–207 (1951).

10. E. S. Deevey and J. E. Potzger, "Peat samples for radiocarbon analysis: problems in pollen statistics," *Amer. Jour. Sci.* 249, 473–511 (1951).

11. R. F. Flint, "Probable Wisconsin substages and late-Wisconsin events in northeastern United States and southeastern Canada," *Bull. Geol. Soc. Amer.* 64, 897–920 (1953).

12. Helmut Gams, "Die Alleröd-Schwankung im Spätglazial," *Zeit. Gletscherkde. Glazialgeol.* 1, 162–171 (1950).

13. H. P. Hansen, "Pollen analysis of two Wisconsin bogs of different age," *Ecology* 18, 136–148 (1937).

14. J. E. Potzger and I. T. Wilson, "Post-Pleistocene forest migration as indicated by sediments from three deep inland lakes," *Amer. Midland Naturalist* 25, 270–289 (1941).

15. D. G. Frey, "Pollen succession in the sediments of Singletary Lake, North Carolina," *Ecology* 32, 518–533 (1951).

16. C. A. Weber, "Grenzhorizont und Klimaschwankungen," *Naturwiss. Ver. Bremen Abhl.* 26, 98–106 (1926).

17. Erik Granlund, "De svenska Högmossarnas Geologi," *Sver. Geol. Unders. Årsbok* 26 (1), 1–193; German summary, pp. 172–182 (1932).

18. Tage Nilsson, "Die Pollenanalytische Zonengliederung der spät- und postglazialen Bildungen Schonens," *Geol. Fören. Stockholm Förh.* 57, 385–562, pls. 6–11 (1935).

19. V. M. Conway, "von Post's work on climatic rhythms," *New Phytol.* 47, 220–237 (1948).

20. H. Godwin, "Studies of the post-glacial history of British vegetation. X. Correlation between climate, forest composition, prehistoric agriculture and peat stratigraphy in Sub-Boreal and Sub-Atlantic peats of the Somerset Levels," *Roy. Soc. Lond. Phil. Trans.* 233B, 275–286 (1948).

21. A. R. Clapham and H. Godwin, "Studies of the post-glacial history of British vegetation: VIII. Swamping surfaces in peats of the Somerset Levels; IX. Prehistoric trackways in the Somerset Levels," *Roy. Soc. Lond. Phil. Trans.* 233B, 233–273 (1948).

22. E. S. Bastin and C. A. Davis, "Peat deposits of Maine," *U. S. Geological Survey Bulletin* 376 (1909).

23. S. A. Waksman, *The peats of New Jersey and their utilization*, New Jersey Department of Conservation and Development, Geological Series, Bulletin 55 (1942).

24. S. A. Waksman, H. Schulhoff, C. A. Hickman, T. C. Cordon, and S. C. Stevens, *The peats of New Jersey and their utilization*, New Jersey Department

of Conservation and Development, Geological Series, Bulletin 55, Part B (1943).

25. A. P. Dachnowski-Stokes, "Records of climatic cycles in peat deposits" (Carnegie Inst. Wash., Report of the Conference on Cycles, 1929), pp. 55–64.

26. A. P. Dachnowski-Stokes, "Peat deposits in USA. Their characteristic profiles and classification," *Handb. Moorkde.* 7, 1–140 (1933).

27. A. P. Dachnowski-Stokes, "Peat resources in Alaska," *U. S. Department of Agriculture Technical Bulletin* 769 (1941).

28. Ernst Antevs, "Climatic changes and pre-white man," in *The Great Basin, with emphasis on glacial and postglacial times* (University of Utah Bulletin 38 [20]; Biol. Ser. *10* [7], 1948), pp. 167–191.

29. Max Welten, "Pollenanalytische, stratigraphische, und geochronologische Untersuchungen aus dem Faulenseemoos bei Spiez," *Geobot. Inst. Rubel Veröff. (Zürich)* 21, 1–201 (1944).

30. F. E. Matthes, "Report of Committee on Glaciers, April, 1939," *Amer. Geophys. Union Trans.* (1939), pp. 518–523.

31. F. E. Matthes, "Committee on Glaciers, 1939–40," *Amer. Geophys. Union Trans.* (1940), pp. 396–406.

32. J. C. Jones, "The geologic history of Lake Lahontan," in *Quaternary Climates* (Carnegie Institution, Washington, Pub. 352, 1925), pp. 1–49.

33. Ernst Antevs, "Retreat of the last ice-sheet in eastern Canada," *Canada Dept. Mines Geol. Surv. Mem.* 146 (1925).

34. F. H. McLearn, "The Mesozoic and Pleistocene deposits of the lower Missinaibi, Opazatika, and Mattagami Rivers, Ontario" (Appendix pp. 45–47 by V. Auer), *Geological Survey, Canada, Summary Report, 1926* (1927), part C, pp. 16–47.

35. L. M. Cranwell and Lennart von Post, "Post-Pleistocene pollen diagrams from the southern hemisphere," *Geograf. Ann.* 18, 308–347 (1936).

36. W. F. Harris, "New Zealand plants and their story — clues to the past," *N.Z. Sci. Rev.* 9, 3–7 (1951).

37. Väinö Auer, "Las capas volcánicas como nuevo método de cronología post-glacial en Fuegopatagonia," *Argentina Minist. Agric. Inst. Suelos Agrotec. Pub.* 6, 311–336 (1948).

38. Väinö Auer, "Las capas volcánicas como base de la cronología postglacial de Fuegopatagonia," *Argentina Minist. Agric. Ganad. Inst. Suelos Agrotec. Pub.* 9, 49–208, 4 pls. (1950).

39. O. H. Selling, "Studies in Hawaiian pollen statistics. Part III. On the late Quaternary history of the Hawaiian vegetation," *Bernice P. Bishop Museum (Honolulu), Spec. Pub.* 39 (1948).

40. Carl-Gösta Wenner, "Pollen diagrams from Labrador," *Geograf. Ann.* 29, 137–373 (1947).

41. Ulf Hafsten, "A pollen-analytic investigation of two peat deposits from Tristan da Cunha," Norske Vidensk.-Akad. Oslo, *Norwegian Sci. Exped. Tristan da Cunha 1937–1938, Results,* No. 22, (1951).

42. H. T. Stearns, "Shore benches on North Pacific islands," *Bull. Geol. Soc. Amer.* 52, 773–780 (1941).

43. H. T. Stearns, "Late geologic history of the Pacific basin," *Amer. Jour. Sci.* 243, 614–626 (1945).

44. H. T. Stearns, "Eustatic shore lines in the Pacific," *Bull. Geol. Soc. Amer.* 56, 1071–1078 (1945).

45. R. W. Fairbridge, "Notes on the geomorphology of the Pelsart group of the Houtman's Abrolhos Islands," *Roy. Soc. West. Austral. Jour. 33*, 1–43 (1948).

46. R. W. Fairbridge, "Recent advances in eustatic research," Austral. N. Z. Assoc. Adv. Sci., *Report of Comm. Invest. Correl. Eustatic changes in Sea-Level*, pp. 181–184 (no date).

47. A. Noe-Nygaard, "Remarks on Mytilus edulis L. in raised beaches in East Greenland," *Medd. Grønland 95* (2), 1–24, pl. 1 (1932).

48. W. R. Browne, "An attempted post-Tertiary chronology for Australia," *Linn. Soc. N.S.W. Proc. 70*, v–xxiv (1945).

49. E. D. Gill, "New evidence from Victoria relative to the antiquity of the Australian aborigines," *Austral. Jour. Sci. 14*, 69–73 (1951).

50. Gertrude Caton-Thompson and E. W. Gardner, "Recent work on the problem of Lake Moeris," *Geog. Jour. 73*, 20–60 (1929).

51. G. Caton-Thompson and E. W. Gardner, "The prehistoric geography of Kharga Oasis," *Geog. Jour. 80*, 369–409 (1932).

52. D. M. A. Bate, "The fossil antelopes of Palestine in Natufian (Mesolithic) times, with descriptions of new species," *Geol. Mag. 77*, 418–443 (1940).

53. D. A. E. Garrod and D. M. A. Bate, *The Stone Age of Mount Carmel. Excavations at the Wady El-Mughara.* (Clarendon Press, Oxford, 1937), vol. 1.

54. L. S. B. Leakey, *Stone Age Africa* (Oxford University Press, London, 1936).

55. H. B. S. Cooke, *A preliminary survey of the Quaternary period in southern Africa.* Union So. Afr. Bur. Archaeol., Archaeol. Ser., 4, 60 pp. (1941).

56. Ernst Mayr, "Timor and the colonization of Australia by birds," *Emu 44*, 113–130 (1944).

57. E. S. Deevey, "Studies on Connecticut lake sediments. III. The biostratonomy of Linsley Pond," *Amer. Jour. Sci. 240*, 233–264, 313–338 (1942).

58. Ruth Patrick, "The diatoms of Linsley Pond, Connecticut," *Acad. Nat. Sci. (Philadelphia) Proc. 95*, 53–110, pls. 11–12 (1943).

59. G. E. Hutchinson and Anne Wollack, "Studies on Connecticut lake sediments. II. Chemical analyses of a core from Linsley Pond, North Branford," *Amer. Jour. Sci. 238*, 493–517 (1940).

60. H. Lohmann, "Planktonablagerungen am Boden der Tiefsee," *Naturwiss. Ver. Schleswig-Holstein Schr. 14*, 399–402 (1909).

61. H. K. Townes, "The Nearctic species of Tendipedini," *Amer. Midland Naturalist 34*, 1–206 (1945).

62. S. A. Cain, Fernando Segadas-Vianna, and Floyd Bunt, "Mollusks of Sodon Lake, Oakland County, Michigan. I. Stratigraphic occurrence of shells in peat and marl sediments," *Ecology 31*, 540–545 (1950).

63. I. I. Messiatzev, "Die fossile Fauna der Seen in Kossino," *Biol. Sta. Kossino Arb. 1*, 16–26, 35; German summary, p. 35 (1924).

64. H. Gross, "Nachweis der Allerödschwankung im süd- und ostbaltischen Gebiet," *Bot. Zentralbl. Beih. 57B*, 167–218, pl. 5 (1937).

65. Knud Jessen and V. Milthers, "Stratigraphical and palaeontological studies of interglacial fresh-water deposits in Jutland and Northwest Germany," *Danm. Geol. Unders.* (2) 48 (1928).

66. Winifred Pennington, "Lake sediments: the bottom deposits of the

314   EDWARD S. DEEVEY, JR.

north basin of Windermere, with special reference to the diatom succession," *New Phytol.* 42, 1–27 (1943).

67. W. Pennington, "Studies of the post-glacial history of British vegetation. VII. Lake sediments: Pollen diagrams from the bottom deposits of the north basin of Windermere," *Roy. Soc. Lond. Phil. Trans.* 233B, 137–175 (1947).

68. D. J. Scourfield, "The Entomostraca of the bottom deposits of Windermere," *Linn. Soc. Lond. Proc. Sess.* 154, 253–258 (1943). See p. 254.

69. R. S. Allan, E. Percival, R. S. Duff, and R. A. Falla, "Preliminary report of excavations at Pyramid Valley Swamp, Waikari, North Canterbury," *Canterbury Mus. Rec.*, Christchurch, 4, 325–353, pls. 43–53 (1941).

70. Roger Duff, *Pyramid Valley, Waikari, North Canterbury* (Assoc. Friends Canterbury Mus., Christchurch, 1949).

71. R. C. Murphy, "The moa deposits of Pyramid Valley Swamp, New Zealand," *Tenth Internat. Ornithol. Cong. Proc.*, 628–630 (1951).

72. August Thienemann, "Tropische Seen und Seetypenlehre," *Arch. Hydrobiol. (Suppl.)* 9, 205–231 (1931).

73. Johannes Lundbeck, "Die Bodentierwelt norddeutscher Seen," *Arch. Hydrobiol. (Suppl.)* 7, 1–473, 17 pls. (1926).

74. G. Lundqvist, "Bodenablagerungen und Entwicklungstypen der Seen," *Binnengewässer* 2 (1927).

75. E. S. Deevey, "On the date of the last rise of sea level in southern New England, with remarks on the Grassy Island site," *Amer. Jour. Sci.* 246, 329–352 (1948).

76. Fritz Overbeck, *Moore (2. Auflage)* (*Wirtschaftswiss. Ges. Stud. Niedersachsens E. V. Schriften* [N.F.] 3, Abt. 4, 1950). See map.

77. K. L. Henriksen, "Undersøgelser over Danmark-Skånes kvartaere Insektfauna," *Dansk Naturhist. For. Vidensk. Medd.* 96, Festskrift 2, 77–355, pls. 6–11 (1933).

78. Otto Harnisch, "Älterer und Jüngerer Sphagnumtorf. Eine rhizopoden-analytische Studie an nordwest europäischen Hochmooren," *Biol. Zentralbl.* 68, 398–412 (1949).

79. Magnus Degerbøl and Harald Krog, "Den europaeiske Sumpskildpadde (*Emys orbicularis* L.) i Danmark," *Danm. Geol. Unders.* [2] 78, English summary, pp. 91–112 (1951).

80. Gerard De Geer, "Geochronologia Suecica Principles," *K. Svensk. Vetenskapsakad. Handl.* (3) 18, no. 6 (1940).

81. Ernst Antevs, "Glacial clays in Steep Rock Lake, Ontario, Canada," *Bull. Geol. Soc. Amer.* 62, 1223–1262 (1951).

82. Harald Johnsson, "Termisk-hydrologiska studier i Sjön Klämmingen," *Geograf. Ann.* 28, 1–154; English summary, pp. 149–154 (1946).

83. W. A. Johnston, "Sedimentation in Lake Louise, Alberta, Canada," *Amer. Jour. Sci.* (5) 4, 376–386 (1922).

84. W. D. Wilcox, "A certain type of lake formation in the Canadian Rocky Mountains," *Jour. Geol.* 7, 247–260 (1899).

85. E. M. Kindle, "Sedimentation in a glacial lake," *Jour. Geol.* 38, 81–87 (1930).

86. A. E. Douglass, *Climatic cycles and tree growth.* (Carnegie Institution, Washington, Pub. 289, 1936), Vol. 3, *A study of cycles.*

87. M. G. Kendall, "On autoregressive time series," *Biometrika* 33, 105–122 (1944).

88. Ph. H. Kuenen, "Mechanics of varve formation and the action of turbidity currents," *Geol. Fören. Stockholm Förh. 73*, 69–84 (1951).

89. Ph. H. Kuenen and C. I. Migliorini, "Turbidity currents as a cause of graded bedding," *Jour. Geol. 58*, 91–127 (1950).

90. B. W. Perfiliev, "Das Gesetz der Periodizität der Schlammbildung und die Tiefwasserbohrung," *Int. Ver. theor. angew. Limnol. Verh. 5*, 298–306 (1931).

91. W. B. Schostakowitsch, "Die Bedeutung der Untersuchung der Bodenablagerungen der Seen für einige Fragen der Geophysik," *Int. Ver. theor. angew. Limnol. Verh. 5*, 307–317 (1931).

92. W. B. Schostakowitsch, "Geschichtete Bodenablagerungen der Seen als Klima-Annalen," *Meteorol. Zeit. 53*, 176–182 (1936).

93. E. S. Deevey, "An absolute pollen chronology in Switzerland" [Discussion], *Amer. Jour. Sci. 244*, 442–447 (1946).

94. Fritz Nipkow, "Vorläufige Mitteilungen über Untersuchungen des Schlammabsatzes im Zürichsee," *Zeit. Hydrol.*, pp. 1–23, pls. 1–3 (1920).

95. F. Nipkow, "Über das Verhalten der Skelette planktischer Kieselalgen im geschichteten Tiefenschlamm des Zürich- und Baldeggersees," *Zeit. Hydrol.* (1928).

96. E. J. Whittaker, "Bottom deposits of McKay Lake, Ottawa," *Roy. Soc. Canada Trans.* (3) *16*, Sect. 4, 141–157, pls. 1–2 (1922).

97. Leo Minder, "Der Zürichsee als Eutrophierungsphänomen. Summarische Ergebnisse aus fünfzig Jahren Zürichseeforschung," *Geol. Meere Binnengewässer, 2*, 284–299 (1938).

98. Leo Minder, "Neuere Untersuchungen über den Sauerstoffgehalt und die Eutrophie des Zürichsees," *Arch. Hydrobiol. 40*, 279–304 (1943).

99. A. D. Hasler, "Eutrophication of lakes by domestic drainage," *Ecology 28*, 383–395 (1947).

100. C. H. Mortimer, "The exchange of dissolved substances between mud and water in lakes," *Jour. Ecol. 29*, 280–329 (1941); *30*, 147–201 (1942).

101. Ken Sugawara, "Liesegang's stratification developed in the diatomaceous gyttja from Lake Haruna, and problems related to it," *Chem. Soc. Japan Bull. 9*, 402–409 (1934).

102. I. T. Wilson, "Some post-glacial time determinations from laminations in sediment" [Abstract], *Bull. Geol. Soc. Amer. 55*, 1486 (1944).

103. Julius Pia, "Kohlensäure und Kalk," *Binnengewässer 13*, 183 pp. (1933).

104. C. R. Baier, "Die Bedeutung der Bakterien für den Kalktransport in den Gewässern," *Geol. Meere Binnengewässer 1*, 75–105 (1937).

105. E. M. Kindle, "The role of thermal stratification in lacustrine sedimentation," *Roy. Soc. Canada Trans.* (3) *21*, Sect. 4, 1–35, pls. 1–3 (1927).

106. E. M. Kindle, "A comparative study of different types of thermal stratification and their influence on the formation of marl," *Jour. Geol. 37*, 150–157 (1929).

107. P. Groschopf, "Die postglaziale Entwicklung des Grossen Plöner Sees in Ostholstein auf Grund pollenanalytischer Sedimentuntersuchungen," *Arch. Hydrobiol. 30*, 1–84 (1936).

108. F. Tidelski, "Untersuchungen über spät- und postglaziale Ablagerungen in Becken der kuppigen Grundmoränenlandschaft Schleswig-Holsteins," *Arch. Hydrobiol. 20*, 345–406 (1929).

109. R. L. Lindeman, "The developmental history of Cedar Creek Bog, Minn.," *Amer. Midland Naturalist 25*, 101–112 (1941).

110. W. H. Twenhofel, "The physical and chemical characteristics of the sediments of Lake Mendota, a fresh water lake of Wisconsin," *Jour. Sed. Petrol. 3*, 68–76 (1933).

111. I. T. Wilson, and D. F. Opdyke, "The distribution of the chemical constituents in the accumulated sediment of Tippecanoe Lake," *Invest. Indiana Lakes & Streams, 3*, 16–42 (1941).

112. W. F. Barbat and John Galloway, "San Joaquin Clay, California," *Amer. Assn. Petrol. Geol. Bull. 18*, 476–499 (1934).

113. Eliot Blackwelder, "Pleistocene glaciation in the Sierra Nevada and Basin Ranges," *Bull. Geol. Soc. Amer. 42*, 865–922 (1931).

114. W. C. Putnam, "Moraine and shoreline relationships at Mono Lake, California," *Bull. Geol. Soc. Amer. 61*, 115–122 (1950).

115. G. K. Gilbert, *Lake Bonneville* (*U. S. Geological Survey Monograph* 1, 1890).

116. R. F. Flint, *Glacial geology and the Pleistocene epoch* (Wiley, New York; Chapman & Hall, London, 1947).

117. H. S. Gale, "Prospecting for potash in Death Valley, California," *U. S. Geol. Surv. Bull. 540*, 407–415 (1914).

118. Eliot Blackwelder, "Lake Manly: an extinct lake in Death Valley," *Geog. Rev. 23*, 464–471 (1933).

119. Reference 116, p. 475.

120. G. E. Hutchinson, "A contribution to the limnology of arid regions," *Conn. Acad. Arts Sci. Trans. 33*, 47–132 (1937).

121. H. S. Gale, "Notes on the Quaternary lakes of the Great Basin, with special reference to the deposition of potash and other salines," *U. S. Geol. Surv. Bull. 540*, 399–406 (1914).

122. H. S. Gale, "Salines in the Owens, Searles, and Panamint basins of southeastern California," *U. S. Geol. Surv. Bull. 580-L*, iii–vi, 251–323 (1914).

123. G. E. Hutchinson and J. K. Setlow, "The chemistry of lake sediments from Indian Tibet," *Amer. Jour. Sci. 241*, 533–542 (1943).

124. E. S. Deevey, "Pollen analysis and Mexican archaeology: an attempt to apply the method," *Amer. Antiq. 10*, 135–149, fig. 7 (1944).

125. Helmut deTerra, "Early Man in Mexico," in *Tepexpan Man* (Viking Fund Pub. Anthropol., No. 11, 1949), pp. 11–86.

126. P. B. Sears, "Palynology in southern North America. I. Archeological horizons in the basins of Mexico," *Bull. Geol. Soc. Amer. 63*, 241–254 (1952).

127. Hildegarde Howard, "A review of the Pleistocene birds of Fossil Lake, Oregon," (*Carnegie Institution, Washington, Pub.* 551, 1946), pp. 141–195, pls. 1, 2.

128. R. R. Miller, "Four new species of fossil cyprinodont fishes from eastern California," *Wash. Acad. Sci. Jour. 35*, 316–321 (1945).

129. C. L. Hubbs and R. R. Miller, "The zoölogical evidence," in *The Great Basin, with emphasis on glacial and postglacial times* (University of Utah Bulletin 38 [20], Biol. Ser. *10* [7], 1948), pp. 17–166.

130. I. C. Russell, *Geological history of Lake Lahontan, a Quaternary lake of northwestern Nevada* (U. S. Geological Survey Monograph 11, 1885).

131. Ernst Antevs, "On the Pleistocene history of the Great Basin," in *Quaternary Climates* (Carnegie Institution, Washington, Pub. 352, 1925), pp. 51–114.

132. Ernst Antevs, "Correlation of Wisconsin glacial maxima," *Amer. Jour. Sci.* *243-A*, 1–39 (1945).

133. W. F. Libby, "Radiocarbon dates, II," *Science 114*, 291–296 (1951).

134. I. S. Allison, "Pumice beds at Summer Lake, Oregon," *Bull. Geol. Soc. Amer.*, *56*, 789–808 (1945).

135. H. P. Hansen, "A pollen study of peat profiles from Lower Klamath Lake of Oregon and California," in L. S. Cressman, *Archaeological researches in the northern Great Basin* (Carnegie Institution, Washington, Pub. 538, 1942), pp. 103–114, figs. 57–62.

136. O. E. Meinzer, "Map of the Pleistocene lakes of the Basin-and-Range Province and its significance," *Bull. Geol. Soc. Amer. 33*, 541–552 (1922).

137. J. D. Solomon, "The Pleistocene succession in Uganda," in T. P. O'Brien, *The prehistory of Uganda Protectorate* (Cambridge University Press, Cambridge, 1939), pp. 15–50. See p. 41.

138. E. J. Wayland, "Rifts, rivers, rains, and early man in Uganda," *Roy. Anthropol. Inst. Lond. Journ. 64*, 333–352, pls. 43–50 (1934).

139. A. T. Hopwood, "The Olduvai fauna," in L. S. B. Leakey, *Olduvai Gorge* (Cambridge University Press, Cambridge, 1951), pp. 20–24.

140. L. S. B. Leakey, *Olduvai Gorge. A report on the evolution of the hand-axe culture in Beds I–IV* (Cambridge University Press, Cambridge, 1951).

141. L. S. B. Leakey, *The Stone Age cultures of Kenya Colony* (Cambridge University Press, Cambridge, 1931).

142. E. Nilsson, "Ancient changes of climate in British East Africa and Abyssinia. A study of ancient lakes and glaciers," *Geograf. Ann. 22*, 1–79 (1940).

143. L. S. B. Leakey, "Tentative study of the Pleistocene climatic changes and Stone-Age culture sequence in north-eastern Angola," Companhia de Diamantes de Angola, Lisboa, *Pub. Cult. No. 4, Museu do Dundo* (1949).

144. C. E. P. Brooks, "The correlation of pluvial periods in Africa with climatic changes in Europe," in L. S. B. Leakey, *The Stone Age cultures of Kenya Colony* (Cambridge University Press, Cambridge, 1931), pp. 267–270.

145. G. Caton-Thompson and E. W. Gardner, *The desert Fayum* (Royal Anthropological Institute, London, 1934), 2 vols.

146. O. H. Little, "Recent geological work in the Faiyûm and in the adjoining portion of the Nile Valley," *Inst. d'Égypte Bull., Cairo 18*, 201–240, 9 pls. (1936).

147. G. Caton-Thompson, E. W. Gardner, and S. A. Huzayyin, "Lake Moeris. Re-investigations and some comments," *Inst. d'Égypte Bull., Cairo 19*, 243–303, 11 pls. (1937).

148. K. S. Sandford and W. J. Arkell, "Prehistoric survey of Egypt and western Asia. I. Paleolithic man and the Nile-Faiyum divide," *University of Chicago Oriental Institute, Publ. 10* (1929).

149. J. R. Arnold and W. F. Libby, "Radiocarbon dates," *Science 113*, 11–120 (1950).

150. C. B. M. McBurney, "Radiocarbon dating results from the Old World," *Antiquity, No. 101*, 35–40 (1952).

151. Reference 116, p. 468.

152. H. P. Moon, "The geology and physiography of the altiplano of Peru and Bolivia," *Linn. Soc. Lond. Trans.* (3) *1*, 27–43 (1939).

153. N. D. Newell, "Geology of the Lake Titicaca region, Peru and Bolivia," *Geol. Soc. Amer. Mem. 36*, 111 pp. (1949).

154. E. W. Gardner, "Lacustrine Mollusca from the Faiyum Depression. A study in variation," *Inst. d'Égypte Mém. 18* (1932).

155. Sven Hedin, *The wandering lake* (Dutton, New York, 1940).

156. N. G. Hörner and P. C. Chen, "Alternating lakes," *Hedin Mem. Vol., Geograf. Ann., 17* (Suppl.), 145–166 (1935).

157. R. F. Black and W. L. Barksdale, "Oriented lakes of northern Alaska," *Jour. Geol. 57*, 105–118 (1949).

158. Stephen Taber, "Perennially frozen ground in Alaska: its origin and history," *Bull. Geol. Soc. Amer. 54*, 1433–1548 (1943).

159. Douglas Johnson, *The origin of the Carolina Bays* (Columbia University Press, New York, 1942).

160. G. E. Hutchinson, G. E. Pickford, and J. F. M. Schuurman, "A contribution to the hydrobiology of pans and other inland waters of South Africa," *Arch. Hydrobiol. 24*, 1–154 (1932).

161. Sheldon Judson, "Depressions of the northern portion of the southern High Plains of eastern New Mexico," *Bull. Geol. Soc. Amer. 61*, 253–274 (1950).

162. H. T. Odum, "The Carolina Bays and a Pleistocene weather map," *Amer. Jour. Sci. 250*, 263–270 (1952).

163. W. H. Bradley, "The varves and climate of the Green River epoch," *U. S. Geological Survey Professional Paper* 158-E, 85–110 (1929).

164. W. H. Bradley, "Origin and microfossils of the oil shale of the Green River formation of Colorado and Utah," *U. S. Geological Survey Professional Paper* 168 (1931).

165. Hermann Korn, "Schichtung und absolute Zeit," *Neues Jahrb. Mineral. Geol. Paläontol.*, Beilage *74A*, 50–188, pls. 4–20 (1938).

166. H. C. Urey, H. A. Lowenstam, S. Epstein, and C. R. McKinney, "Measurements of paleotemperatures and temperatures of the upper Cretaceous of England, Denmark, and the southeastern United States," *Bull. Geol. Soc. Amer. 62*, 399–416 (1951).

167. Samuel Epstein, Ralph Buchsbaum, Heinz Lowenstam, and H. C. Urey, "Carbonate-water isotopic temperature scale," *Bull. Geol. Soc. Amer. 62*, 417–426 (1951).

168. G. E. Hutchinson, "Limnological studies in Indian Tibet," *Int. Rev. ges. Hydrobiol. Hydrogr. 35*, 135–177 (1937).

169. C. W. Thornthwaite, "An approach toward a rational classification of climate," *Geog. Rev. 38*, 55–94, pl. 1 (1948).

170. Reference 163, pp. 90–95.

171. R. E. Moreau, "Pleistocene climatic changes and the distribution of life in East Africa," *Jour. Ecol. 21*, 415–435 (1933).

172. R. E. Moreau, "Africa since the Mesozoic: with particular reference to certain biological problems," *Zoöl. Soc. Lond. Proc. 121*, 869–913 (1952).

173. Wolfgang Soergel, "Apopiden aus dem Chirotherium-Sandstein. Die Geschichte eines fossilen Tumpels," *Paläontol. Zeit. 10*, 11 (1928).

174. Erich Wasmund, "Die Verwendung biosoziologischer Begriffe in der Biostratonomie," *Naturhist.-Med. Ver. Heidelberg Verh. 16*, 466–512 (1929).

175. S. H. Scudder, *The Tertiary insects of North America* (U.S. Geological Survey Terr. *13*, 1890).

176. Oswald Heer, *Die Urwelt der Schweiz* (Friedrich Schulthess, Zürich, 1865).